Thomas Wm. Wright, Jr.
1334 Paso Hondo St.
San Antonio
CA- 63520

Experimental Physics
FOR COLLEGES

THE MACMILLAN COMPANY
NEW YORK • CHICAGO
DALLAS • ATLANTA • SAN FRANCISCO
LONDON • MANILA
IN CANADA
BRETT-MACMILLAN LTD.
GALT, ONTARIO

Experimental Physics

FOR COLLEGES

Revised Edition

(with corrections and emendations)

WALTER A. SCHNEIDER, PH.D.

*Late Professor of Physics and Director of the Physics
Laboratories, Washington Square College,
New York University*

LLOYD B. HAM, PH.D.

*Emeritus Professor of Physics, Former Head of
the Department of Physics, University of
Arkansas*

THE MACMILLAN COMPANY

New York

First Printing

Library of Congress Catalog Card Number: 60–5044

Printed in the United States of America

Within the past decade most authors of general physics texts for technical students have been turning to the mks system of units because of its usefulness in the applied electrical and magnetic sections of physics. The trend in other general physics courses has not been so well defined. The incorporation of the two metric systems (i.e., cgs and mks) for parallel presentation was a major consideration in the type of alterations made in this corrected and emended reprint of the Revised Edition. All new material, including any accompanying tables, has been woven into the text in a manner that will allow use of either metric system.

In reality, there were three main objectives in the present limited revision, namely: the removal of some printing and author errors, the substitution of some new material, and the introduction of the mks units.

The alterations range from a few words or characters in some paragraphs to a few whole page substitutions, including a new experiment (Experiment 12). The approximate sixty-two pages of changes in the text have been made by replacement methods that leave the page numbering the same as in earlier printings of the Revised Edition.

The flexibility in use of the mks units has been increased by setting up the formulae so that they are applicable to either the normal or rationalized units with symbols chosen for the space constants that will be in keeping with one of the generally recognized systems. A perusal of pages 236, 241, and 297 will disclose the adopted procedural methods. The symbols for the relative permittivity (ϵ_r) and for the relative permeability (μ_r) as used in this printing will occasion little, if any, conflict with the many possible accompanying lecture texts.

The second author regrets very much the death of Walter A. Schneider who has collaborated with him on many laboratory problems over a period of about thirty years.

L. B. H.

7915

An outline for revision of *Experimental Physics for Colleges* was prepared before World War II. Returns from a previously circulated questionnaire were used freely in our discussions at that time. Plans for completion of the revision were delayed for the duration, but the teaching program during the war gave us much opportunity for testing many new experiments. As a result, more than half of the book has been completely rewritten. Some experiments have been extended in length and in theory where experience indicated the need; as, for example, in Experiments 9, 13, 29, 40, and 53. There have also been many regroupings of experiments. Those in sound now appear following the experiments in mechanics.

The many new experiments fall under two general classifications: (1) those involving theory and experiences that have gradually assumed greater importance, as in Experiments 25, 45, 47; (2) those for which suitable apparatus or techniques had not been very well worked out at the time of the first edition, as illustrated in Experiments 5 and 56. In order not to increase unduly the size of this text, it has been necessary to omit some experiments listed in the original textbook. The new experiments have, however, been chosen with great care and after extensive trial, and replace only those which were not often performed.

We have tried to make this edition more flexible as to experimental procedure and as to type of apparatus required. Optional parts have been introduced for varying the length of almost every experiment, but especially Experiments 9, 11, 13, 23, 34, 40, and 49.

Certain alternate experimental methods are introduced especially where new apparatus or considerably modified techniques are employed. Examples for the latter in the section on mechanics are found in Experiments 4–0, 5–0, where the letter O indicates "optional."

When adding new experiments we have tried to live up to our original intent of describing only those that lend themselves to the "even-front" principle. The exception to this occurs in Experiment 5 where it is unlikely that the laboratory will be equipped with more than one piece of apparatus. However, the experiment is automatic and is performed by the instructor with his students looking on, and each pair of students is supplied with a record on waxed paper which they then proceed to analyse.

Chapter XXXIV, "Notes on Useful Instruments and Procedures," has been introduced to describe certain optional instruments and procedures. It is to be hoped that laboratories using apparatus with some variations in measuring instruments from the experiments as described will find this section useful.

We are sympathetic to the idea of standardization of letter symbols and have followed usage as proposed by the Committee on Letter Symbols and Abbreviations* in many instances. Departures are due usually to use of another letter by the majority of elementary texts. We are, however, using ρ for density instead of the letter d or D.

The method for calculating errors has been modified. It is not new, nor accurate, but is a little more extended than before, and appears to be a reasonable compromise over the more complicated but precise least squares method.

We are very grateful to the many fellow physicists in our own as well as in other institutions who have offered suggestions for the revision, and in particular to Prof. W. F. C. Ferguson of New York University who has offered much help and criticism in the field of light, to Prof. P. C. Sharrah of the University of Arkansas who has helped with many of the new experiments, and to Prof. T. N. Hatfield of Louisiana State University who offered many generous suggestions at the time we first outlined the revision before the war. Apparatus companies have been very helpful in supplying cuts, acknowledgment of which accompanies each diagram.

W. A. S.

L. B. H.

New York City
Fayetteville, Arkansas

---

*Am. J. Phys. **8**, 300-315, Oct., 1940.

This book is essentially a *text* on experimental physics for elementary students. The authors feel that students should be given more than a set of laboratory instructions for performing an experiment and have tried to bring out the connection which an experiment has with other experiments of a similar nature. In other words, students should look upon a laboratory physics experiment as part of the larger subject of "Experimental Physics." This book can be used as a laboratory text in conjunction with any general college physics text.

The chapters are so planned that experiments illustrating laws which are governed by the same or by a similar set of physical principles may be grouped together. Each chapter begins with a discussion of the general theory, followed by directions for each specific experiment. If any experiment requires more details as to the theory, these are given under the experiment heading.

The experiments are designed for *even front;* that is, enough sets of apparatus are utilized to enable a whole class to work in pairs on the same experiment. This makes it possible to use apparatus which is of a simpler and less expensive type. Occasionally, when experiments are inserted for completeness which by their nature require a more expensive piece of apparatus, a demonstration laboratory period may be substituted.

The authors' aim has been to make many of the electrical experiments inexpensive by the substitution of commercial rheostats, resistance units, etc., in place of the more expensive resistance boxes when the experiment does not warrant the accuracy of the latter. The apparatus mentioned is listed at the beginning of each experiment. Many pieces of apparatus mentioned in this text may be made cheaper and often better than those which can be bought, provided the facilities of a machine shop are available.

The experiments are designed for at least a full two-hour period of laboratory experimental work, but if one wishes, the period may be shortened by leaving out parts of the experiment or by taking fewer readings.

The book starts with a study of the *precision of measurements* so that the student may make a statement as to the accuracy of his work in every experiment performed. In the beginning, sample data are given and tabular forms suggested. Such details are made less definite, however, as the experiments progress. The purpose of this procedure is an attempt to teach the student to do his work in an orderly and systematic manner, first by example, and finally, by working out some orderly system of his own. The student is quite free to use his own ingenuity when obtaining his data in any way that he thinks will give him the best results. Every experiment is written in sufficient completeness, as to theory and laboratory instructions, so that the student may start his laboratory work immediately upon entering the room without instruction as to theory or procedure.

In order to make sure that the student will read the theory as well as the experiment before he enters the laboratory, it is well to require each student to solve, before the laboratory hour, the *problems* which have been placed at the end of each chapter for that experiment. It should be noted that these problems, which involve making statements concerning the theory as well as solving equations for numerical answers, cannot be done without some knowledge of the theory contained in the chapter.

In addition, at the end of every experiment there are *questions* concerning data, to be answered and passed in with the finished report. These questions, when answered and submitted, will help to make the student more careful in the taking of data and will give him a better understanding of his experiment as a whole. These questions will also serve, it is hoped, to suggest many other and perhaps more helpful ones to the instructor.

The authors take this opportunity to thank their fellow-members of the Physics Department at Washington Square College who have contributed valuable criticism and help in the choice and arrangement of material used in this text.

W. A. S.
L. B. H.

New York City
April, 1932

TABLE OF CONTENTS

PART 7   NOTES AND TABLES

PART 1   UNITS AND MEASUREMENTS

CHAPTER I

INTRODUCTION

Physics, like the other sciences, is playing an ever-increasing part in shaping our environment and our mode of living. Were it not for the knowledge and application of the laws of physics, one could not travel through space, ride under the sea, view the hitherto unknown celestial bodies, or examine the minutest forms of life and matter. Present-day laborsaving devices — electric lights, radio, telegraphy, telephones, and the ocean cable — are often taken for granted and little thought is given to the years of scientific research which produced them. What is the fascination which makes great minds devote years of study to physical phenomena in order to present to the world wonders which will all too soon be labeled necessities? Is it not because there are always untold possibilities ahead — a story of surprises awaiting?

THE LABORATORY

Let us then consider the laboratory, which is the workshop of the scientist, as a place of interest where each one can perform for himself the experiments which brought joy to the heart of the man who first worked them out. Consider it a place where one can learn by actual practice to understand better the principles of and the care of mechanical devices which are used in everyday life. Remember that seeing and working with objective material and apparatus gives one the first-hand knowledge which is so valuable in rendering the descriptive more concrete, comprehensive, and usable, and that it initiates a better understanding of the formulation of laws, illustrates the working of a principle, concentrates attention to detail, and stimulates the exercise of deliberate judgment.

Success with an experiment comes only when all possible knowledge and underlying theory of the experiment have been obtained before starting. The teacher helps the student to acquire this in

3

ways that he sees fit, and he points out certain delicate adjustments of apparatus and means of taking advantage of situations to obtain more accurate results, *but* it is up to the student to grasp and retain the lessons taught in the laboratory. Others cannot do this for him.

Conduct The instructor expects his students to be honest and interested in their experiments, careful of University property, and methodical in replacing or leaving apparatus at the end of each class session. If the semester's work in the laboratory does not develop the habit of inquiry, respect for seasoned opinions, ability to handle apparatus carefully and intelligently, and the value of system and order in any work then it has not accomplished its purpose.

Written reports The instructor decides upon the particular method and form of the written report, but the following headings might be remembered as important in any write-up of an experiment: object, description, conventional drawing of apparatus, theory, data, conclusion, and discussion of errors. The treatment of each of these divisions will depend upon the wishes of the instructor. Avoid the use of personal pronouns in written reports.

UNITS

In laboratory work, generally speaking, results not given in definite units mean little or nothing. For instance, the numerical values of density depend upon the system of units used. Some results, such as specific gravity and specific heat, appear as abstract numbers because they are defined as ratios of numbers having the same units.

There are *three systems* of units in common use: the cgs system (centimeter, gram, second), used almost exclusively by scientists; the fps system (foot, pound, second); and the gravitational system. A *fourth system*, called the mks system (meter, kilogram, second) has been added more recently to this list. The first two and the fourth are called absolute systems because the derived units bear the simplest possible relation to the fundamental units of length, mass, and time. Thus, in the three absolute systems as stated, the unit of force (i.e., dyne, poundal, newton) is defined as that force which will give a unit mass unit acceleration. In the gravitational system, the unit force (pound weight) is the force acting on a unit mass (pound) due to the attraction of the earth. Since this force varies, depending upon the location, it is seen that the pound weight is not an absolute unit of force. It is sufficiently accurate, however, for practically all engineering work.

The mks system was approved by the International Committee of Weights and Measures in 1935. This system has for its fundamental units the meter, kilogram, and second. The unit of force is the *newton*, which is defined as the force required to give a mass of one kilogram an acceleration of one meter per second per second. The object of this system is to provide an absolute system of units that will unify the existing systems of units in electricity, and use at the same time a number of units occurring in practical measurements. The new system of units is becoming more widely used, although many American scientific societies have not yet taken any official action. The Committee on Electric and Magnetic Units of the American Physics Teachers Association made a report* on the mks system in 1938 (see Table 2, page 426).

As an example of the use of units, suppose that a train is observed to have a steady velocity of 36 kilometers per hour for 30 seconds. What distance was traversed in this time interval? The distance (s) traveled would be the velocity (v) times the time (t), i.e.,

$$s = vt.$$

The answer in centimeters is

$$s = \frac{36 \times 1000 \times 100}{60 \times 60} \times 30$$
$$= 3 \times 10^4 \text{ cm.}$$

It is better practice in general to convert all units, before using them in equations, to fundamental units, i.e., 36 kilometers per hour $\backsim$ (is equivalent to) $36 \times 1000 \times 100$ centimeters per hour or $\dfrac{36 \times 1000 \times 100}{60 \times 60}$ centimeters per second, which in turn =

* *Am. Phys. Teacher*, **6**, 144 (1938). The International Committee set the date of January, 1940 for adoption of the new system of units. All essential details, except the question of rationalization, have been worked out. For further information on the mks system see the following articles in the same journal; **8**, 30, 222, 318 (1940). See also G. E. M. Jauncy and A. S. Langsdorf, *M.K.S. Units and Dimensions and a Proposed M.K.O.S. System*, New York, The Macmillan Company, 1940 .

(equals) 1000 centimeters per second. Notice that dimensionally the product, vt, gives $\frac{cm}{sec} \cdot sec = cm$. (The dot is often used to denote multiplication.) This is the same as the dimension found on the left-hand side of the equation (in other words, s).

Whenever large numbers are involved, it is better to express them in positive powers of ten. Thus, the number 237,000,000 may be expressed as 2.37×10^8. Likewise, all small decimal quantities may be expressed in negative powers of ten, i.e., 0.0000000237 = 2.37×10^{-8}.

Often a preferable method of indicating powers of ten, especially in electricity, is to write the prefix micro (μ), milli (m), kilo (k), and mega instead of employing 10 with superscripts. Thus, we may write 12×10^{-12} farads as 12 micromicrofarads (also, $12\mu\mu f$), 0.003 amperes as 3 milliamperes (ma), 0.000013 meters as 13 micrometers (13 microns), 125×10^6 cycles as 125 megacycles, 1.253×10^9 ohms as 1253 megohms, 0.0015 henries as 1.5 millihenries (mh), etc.

CHAPTER II

PRECISION OF MEASUREMENTS

Errors that enter into the results of a series of observations may be classified as personal, accidental, systematic, and instrumental. The magnitude of the personal errors depends upon the observer's experience and follows the law of chance unless there is a personal bias.

Personal bias A common example of the personal bias of beginners is their tendency to give to a first reading of a series greater significance than the succeeding readings. A beginner asked to take three readings of the length of a table with a meter stick, to the nearest tenth millimeter, will bring back, generally, three readings all alike. Consider Figure 1, which represents a plan of the table top. Besides inaccuracies in the placing of the meter stick, it should be observed that the length must vary, depending upon whether the measurements were taken at A, B, or C.

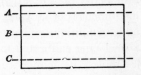

Fig. 1. Measuring the length of a table top.

Personal errors Personal errors include inaccurate settings, inaccurate estimations of a fractional division, insufficient development of one or more of the six senses, and parallax. The matching of colors, of loudness, pitch of two sounds, and timing results are examples of measurements depending upon the use of sense organs. The error due to parallax will be discussed later (see page 25).

Accidental errors Errors which are beyond the control of the observer are called *accidental*. For instance, suppose galvanometer readings are to be taken every fifteen seconds. A sudden jar will cause the galvanometer to alter its readings from an otherwise good result. Other examples of accidental errors are found in fluctuations in magnetism, noise, temperature, pressure, electricity, wind, and the like.

7

Systematic errors Such errors are characterized by their tendency to one direction only, i.e., positive or negative. They may or may not be easily traced. For instance, if a meter stick is always used by taking measurements from one end, then this end may get worn and a constant error will occur in all measurements made with this meter stick when measuring from this end. If not detected, systematic errors may give a result far from the true result, and are, moreover, not accounted for in any calculations of the experimental error.

Instrumental errors New instruments are usually calibrated to a certain degree of accuracy. If not, they should be calibrated in the laboratory or sent to some place, such as the National Bureau of Standards for calibration. Once the required per cent accuracy is decided upon as necessary for the experiment, one should see that the apparatus used for any measurement has an accuracy a little better than that demanded for the tests. However, a calibrated instrument is of no value as a precision instrument unless operated under conditions similar to those used in its calibration. For instance, a steel tape calibrated for 20°C would not be accurate for winter use unless its temperature coefficient is known. Furthermore, a calibrated instrument is reliable only with careful and intelligent use.

Arithmetical mean — most probable result The accuracy of an experiment, then, depends upon a number of factors or conditions, many of which are not easily ascertained. In our discussion we shall assume that the apparatus is sufficiently accurate for the experiment and that there exists no personal bias nor any systematic error. This leaves us with certain personal and accidental errors which are subject to pure chance. With these limitations as to the nature of errors to be considered, our judgment tells us that the arithmetical mean of a number of observations will give us the most probable result. Actually, this represents the most probable reproducible result with the apparatus available rather than accuracy. Accuracy is better checked by other independent experiments using different methods of experimentation. Hence, such expressions as *per cent of error, probable error,* etc., refer to the mean result as found, since the true result is seldom known.

CALCULATION OF ERRORS AND PER CENT ERRORS

When an experimental result is to be obtained by direct measurement, we take one or more readings, depending upon the accuracy desired. Suppose a single measurement of length, less than a meter, is to be made with a meter stick. Let the measurement be 34.3$\bar{5}$ centimeters. All figures, except the last digit which has the dash over it, are measured digits. The last digit ($\bar{5}$) is doubtful. The most inexperienced observer could estimate probably to a half millimeter division. For the single reading above, we will designate as the error ± 0.05, the plus or minus sign (±) indicating that the reading may be too small or too large by this amount. Such estimations on a single reading are generally taken large enough to be called, with some reservations, a maximum possible error. For this reason, the term *maximum possible error* is used by some authors. Our reading now becomes 34.35 ± 0.05 cm, which gives a per cent error of 0.15 $\left(\text{i.e.,} \dfrac{0.05}{34.35} \times 100 \right)$. If anything more than an approximate answer is required, more than one reading is essential. However, *when a single measurement only is taken, we shall designate all digits, including the first doubtful figure, as significant figures.* That is, we designate as significant figures all digits that have any trustworthy meaning for our purposes.

When a number of independent readings of a given length are taken, we must deal with an average having a certain error. Calculations of the precision from such considerations is our present problem and is important since the result of our experiment must represent an average of various readings and calculations. Consider, for instance, the following readings to have been taken for a given distance: 152.2$\bar{8}$, 152.3$\bar{6}$, 152.3$\bar{0}$, 152.3$\bar{2}$, and 152.3$\bar{8}$ cm.

Reading (cm)	Deviations
152.2$\bar{8}$	−0.048
152.3$\bar{6}$	+ .032
152.3$\bar{0}$	− .028
152.3$\bar{2}$	− .008
152.3$\bar{8}$	+ .052
5)761.64	5) ±0.168
152.328	±0.033$\bar{6}$

Length = 152.328 ± 0.034 cm

Notice that since the meter stick must be reset at least once for each measurement of length, the individual readings show greater variations, and therefore greater deviations, than was obtained with the single measurement of length described in the previous paragraph.

In view of the deviations inherent in the above measurements of length, the question arises as to the magnitudes of the residuals and how the reliability of a given set of measurements is determined. What then is the most probable length and the per cent of error that may be expected? We will assume that the arithmetical mean *am*, found by adding the five readings and dividing by five, is the most probable length. It should be carefully noted that the calculated average is only the *most probable* result that can be obtained from the observations. It is *not* the true or exact result, because this value cannot be found from the measurements, and hence must remain unknown. When the word *error* is used in its strict sense, it should refer to the difference between the true value (which is unknown) and the most probable value found from the measurements. When the word *error* is used in this chapter, it therefore refers to a quantity calculated from the deviations (or residuals) from the mean value, and also from the number of readings taken, and is really an index of the precision which one might associate with these measurements. The true value might lie anywhere between the limits of the most probable value plus or minus the average deviation of the arithmetical mean *AD*. This latter quantity is often rather loosely referred to as the error.

Note that the arithmetical mean is 152.328 and that a total of six digits is retained. If the division had not turned out to give exactly six figures, then the additional digits would have been omitted. That is, two doubtful digits have been retained for the arithmetical mean of the five measurements. Although partly arbitrary but definite, we shall adopt this procedure of retaining two doubtful figures whenever averages are involved. Hence, *the number of significant figures where averages are concerned will be designated as all digits including the first two doubtful figures.*

Calculation of the per cent of error of the mean   There are two essential steps to be taken to calculate the per cent of error of the mean, namely, determine (1) the average deviation of the five *single* observations *ad*, and (2) the average deviation of the *mean* of the five observations *AD*. The *ad* is a measure of error of a single observation while the AD is a measure of error of the mean of n observations.

We have seen that the arithmetical mean am of our five measurements of length was 152.328 cm. The *error* in each reading is calculated by subtracting from each reading the arithmetical mean. These departures from the arithmetical mean are called *deviations d*, or *residuals*. The average of the individual deviations ad is found by adding the individual deviations (neglecting the signs) and dividing by the number. The average error or deviation ad in the above five measurements of the lengths is $ad = 0.034$. The digit 6 is dropped since its retention would be equivalent to assumption of seven significant figures in the arithmetical mean. When digits are dropped if the rejected digit is greater than 5, the retained digit immediately to the left is increased by unity. In general, *the average deviation of individual readings* (ad) is found by the equation,

$$ad = \frac{d_1 + d_2 \cdots \cdots d_n}{n} \equiv \frac{\Sigma d}{n}$$

where n is the number of readings which made up the arithmetical mean. The arithmetical mean will be closer to the true result the larger the number of readings. Actually the true result cannot be found. Theory shows that the arithmetical mean is more reliable than a single observation by the ratio $\sqrt{n}$ to 1. Hence, the *average deviation of the arithmetical mean* *AD from the true value is given by the equation,

$$AD = \frac{ad}{\sqrt{n}}.$$

The average deviation of the mean (AD) in our measurements of length found on page 9 is $AD = 0.034/\sqrt{5} = 0.015$ cm with a per cent deviation of the mean ($\% \, AD$) of 0.0098 (i.e., 1.5/152).

* The least squares method of calculating errors is much more satisfactory but the details of calculation are too involved for present purposes. The theory used in the least squares method shows that the best average value is obtained when Σd^2 is a minimum. In any case, once Σd^2 is obtained from the arithmetical mean, the following terms are used: dispersion (σ^2) is, $\sigma^2 = \Sigma d^2/n$; standard deviation (σ) is, $\sigma = \sqrt{\Sigma d^2/n}$; probable error of a single observation is, $pe = 0.6745 \sqrt{\Sigma d^2/(n-1)}$ and probable error of the arithmetical mean is, $PE = 0.6745 \sqrt{\Sigma d^2/n(n-1)}$. By probable error, one means that the true result is equally likely to be larger or smaller than the arithmetical mean by an increment which is plus or minus the probable error.

We shall refer often to the per cent deviation of the mean as the per cent of error.

$$\% AD = \frac{AD \times 100}{am}.$$

Since the per cent of error depends upon the square root of n, the number of observations, increasing the number of readings yields less and less returns. For practical purposes, from 3 to 5 readings will prove to be quite satisfactory for routine work. Thus, 16 individual observations are required rather than 4 in order to increase the precision of the result in a ratio of 2 to 1.

A summary of the steps used in the calculation of the per cent of error follows: Obtain the average deviation ad from your set of readings. Then calculate the average deviation of the mean AD by the equation $AD = ad/\sqrt{n}$. The per cent of error ($\% AD$) will be the AD multiplied by 100 and divided by the arithmetical mean am; i.e., $\% AD = (AD/am) \times 100$. Without going through the rather tedious calculations of the method of least squares, the above method will suffice to give a fairly reliable estimate of the precision to be expected from a series of measurements.

The average when readings are dependent. Method of differences. In many experiments the data are not independent as was assumed on page 9. That is, the readings are obtained in some ordered sequence where a constant increment is made in one quantity. Experiments 14 (Young's modulus), 5 (Behr free fall), and 17 (period of oscillation and force constant of a spring) are examples of such experiments. The method suggested in Experiment 14 to obtain Young's modulus is to average the data graphically. An alternative method of averaging data, such as is shown for obtaining the acceleration in the Behr fall apparatus (Experiment 5), is the method of differences.

The method of differences will be illustrated by means of hypothetical data for Experiment 17, (period of oscillation and force constant of a spring). Suppose we are to make three independent calculations of the force constant of the spring shown in Figure 2. Place an initial mass on the scale pan. This mass should be sufficient to free the spring of any negative tension due to any adjacent coils touching. Suppose that under these conditions a reading of a_0 is obtained on a vertical scale. Then add successively five equal masses giving readings a_1, a_2, a_3, a_4, and a_5. The five masses should be large enough so that the total mass will stretch the spring considerably but not exceed the elastic limit. We can now, by the subtraction shown in Table I, obtain three independent values of the stretch produced by a given load from which an average may be obtained. Table I was obtained by dividing the consecutive observations (a_0, a_1, a_2; a_3, a_4, a_5) into two halves and subtracting a number in one half from the corresponding successive observation in the other half. There are now three independent sets of data that may be averaged. The differences shown in Table I give three of the desired intervals. If the problem had required a knowledge of the sum of two observations, then the data would have furnished nine intervals. All such sums or differences will be independent.

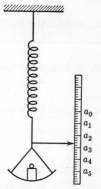

Fig. 2. Measurement of the force constant of a spring.

If successive differences, as in Table II, had been used, and in the process of averaging their sum had been found, then only the

(Table I)	(Table II)
$a_3 - a_0$	$a_1 - a_0$
$a_4 - a_1$	$a_2 - a_1$
$a_5 - a_2$	$a_3 - a_2$
	$a_4 - a_2$
	$a_5 - a_3$
	$a_5 - a_0$

first and last readings really count since all the other readings cancelled out. Individual errors in readings may be noted by subtracting consecutive readings, but a large error in determining the average may occur because the average depends only upon the values of a_0 and a_5. Any errors in a_0 or a_5 do not affect the average as greatly in the method illustrated in Table I, because *all* the readings are averaged independently.

Errors in indirect measurements So far we have assumed that the desired results depended only upon certain direct measurements.

An extension of the above rules for finding errors will be necessary when the result is obtained by computation. Thus, to find the moment of inertia I from the equation:

$$I = I_0 + mh^2,$$

or, to find the surface of the sides of a cylinder from the equation:

$$S = 2\pi rl,$$

or, to find the area of a circle from the equation:

$$A = \pi r^2,$$

or, to find the value of g from the equation:

$$g = \frac{4\pi^2 l}{T^2},$$

one must perform the arithmetic calculations of addition, multiplication, squaring, and division respectively. It is assumed that each of the factors involved is an average obtained from several readings and that the error in each factor has been computed. Upon these assumptions, the following rules for errors in computing results are given:

Rule I In *addition* or *subtraction*, retain as the error in the final result the sum of the numerical errors found in each one of the quantities, e.g.:

Addition	Subtraction
Distances in cm	Distances in cm
25.20 ± 0.23	13.210 ± 0.022
5.312 ± 0.021	7.315 ± 0.026
1.2534 ± 0.0025	5.895 ± 0.048
31.76 ± 0.25	

Thus, in the example of addition shown above, the result is 31.76 ± 0.25 cm, while in the example on subtraction, the result is 5.895 ± 0.048 cm.

There is no way of knowing whether the errors are accumulating or subtracting out in a sum.

In any case, with additions and subtractions, the sum of the individual errors is important. If the measurement of 25.20 cm in the addition problem was taken with a meter stick, the other distances which were added to it could be measured equally well with a meter stick. The accuracy of the other two figures (5.312 and 1.2534) show that they were measured with more accurate instruments. The additional digits to the right of the decimal beyond the two found in the first measurement (25.20) have no significance.

Rule II   In *multiplication* or *division*, retain as *the per cent of error* the sum of the per cents of error found in each of the terms. Thus, the product, $(135.27 \pm 0.17\%) \times (1.325 \pm 1.3\%)$, is $179.2 \pm 1.5\%$.

$$135.\overline{27}$$
$$\underline{1.3\overline{25}}$$
$$\overline{67635}$$
$$2\ \overline{7054}$$
$$40\ \overline{581}$$
$$\underline{135\ \overline{27}}$$
$$179.\overline{23275}$$

Answer $= 179.2 \pm 1.5\%$

The per cent of error is important in multiplication since multiplication of an accurate measurement by a highly inaccurate measurement propagates the large uncertainty to the product. Hence, in multiplication and likewise in division, small quantities should be measured more accurately so that the per cents of errors in all quantities are reasonably equal. One may raise a question as to the reason for retaining only four figures in the result of the multiplication in the previous paragraph. The reason for this will be seen by observing that in the multiplication each doubtful figure has a dash over it. One of the quantities to be multiplied shows doubtful figures beginning with the third. Therefore the number of significant figures in the result is four.

When multiplying or dividing two factors, retain a number of digits in the result equal to the number of digits in the factor containing the smaller number of significant figures. In the multiplication shown, the number of significant figures was four in one quantity and five in the other. Therefore, the number of significant figures in the result is four. (In a product, such as $125\overline{72} \times 1\overline{34} = 1\overline{684648}$, the result may be expressed as $16\overline{8} \times 10^4$.) This rule concerning significant figures is important especially where the result obtained is to be multiplied or divided by a third factor.

Slide rule The number of significant figures in one's result indicates whether one could use a slide rule profitably. There are few calculations in the elementary laboratories which have more than three or four significant figures. Consequently, a slide rule is a very great timesaver in the laboratory.

When a number is squared, its per cent of error is multiplied by two. Similarly in taking a square root, the per cent of error is divided by two. The reason for this is seen when one considers that in such cases the errors must be cumulative or subtractive.

SUPPLEMENTAL CONSIDERATIONS IN TREATMENT OF DATA FOR ERRORS

Per cent of error from some standard value Occasionally, the student is asked to determine the value of a physical constant, such as the acceleration g of a freely falling body, with his apparatus, and then check his value with the standard known value. This procedure is useful in order to check against personal bias and systematic or instrumental errors. Assume that he obtains an arithmetical mean of 978.5 cm per sec per sec. If the value of g for his location is 980.2 cm per sec per sec, the per cent of error from the accepted value is given as

$$\frac{980.2 - 978.5}{980.2} \times 100 = 0.17\%.$$

This error when compared with the $\%$ AD obtained from the experiment will give considerable information on the experimental technique and the apparatus used.

Per cent of error from the mean Certain experiments, as Experiment 25 on the linear coefficient of expansion, are performed by taking only one reading of each of the variables and the result calculated from this set of readings. The experiment is then repeated. Assume that the two results found are 1.281×10^{-5} and 1.253×10^{-5} and are considered equally probable. Then the per cent of error from the mean is given as

$$\frac{1281 - 1253}{1281 + 1253} \times 100 = 1.1\%$$

This method does not give as much information on precision of the result as the method of residuals. The method may lead in certain instances to a better preliminary understanding of the experiment because of absence of detail on single measurements.

SUMMARY OF METHODS FOR DETERMINATION OF ERRORS

1. Method of Deviations (or Residuals) We assume that the deviations were brought about by pure chance and therefore that the arithmetical mean am is the most probable result. Let the n individual readings be $s_1, s_2, s_3, \ldots s_n$; then the following definitions may be written:

(a) The arithmetical mean $= am = \dfrac{\Sigma s}{n}$

(b) The deviations (d_1, d_2, etc.) are

$$d_1 = s_1 - am$$
$$d_2 = s_2 - am$$
$$. \quad . \quad .$$
$$. \quad . \quad .$$
$$. \quad . \quad .$$
$$d_n = s_n - am$$

(c) The average deviation of individual readings $= ad = \dfrac{\Sigma d}{n}$

(d) The average deviation of the arithmetical mean (or *deviation of the mean* for briefness) $= AD = \dfrac{ad}{\sqrt{n}}$

(e) The fractional deviation of the arithmetical mean $= \dfrac{AD}{am}$

(f) The per cent deviation of the arithmetical mean $= \dfrac{AD}{am} \times 100$

2. Per cent of error from some standard value This method is useful to check against errors that are thought to be due to some cause other than chance. The accuracy of a new piece of apparatus may be tested in this way. Thus, in the Behr fall method (Exp. 5) to obtain the value of g, the standard value may be expected to be found within the mean value $\pm \% AD$ if the experiment is performed carefully.

3. Per cent of error from the mean This method may be used in place of (1) but does not give as much information on the precision of measurements.

GRAPHICAL RESULTS

To show the relation between one variable and another, if any definite relation does exist, it is often best to resort to plotting a curve. By this method, the mathematical relation existing between the two quantities may sometimes be determined. In any case, a graph represents pictorially and in concise form the nature of the results obtained. The curve should be drawn *smoothly* so as to fall on as many points as possible. The points which are noticeably in error should fall in approximate equal numbers on each side of the curve. When such a curve has been drawn, the magnitude of the errors is shown qualitatively by the distance which the points in error fall outside the smooth curve. If one wishes to find the value of the quantity for intermediate positions on the curve where readings were not actually taken, the curve is sufficiently accurate for that purpose. If the accuracy of the final result is desired, the per cent of error should be found by the methods outlined previously.

Whenever possible, the coördinates used for abscissae and ordinates should be so chosen from the experimental data that the plotted points will fall on a straight line within the limits of experimental error. A straight line is the only graph easily examined. If the graph is a curve, one might have considerable difficulty in determining whether it is a parabola, hyperbola, or even an ellipse, particularly if only a small portion is shown. A few illustrations of curve plotting are given.

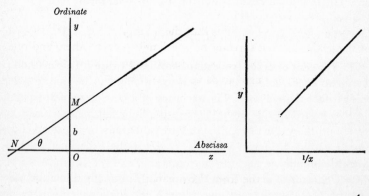

Fig. 3. Graph of $y = asc + b$.

Fig. 4. Graph of $y = c\left(\dfrac{1}{x}\right)$.

Example 1 Suppose that in a certain experiment it is found that y varies directly with x, as shown in the diagram. The graph is a straight line and any straight line can be represented mathematically by an equation of the form,

$$y = ax + b.$$

If this line cuts the x and y axes at N and M respectively, then it can easily be shown that the distance OM is equal to b, and that its slope (i.e., $\tan \theta$) is a (Fig. 3). The kinematical equation, $v = u + at$, is an example in physics of the above form of equation.

Example 2 If we plot y against $1/x$, and obtain a straight line (Fig. 4) through the origin, it means that

$$y = c \left(\frac{1}{x}\right),$$

where c is a constant. If y represents the pressure and x the volume of a gas, then we have an experimental verification of Boyle's law ($pv = c$) if, when p is plotted against $1/v$, a straight-line graph results.

Example 3 If the electric current I is plotted against the heat developed H, the curve is not a straight line but will be a straight line if I^2 is plotted against H. The known relation existing between these two quantities is

$$H = I^2 \frac{R}{J},$$

where R and J are constants.

Example 4 When one finds that the quantities which are plotted on the graph are not directly proportional to each other, and one suspects that one of the variables raised to some power is proportional to the other raised to some different power, then it is better to take the logarithms of both quantities before plotting them.

Thus, suppose the actual relation between x and y is

$$y^n = ax^m,$$

it being necessary to find the constants a, n, and m from the experimental data. When the logarithm of both sides is calculated, we have

$$n \log y = \log a + m \log x.$$

Now plotting log x against log y (Fig. 5), instead of x against y, we get a straight line; and from the intercepts on the log x and

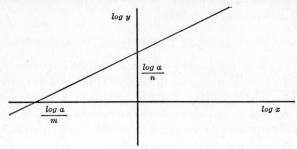

Fig. 5. Graph of $n \log y = \log a + m \log x$.

log y axes, we can find the constants log a, n, and m. In order to facilitate this procedure and save time in calculating the logarithms of the different values of x and y, it is possible to purchase log-log graph paper in which the axes are marked off in logarithmic units. In using this paper it is then only necessary to plot values of x and

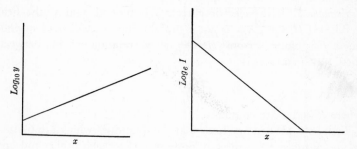

Fig. 6. Graph of $\log y = \log k$ + $x \log a$.

Fig. 7. Graph of $\ln I = \ln I_0 - kx$.

y directly, and if a relation of the above type exists, a straight line will result.

Example 5 Occasionally, *only one* of the two axes needs to be marked off in logarithmic units to obtain a straight line, since the equation is logarithmic on one side only. An example of this type of equation is $y = ka^x$. Taking the logarithm of both sides yields $\log y = \log k + x \log a$. If $\log y$ is plotted against x (Fig. 6), a straight line is obtained at once and from it a can be found from its slope, and k from its intercept on the log y axis. Another representative example involving natural logarithms is $I = I_0 e^{-kx}$. Taking the logarithms of both sides gives $\ln I = \ln I_0 - kx$. A straight line is obtained when x is plotted against $\log_e I$ as in Figure 7.

Graph paper with logarithmic scales in one or both directions comes with the logarithmic *cycle*, that is, the space occupied by numbers in the ratio of 1 to 10, repeated once or twice or not at all. These are called two, three, or one cycle paper. The range of values for which they are suited are 1 to 100, 1 to 1000, and 1 to 10 respectively.

The following directions will be found helpful in plotting a useful curve:

1 Use coördinate paper with rulings of one millimeter or some similar decimal scheme on sheets of convenient size (say $8\frac{1}{2}$ by 11 inches).

2 Plot to such a scale that all significant figures will be used. The curve should be drawn to as large a scale as the sheet will allow.

3 Place a small dot (or cross) at every located point (Fig. 8).

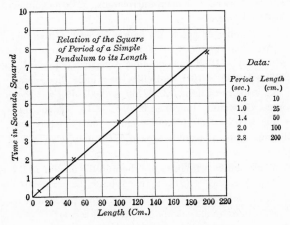

Fig. 8. An example of curve-plotting.

If many curves are to be drawn on the same graph, the appropriate points may be located by use of small circles, triangles, or squares.

4 Every curve should have a title indicating which two quantities are plotted along the two axes.

5 Draw heavy lines for the coördinate axes and label the axes, the independent variable along the x axis and the dependent variable along the y axis.

6 The origin of the coördinate axes need not be shown on the curve.

7 If a relation exists between the quantities, draw, by means of a flexible rule, a smooth curve through the points. If all the points do not actually fall on a smooth graph, then draw the curve so that approximately as many points will be on one side as on the other. A point that deviates from the curve markedly should be discarded as an accidental error.

PROBLEMS

1 Express the following numbers in powers of 10 so that only one digit is to the left of the decimal point; 0.00231, 10352, 6370, 0.00003002, 921000.

2 Assuming that each of the above figures is an arithmetical mean, state the number of significant figures in each.

3 Write the following in powers of 10 after conversion to the usual mks units, with one digit only to the left of the decimal point; 377 megamegacycles, 27 microampers, 125 micromicrofarads, 3278 megohms, 3.7 millihenries, 3010 kilocycles.

4 State the number of significant figures for each of the following constants;[*] electron mass $(9.1066 \pm 0.0032) \times 10^{-28}$ g; charge on the electron, $(4.8025 \pm 0.0010) \times 10^{-10}$ statcoulombs; Avogadro (chemical scale) number $(6.0228 \pm 0.011) \times 10^{23}$ molecules per mole; ice point, (273.160 ± 0.020) K; velocity of light, $(2.997760 \pm 0.000040) \times 10^{10}$ cm per sec; gravitational constant, $(6.670 \pm 0.0050) \times 10^{-8}$ dyne cm^2/g^2; liter $(= 1000$ ml$) = 1000.0280 \pm 0.0020$ cm^3; Joule's equivalent, 4.18550 ± 0.00040 joule/cal_{15}; mass of hydrogen $(_1H^1)$ atom, $(1.67339 \pm 0.00031) \times 10^{24}$ g.

5 How many significant figures are there in the answer to the following calculation: $(1354 \pm 24) \times (972 \pm 15)$? What is the per cent of error?

6 Find the above product with a slide rule. What per cent of error do you actually find by making the calculation with a slide rule?

7 The following readings (in mm) of the side of a cube are found to be 78.9, 78.2, 78.2, 78.1. Calculate the ad, the AD, and the per cent of error. What is the per cent of error of the volume of the cube? How many significant figures has the resulting volume of the cube?

---

[*] Taken in part from R. T. Birge, "A New Table of Values of the General Physical Constants," *Rev. Mod. Phys. 13*, 233 (1941).

8 Suppose that the mass of the cube in problem 7 above is 131.2 ± 1.6 grams, what are the density and the per cent of error in the density?

9 Add the following, stating the error; (132.2 ± 3.1), (2.41 ± 0.32), (4.61 ± 0.41), (1375 ± 10).

10 Calculate the standard deviation and the probable error of the individual readings and the probable error of the *am* for the data on page 9 by the method of least squares. (See notes on calculation of errors by least squares at the bottom of page 11.) Compare with the average deviation of the individual readings *ad* and the average deviation of the arithmetical mean *AD* as described on pages 10 and 11.

11 Show by squaring that, if a quantity is in error by 1 per cent, the squared quantity is in error by 2 per cent.

12 Plot the data used in Figure 8 on (1) equal interval coördinate paper, (2) log-log paper (use coördinate paper with two cycles in both the x and the y direction), (3) semilog paper (two cycles along the x axis). (Plot the period as ordinates.)

13 Plot $y = 5 \log x$ on semilog paper showing the points on the graph where $x = 1, 10, 50, 100, 300, 600,$ and 1000. (Use a three-cycle paper for plotting the abscissas. You may approximate logarithmic spacing between cycles on plain white paper by noting that the numbers 2, 3, 4, 6, and 8, are distant from the position 1 to the next position 1 on the cycle paper approximately $\frac{1}{3}$ (0.301), $\frac{1}{2}$ (0.477), $\frac{6}{10}$ (0.602), $\frac{3}{4}$ (0.778), and $\frac{9}{10}$ (0.903), respectively. The more exact relationships as to distances are shown in parentheses.

CHAPTER III

FUNDAMENTAL UNITS.
MEASUREMENT OF LENGTH AND MASS

THE MEASUREMENT OF LENGTH

This is perhaps the most widely performed, as well as the simplest of the three fundamental units, length, mass, and time. In our everyday experiences, we frequently have to measure some length or other. Very seldom, however, do we stop to consider whether we are really performing the measurement with the best rule or apparatus for that particular purpose. Still less do we concern ourselves with the question of accuracy of measurement. The reason for this unconcern is to be found in the fact that someone has already considered these points very carefully and the apparatus which we have used has been designed accordingly. The same is true when we have to measure mass and time, the other two fundamental quantities.

In the physical laboratory, we cannot be satisfied with such a superficial view, but must consider both the accuracy of our instruments and our measurements carefully. They become of much greater importance when a student of physics has devised some new and easier method of performing a certain measurement, which, according to his ideas, will give more accurate results. In such a case, knowledge of the accuracy and reproducibility of his apparatus and of the precision of his result is necessary. The research worker in the field of physics or chemistry must be familiar with the different methods at his disposal, and with their relative accuracy, as well as the methods of calculating or estimating the errors of observations.

In these first two experiments, therefore, the student should try to discover for himself the precision that he has obtained with his apparatus; and in the future, when measuring a length, mass, or time interval, adapt the method to the precision required in the result. A discussion on the fundamental unit of time will be found in Chapter XXXIV.

The meter rule The simplest way of measuring length is with the aid of an ordinary scale or rule. (A metric scale or "meter bar" is most frequently used in the laboratory.)

There are several errors to be considered when using such an instrument. The inherent accuracy in the instrument is limited by the fact that the lines on the scale have a finite thickness. *Observational errors* occur when estimating the fraction of the smallest division. When estimating the fraction of a millimeter on an ordinary meter rule, an uncertainty of 0.1 mm is about the limit of accuracy for all but the most skilled observers. An error of equal or larger amount is probable in placing the object on the zero reading from which the measurement is made. Errors of this type can be mini-

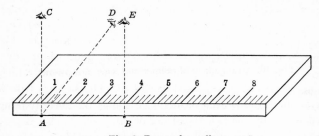

Fig. 9. Error of parallax.

mized only by taking a sufficiently large number of readings. Another frequent source of error is the *error of parallax*. This error occurs when a scale of finite thickness is used and the eye is not always vertically above the scale and point being read, or even in the same relative position with regard to the scale. This will be more clearly seen in Figure 9. When the eye is placed at *C* and *E*, the distance *AB* will be read correctly. This will not be the case, however, if the eye is placed at *E* and *D*. In practice, therefore, whenever it is possible, the rule should be placed in such a position — on edge in this case — so that the markings on the scale fall right on the points *A* and *B*. The nearer the division marks on the scale to the points being read, the smaller is the error due to parallax. In many pieces of physical apparatus this error of parallax causes additional difficulties, and consequently a large number of ingenious artifices have been invented to overcome this error. Such an example is shown in Figure 10, which represents the method used often with the better class of electrical voltmeters and ammeters. Since in these cases the pointer has to swing freely over the scale, the error of parallax may be present. It is overcome in this type of instrument by mounting a mirror underneath the pointer. When looking into the mirror, right underneath the pointer, an image of the latter will be seen. By adjusting the position of the eye above the pointer, this image can be made to disappear underneath the pointer. When this is the case the eye is vertically above and the reading on the scale, keeping the eye in this position, can then be taken accurately.

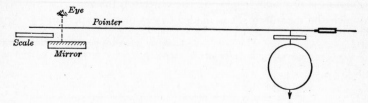

Fig. 10. Arrangement of pointer and scale in a voltmeter.

Very often the object or distance being measured cannot be placed along the side of the scale, or *vice versa*. Such cases as the inside or outside diameter of a vessel, the outside diameter of a sphere, etc., come into consideration here. The method used involves the use of transfer instruments whereby we transfer the original dimension to a pair of dividers, or *calipers* as they are called, and then measure the distance on a scale between the legs of the transfer caliper. Figure 11 shows both inside and outside calipers.

The vernier scale   In taking a measurement with an ordinary meter scale, we try to estimate to tenths of a division. This requires a large amount of skill, and, even then, when the divisions on the scale are small, an error of one- or two-tenths is quite probable. A microscope will help in such cases.

A very ingenious device was devised by P. Vernier (1580–1637) for the purpose of estimating this fraction of a division with great accuracy. The great advantage of his method is that we can measure to any fraction of a division, be it to tenths, twelfths, twenty-fifths, hundredths, etc.

The instrument consists of a scale — called the vernier scale — which can slide next to the ordinary scale. This vernier scale has divisions on it which may be either a little smaller or a little larger than the divisions of the ordinary main scale along which it slides. In most cases the divisions on the vernier are smaller than those on the main scale, and it is this case which we will consider here in detail. The vernier scale is marked off into n equal divisions; the one end being called zero and usually marked correspondingly or

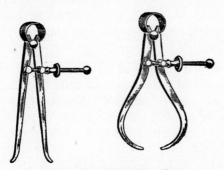

Fig. 11. Inside and outside calipers.

with an arrow. Placing this zero mark of the vernier on any main scale division, it will be seen that in the case under consideration n divisions of the vernier correspond to $(n - 1)$ divisions on the main scale. Hence each vernier division is $(n - 1)/n = (1 - 1/n)$ of a main scale division. Consequently the vernier division is $1/n$ shorter than a main scale division. This quantity $1/n$ of a main scale division is called the *least count* of the vernier and is usually expressed in centimeters or inches. Always determine the least count of a vernier before attempting to make a measurement.

Suppose next that we wish to make a measurement and find the zero of the vernier somewhere between two main scale divisions. From what has been said above about the least count, we can readily see that if the zero of the vernier is $1/n$ division (main scale) beyond the division line of the main scale (Fig. 12), then the first vernier division should coincide with a division line on the main scale.

Similarly, if the zero of the vernier should be $2/n$ divisions to the right of the main scale division, we should expect the second line beyond the zero on the vernier to correspond with a main scale division. The reason for this, of course, is that the first vernier division reduces the discrepancy between vernier division and main

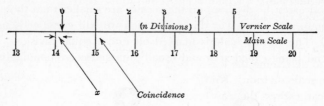

Fig. 12. Reading 14.1 if $n = 10$.

division by $1/n$, and the second by $2/n$, therefore making them coincide on the second division of the vernier (see Fig. 13).

In general, then, if we find the kth division of the vernier coincides with a scale division, we will be able to make out that the part x, which we had to estimate with our eye previously, is exactly

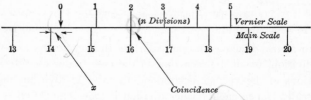

Fig. 13. Reading 14.2 if $n = 10$.

k/n main scale divisions.* *Always bear in mind that it is the zero mark on the vernier the position of which we are trying to locate as accurately as possible on the main scale.*

---

* A vernier may have a length of $(n - 2)$, $(n - 3)$, etc. scale divisions provided that n is not an exact multiple of any of these vernier lengths. However, the order of coincidences will not appear in succession of vernier divisions and will not be convenient to use. The retrograde verniers have lengths of $(n + 1)$, $(n + 2)$, etc. scale divisions. The theory, except for numbering the vernier in the opposite direction, is much the same as for the direct-reading verniers. Verniers are often made to have a scale length less by one than some multiple of the number of vernier divisions, i.e., $(2n - 1)$, $(3n - 1)$, etc. An arrangement of this type is found often on circular scales that measure to some fraction of a degree. A vernier divided into 30 divisions covering 59 of the main scale is an example, where $n = 30$.

The procedure in reading an instrument having an attached vernier scale is as follows:

1   First determine the least count. This is usually done by moving the vernier along the main scale so that the zero mark on the vernier coincides with some division on the main scale. Find out, by looking along the vernier, how many divisions on the vernier are necessary until a vernier and a main scale division coincide again. This enables one to determine the least count, as described above (i.e., $1/n$ of a main scale division). Knowing the value of the main scale division one can express the least count in inches or centimeters.

2   Set the vernier on the instrument so as to measure the length of the required object and estimate approximately its length, by noting the position of the zero of the vernier. In Figure 13 this would be 14+ · · · ·

3   Determine the fraction x by noting which vernier division coincides with a main scale division. In the above figure this would be the second. This gives for a final result, then, $14(2/n)$ main scale divisions.

The least count is usually chosen as to give the required measurement in convenient and practical cgs or fps units. Common arrange-

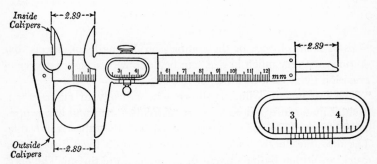

Fig. 14. Vernier caliper, reading 2.89 cm.

ments on instruments are: in the cgs system 0.01 cm (Fig. 14), and in the fps system $\frac{1}{128}$ or $\frac{1}{1000}$ inch.

In the accurate measurement of angles by means of a vernier the procedure is exactly the same. The verniers are usually arranged to read to a minute of arc (i.e., $\frac{1}{60}$ degree). This is very often accomplished by using for the main scale division a unit of $\frac{1}{2}$ degree and placing thirty divisions on the vernier to correspond with twenty-nine divisions ($\frac{1}{2}$ degree) on the main scale. When this is the case, one should not forget part 2 of the above procedure. Be sure to see whether the fraction x is in the first or second half of the larger degree divisions. If it should fall in the second half, then we must add a half-degree to x in expressing our result in degrees.

A little practice will help considerably in understanding the above principles. A well-made vernier scale forms one of the most useful, and therefore most frequently used, adjuncts to physical apparatus having to do with the measurement of lengths or angles.

The micrometer caliper   The measurement of the linear dimen-

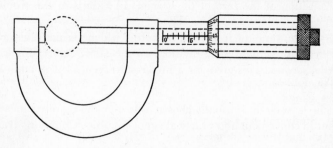

Fig. 15. Micrometer caliper.

sions of small objects, or the comparison of lengths of objects that do not vary very much in size, can be done with a higher degree of precision by using a micrometer screw.

The instrument, which is shown schematically in Figure 15, is usually made in a more or less semicircular form and has two so-called "jaws." One of the jaws is fixed and the other is movable. The movable one is made to advance a certain fixed distance for every revolution by having cut on it an accurate thread. The *pitch*, or distance that the movable jaw advances per revolution, is usually made to be 1 mm or 0.5 mm in the cgs system and $\frac{1}{40}$ inch in the fps system. If now we attach a "head" on the end of the screw, which we divide up into a large number of equally spaced divisions, we can measure the fraction of a turn that the screw is advanced. In the case of a 0.5 mm pitch screw with fifty divisions on the head, we can therefore measure to $\frac{1}{50}$ of $\frac{1}{2}$ mm $= \frac{1}{100}$ mm $= 0.01$ mm.

In addition to the divisions on the screw head a horizontal scale is usually engraved along a fixed cylindrical barrel so that the whole number of turns will be indicated. Remember again that in this case the reading on the head, which goes up to fifty, may be in the first or second half of the millimeter, and if the latter is true, then 0.5 mm must be added. When the pitch happens to be 1 mm and there are 100 divisions on the head, then the last precaution mentioned is not necessary.

A good micrometer gauge or caliper has at the end of the movable jaw a friction or ratchet device which, when used, prevents too much pressure being applied to the jaws. This ratchet device serves a double purpose. First, it prevents the operator from applying too great a force to the jaws, thus damaging the thread and jaws and so making them useless for accurate measurements. Secondly, in many cases when too great a pressure is applied, the object being measured will be slightly deformed and an error introduced in the result.

The following *procedure* is suggested when using a micrometer screw gauge:

1 Study the *pitch* of the screw by turning the head through a certain number of counted revolutions and noting the movement on the horizontal scale. Observe how many divisions there are on the head and from this determine the amount that the screw advances for a rotation of one division on the head (this might be called the least count in this case). In the above example this amount is $\frac{1}{50}$ of $\frac{1}{2}$ mm = 0.01 mm.

2 Study the *zero setting*. To test the zero, screw up the movable jaw, using the ratchet head, until it just touches the fixed jaw, and see whether the zero checks. If it does not, allowance must be made for a zero correction in future readings. In the better-made instruments the zero settings can be adjusted. This adjustment, however, should not be done by the student. Note that the pressure at contact is governed by the friction device on the ratchet head.

3 Insert the object between the jaws, using the *ratchet device* to insure just the right pressure, and take the readings. If the micrometer gauge has no ratchet head, a light contact can be made fairly reproducible only by practice.

EXPERIMENT 1

THE MEASUREMENT OF LENGTH.   VOLUME

To measure the volume of a block or a cylinder by means of a meter rule, vernier caliper, and micrometer screw, and to determine the error in each case.

APPARATUS: A numbered block or cylinder (metal) about 2 cm in length but not carefully machined, a metric rule, a vernier caliper, a micrometer screw gauge.

The volume of the metallic mass will be calculated by accurately measuring all necessary lengths. It will be necessary to measure three lengths for a rectangular block, two lengths for a cylinder, and one length for a sphere. Three separate calculations for the volume will be obtained: first, with the meter rule; second, with the vernier caliper; and third, with the micrometer screw. Then a comparison of their respective accuracies will be made. This will be your opportunity to make a practical study of significant figures outlined in Chapter II.

1 Determine the dimensions of the object using the *metric rule*. Avoid errors of parallax as described in Chapter II. Take three readings of each of the dimensions yourself, using various parts of the metric rule. Ask your partner to do the same. In each case estimate the fractions (tenths) of a millimeter. Record all your readings in tabular form.

From your data obtain for each of the measured dimensions, the following: arithmetical mean, deviations (or residuals), the average deviation of the individual readings (ad), the average deviation of the arithmetical mean (AD), and the per cent of error of the mean ($\% AD$). Calculate the resulting volume with the per cent of error in accordance with the instructions in Chapter II.

2 Determine the dimensions of the object using the *vernier caliper*. Having studied carefully the least count, etc., determine first the zero correction. Next insert the object in the caliper, being careful not to force the jaws, and take three readings of one of the dimensions. Choose various positions on the object so as to get an average value. Ask your partner to take three more. Proceed in like manner with any remaining dimensions. Record all the readings in tabular form. Use your data to find the volume and the resulting error in the same manner as with the meter rule.

3 Determine the dimensions using the *micrometer screw*. After having studied the instrument determine first the zero correction. The sign of the zero correction is easily mistaken. Insert the object and obtain all together six readings for each dimension. *Be sure to use the auxiliary milled head with ratchet device to insure constant pressure on the object and to preserve the accuracy of the micrometer screw.* From the data determine, as before, the volume and the error.

DATA

OBJECT: **A Metal Cylinder**   Number_II____

1 Volume of a cylinder, using a metric rule

Trials	Diameter (cm)	Residuals (cm)	Length (cm)	Residuals (cm)
1	1.90	−0.02	2.39	+0.002
2	1.94	+0.02	2.40	+0.012
3	1.91	−0.01	2.38	−0.008
4	1.92	0.00	2.37	−0.018
5	1.93	+0.01	2.41	+0.022
6	1.92	0.00	2.38	−0.008
Mean	1.920	±0.010	2.388	±0.012

Name of calculation	Diameter (cm)	Length (cm)
$am \left(= \dfrac{\Sigma s}{n} \right)$	1.920	2.388
$ad \left(= \dfrac{\Sigma d}{6} \right)$	0.010	0.012
$AD = \dfrac{ad}{\sqrt{6}}$	0.0041	0.0049
$\%AD \left(= \dfrac{AD}{am} \times 100 \right)$	0.21	0.21

Volume $(V) = \pi r^2 l$
$V = \pi(0.960)^2(2.388)$
$= 6.915 \text{ cm}^3 \pm 0.63\%$

NOTE that the per cent of error $(\%AD) = (2 \times 0.21) + 0.21 = 0.63\%$.

2 Volume of a cylinder using a vernier caliper.

Zero correction = 0.000 cm.   Least count = 1/10 main scale
                                                        (i.e., 1/100 cm)

Trials	Diameter (cm)	Residuals (cm)	Length (cm)	Residuals (cm)
1	1.900	−0.0050	2.360	−0.0175
2	1.910	+0.0050	2.375	−0.0025
3	1.900	−0 0050	2.380	+0.0025
4	1.910	+0.0050	2.385	+0.0075
5	1.905	0.0000	2.380	+0.0025
6	1.905	0.0000	2.385	+0.0075
Mean	1.9050	±0.0033	2.3775	±0.0067

Name of calculation	Diameter (cm)	Length (cm)	
$am \left(= \dfrac{\Sigma s}{6} \right)$	1.9050	2.3775	
$ad \left(= \dfrac{\Sigma d}{6} \right)$	0.0033	0.0067	$V = \pi r^2 l$ $V = \pi (0.9525)^2 (2.3775)$ = 6.776 cm^3 ± 0.25%
$AD \left(= \dfrac{ad}{\sqrt{6}} \right)$	0.0013	0.0027	
$\%AD \left(= \dfrac{AD}{am} \times 100 \right)$	0.068	0.11	

3 Volume of a cylinder using a micrometer gauge.

Zero correction = 0.0000 cm.   Least count = 1/1000 cm.

Trials	Diameter (cm)	Residuals (cm)	Length (cm)	Residuals (cm)
1	1.9052	+0.00038	2.3722	−0.00833
2	1.9047	−0.00012	2.3772	−0.00333
3	1.9052	+0.00038	2.3827	+0.00017
4	1.9048	−0.00002	2.3813	+0.00077
5	1.9051	+0.00028	2.3855	+0.00497
6	1.9039	−0.00092	2.3843	+0.00377
Mean	1.90482	±0.00035	2.3805	±0.0036

Name of Calculation	Diameter (cm)	Length (cm)	
$am \left(= \dfrac{\Sigma s}{6} \right)$	1.90482	2.3805	$V = \pi r^2 l$
$ad \left(= \dfrac{\Sigma d}{6} \right)$	0.00035	0.0036	$V = \pi (0.95241)^2 (2.3805)$
$AD \left(= \dfrac{ad}{\sqrt{6}} \right)$	0.00014	0.0015	$= 6.784 \text{ cm}^3 \pm 0.078\%$
$\%AD \left(= \dfrac{AD}{am} \times 100 \right)$	0.0074	0.063	

OPTIONAL EXPERIMENT 1-0

HOMEMADE VERNIER SCALE

To Construct and Use a Vernier Scale

Draw a main scale and a vernier scale on some bristol board or heavy drawing paper. Refer to Figure 16 for suggestions. The divisions on the main scale should represent some definite unit intervals such as $\frac{1}{4}$ inch or $\frac{1}{2}$ cm.

Construct the vernier to read $\frac{1}{8}$, $\frac{1}{10}$, or some other fractional unit on the main scale as suggested by the instructor.

Having drawn the scale and vernier, cut them so that they may be combined to use for measurement of the objects provided. Express your results in scale units as well as in the metric or the English system of units.

Questions (Exp. 1 or 1-0)

(There are two arbitrary scales in Figure 16, each with a vernier appropriate to the chosen scale. Thus, the vernier P_1 goes with scale P. You will note that to the right of the fixed jaw of the scale, there are some lettered straight lines. The object is to measure the distance between the fixed jaw of the arbitrary scale and some lettered line in accordance with the question asked. To make a measurement, trace over the vernier with some fairly transparent white sheet of paper, and then cut out the resulting vernier from your tracing. Or, if you use the corner of a sheet for the vernier jaw, the vernier may be constructed without cutting the paper. Now slide the re-

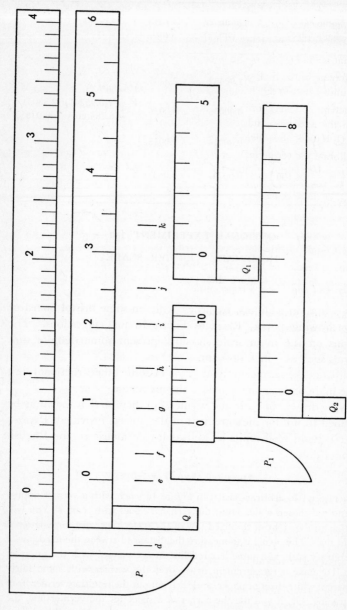

Fig. 16. Two arbitrary vernier scales P and Q. Scale P has one vernier P_1. Scale Q has two verniers, Q_1 and Q_2.

drawn vernier along the scale for the reading or readings. Make proper corrections for the initial reading if any error exists. The same directions apply to the scale Q of Figure 16 and its verniers, Q_1 and Q_2.)

(a) What is the reading of the micrometer screw of Figure 15, page 30?

(b) Referring to the main scale P of Figure 16, what is the distance in arbitrary units between the fixed jaw and the parallel line (1) d, (2) f, (3) h?

(c) Referring to scale Q of Figure 16, what is the distance in arbitrary units between the fixed jaw and the parallel line (1) e, (2) g, (3) i, when the vernier Q_1 is used, also when vernier Q_2 is used?

(d) Calibrate the vernier caliper P of Figure 16 by measuring the length of some object first with a standard vernier caliper and then with the vernier caliper P_1. What is the ratio of standard vernier units in centimeters to the arbitrary units of the scale?

(e) Repeat question d for the scale Q with vernier Q_2 (Fig. 16).

(f) Now measure the actual distance between the lines designated by letters, d and h. Compare with questions (b) and (d).

(g) Make a vernier for the scale P so that 10 divisions of the vernier cover 11 divisions on the scale. What difference, if any, do you note in use of the vernier?

(h) If a circular scale is divided into degree divisions and 30 vernier divisions cover 29 on the main scale, what is the least count?

(i) A circular scale is divided into degrees. A vernier of 10 divisions covers 21 divisions on the main scale. What is the least count?

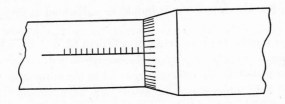

Fig. 17. Partly drawn barrel and head of a micrometer gauge.

(j) Figure 17 represents a portion of the arm and movable sleeve of a micrometer screw. Trace this drawing three times on some reasonably transparent paper and fill in the scale numbers on the arm and the movable sleeve so that the micrometer reading will be (1) 2.32 mm, (2) 4.77 mm, (3) 3.82 mm. (*Note.* Lengthen the divisions on the movable sleeve and on the arm at 5 mm intervals in accordance with conventional practice. Assume that the divisions on the arm represent 0.5 mm and that the pitch is 0.5 mm.)

THE MEASUREMENT OF MASS

There are two common methods by which the mass of an object may be determined. The one utilizes the principle of the lever, while the other is based upon the principle of elasticity.

The principle of the lever states, for our purpose, that, given a bar (called a lever), it is always possible to place it on some knife edge (or fulcrum) on which it may turn and be made to balance by placing weights properly on either side. With equal arm balances, such as the platform and fine balance, equilibrium will be established with an equal quantity of mass on each side. Hence, any standard series of masses may be used to determine the mass of an unknown with equal arm balances. With unequal arm balances, such as the fish scales and many standard scales which employ more than one lever, the masses used in the process of determining the unknown must be calibrated for the particular scale.* In any case, the result of the determination of mass is not affected by changes in the force of gravity.

The principle of elasticity explains the behavior of elastic bodies under twisting, stretching, or compressional forces. Any body which returns to its former position after a given distortion is serviceable for a balance. The spring balance is the commonest and can be made quite sensitive. While it may be calibrated and used to measure mass, it actually records the gravitational attraction on the mass. For accurate work, it should be calibrated at every place used.

Two very useful kinds of balances sufficient for our purposes will be described: the one, a *platform balance* which will weigh objects up to about 1000 g with an accuracy of 0.1 g; the other, a *fine balance* which will weigh objects up to approximately 100 g with an accuracy of 0.0001 g. Both of these balances are characterized by having pans supported by knife edges (called fulcrums) at either end of a lever arm and a third fulcrum at the center of the lever. The center fulcrum knife edge is raised slightly above the other two so that the balance arm will be in stable equilibrium.

The **platform balance** is used for quick weighings and is very useful where great accuracy is not necessary. The pans or platforms supporting the known and unknown weights are of heavy con-

* See Chapter XXXIV for description of other types of balances.

struction and are kept rigidly in an upright position by supporting rods under the balance (Fig. 18). The knife edges, which constitute the fulcrum positions, are of steel construction and rest on hardened steel or agate plates. The pans are balanced at the factory by loading cups near the bottom of the balance under the platform. An adjustment for student use is found over the center fulcrum in the form of a threaded cylindrical nut which advances on a screw either to the left or to the right. A pointer travels in front of a scale marked in arbitrary divisions. The last 10 g of mass may be added to the load by a sliding weight placed on a graduated scale in front of the balance. This scale is graduated in 0.1 g divisions. Because of this

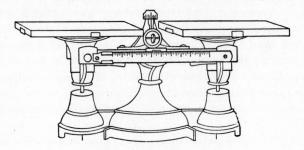

Fig. 18. Platform balance.

scale, the unknown is generally placed on the left while the known masses are placed on the right pan. Should the unknown be placed on the right-hand side, that mass indicated by the slider must be subtracted from the known masses placed on the left-hand pan.

The **fine balance** is used wherever an accurate determination of the mass is necessary. The ordinary fine balance will weigh to about 0.1 mg. If much greater accuracy is desired, the buoyancy effect of the air, due to the volumes occupied by the known and unknown masses, must be taken into account.

The pans are suspended from agate planes on either end, which in turn are supported by knife edges. The central fulcrum knife edge is supported on an agate plane which is imbedded in a pillar. A pointer fastened to the lever arm swings in front of the pillar and in front of the scale, which is graduated in arbitrary divisions and located behind the lower end of the pointer. A small weight, clamped by a set screw, is fastened on the pointer and may be moved up or down so as to raise or lower the sensitivity. When the weight is raised on the pointer, the stability of the lever system is lessened, but the balance becomes more sensitive. When the balance is made very sensitive, a long period of swing of the lever system results, and a longer time is required for the weighing. Hence the sensitivity of the balance for general use is adjusted to compromise between sensitivity and quick weighing. The zero position of the pointer on the scale can be adjusted by small threaded weights placed at the two ends of the lever arm. Every fine balance has some kind of a "rider" or chain system to make adjustments from 0.1 to 5 mg. Very often the rider will add or subtract from a load a maximum of 10 mg. The whole mechanism is placed in a glass case. When not in use, an arrestment mechanism is provided to release the agate planes from the knife edges or to raise the lever arm itself from its agate plane. This is accomplished by use of a screw head at the bottom of, and outside, the glass case of the balance. There is also a button at the left of this screw head, which may be pressed in to release the pans so that they will swing freely. When the button is pressed in and turned slightly, it will catch, so that the pans will be free without further pressure. A level is provided at the back of the balance, so as to indicate when the balance is horizontal. The balance itself is supported on three legs. The two front legs are threaded and adjustable in length.

Before attempting to weigh an object, especially when the balance is first set up, notice whether (1) the balance is level, (2) the knife edges are in position, and (3) the pointer is swinging so that the initial resting point is near the central division of the arbitrary scale. If the lever arm does not swing freely upon release by the screw head, the knife edges should be examined to see if they are properly seated when lifted by the screw head. If the pans are free to turn and the pointer does not have its zero position near the central division of the scale, an adjustment of one or both of the threaded units at each end of the lever arm should be made. All such adjustments are generally made by the instructor. With continued use, the student learns to make these adjustments himself at the direction of the instructor.

The knife edges are frequently found out of position, because of carelessness on the part of the student when weights (i.e., standard masses) are added or taken off the balance. Weights should never be added or removed from the scale pan unless the balance arms are locked by the arrestment devices. Moreover, weights should always be lifted by tweezers, since the hand leaves grease marks, which increase the mass of the weight.

Suppose that the unknown is on the left pan and certain known masses are on the right pan, and we wish to see whether a balance exists. First, turn the screw head. Then if the pans do not tip, press in the button which frees the pans. If a balance does not exist, release the button so as to bring the pans to rest and then turn the screw head so as to lock the balance arms. The known masses are generally placed on the right-hand pan because of the fact that the rider is attached to the right-hand balance arm. Each scale must be studied by itself to learn its particular arrestment device.

Because of friction at the knife edges the exact *resting point* cannot be found by allowing the pointer to come to rest because it does not always come to rest at the same point. In a sensitive balance the time taken to come to rest is also inconveniently long. Hence a *method of swings* is used to overcome these difficulties. Turn the screw head so as to release the balance arms and then press in the button gently so as to give an initial swing of about 4 to 10 divisions. If the initial swing is not enough, wave the hand in front of one of the pans to give it the desired initial swing. Close the window so

Fig. 19. Pointer scale of a balance.

that air currents will not affect the to-and-fro motion of the pointer. Then take an odd number of consecutive readings of the extreme positions of the pointer. Assume the readings to have been 8, 18, 8.5 (Fig. 19). Now in order to calculate where the pointer would come to rest on the scale, first average the two left-hand readings. Then find the mean between this average reading and the reading on the right. In the example shown, the resting point would therefore be 13.12. This is so because the average left-hand reading is 8.25, and when the mean is found between this average and 18, the result becomes $\dfrac{18 + 8.25}{2}$, which equals 13.12.

The *sensitivity of a balance* is a very important constant in comparing balances and estimating the accuracy to be expected. It is defined as the mass which must be added to the scale pan in order to deflect the pointer one division. A little consideration will show that the sensitivity decreases somewhat, on account of friction, with the increase of the load on the balance arms. Note also that bending of the balance arms with increased load causes a decrease in sensitivity.

Because of the large number of small standard masses (i.e., weights) used in weighing with a fine balance, one tries to minimize the number of weights both for simplicity and to cut down the number of accumulative errors incident with each weight. The minimum number of masses will be used when we start with the weight next smaller to the one which overbalances the unknown mass and continue to add each time that weight which is next smaller than the one which overbalances the unknown. This process continues until the smallest weight is used or until the pointer stays on the scale without further addition of weights. Most fine balances have a rider or other mechanism to furnish readings of 5 mg or less.

With a large number of standard masses on the scale pan, there is a fair probability of error in adding these masses mentally. To avoid this it is good practice to write down the masses of the weights taken from the box by a study of the empty spaces in the box. Then check off the weights as they are taken from the scale pan and replaced in the box. This method is sure, saves one from doubt, and often also the necessity of repeating a whole experiment.

If the arms are found to be unequal, the correct mass of the unknown is found by placing it on each scale pan in turn and weighing. Suppose that, when the unknown mass is in the left-hand pan, the known mass in the right-hand pan is m_1, while when the unknown mass is in the right pan, the known mass in the left-hand pan is m_2, then the correct mass M is found by theory to be

$$M = \sqrt{m_1 m_2}.$$

EXPERIMENT 2

THE MEASUREMENT OF MASS

Part (a)   *To measure the mass of an object with a platform balance.*

Part (b)   *To find the sensitivity of a fine balance and to use this sensitivity in weighing an object with the greatest possible accuracy.*

APPARATUS:

Part (a) Platform balance, set of weights (10−500 grams), unknown mass.

Part (b) Fine balance, set of weights, unknown mass (e.g., a coin), tweezers.

Part (a) Place the unknown first on the left-hand pan and weigh, than on the right-hand pan. Repeat three to five times, alternating the unknown weight from one pan to the other. Since the sliding weight in front of the scale is made for weighing when the known weights are on the right-hand pan, one should remember to subtract this weight when the known masses are placed on the left. From the data calculate the average mass for each side and its accompanying deviation. Find the per cent of error on each side, also the true weight.

$$A.D = \frac{\partial \cdot d}{\sqrt{n}} ; \quad \% A.D = \frac{A.D}{m} \times 100\%$$

DATA: UNKNOWN MASS IN GRAMS $\% = \frac{M - m_t}{m_t} \times 100\%$

LEFT PAN		RIGHT PAN	
Known Mass on Right Side	Deviations	Known Mass on Left Side	Deviations
165.3	+0.10	164.6	−0.17
165.2	0.00	164.6	−0.17
165.0	−0.20	164.9	+0.13
165.3	+0.10	165.0	+0.23

Averages 165.20	±0.10	164.77	±0.17
Per cent of error (%AD)	0.030%		0.053%

$$M = \sqrt{165.20 \times 164.77} = 164.98 \text{ grams.}$$

Mass (M) = 164.98 grams with 0.083 per cent of error.

Part (b) First determine the *zero resting point* of the balance when no load is on either pan. This should be found by the method of swings (as described in a previous section) by taking three consecutive readings of the position of the pointer on the scale (say two on the left and one on the right). From these three readings the zero resting point can be calculated. Repeat these three observations three times, obtaining an average value for this resting point. Record every reading on your data sheet.

Next place on the left pan the object to be weighed (having of course first clamped the balance arm) and on the right pan the standard weights until a balance point is found somewhere near the zero resting point as determined in the first part of this procedure. Determine this resting point now by taking as many readings for it as were taken for the zero resting point. Let us call the average value of this resting point the *load resting point 1*.

The next part of the procedure is for the purpose of finding the "sensitivity" at this load. This is done by adding (or subtracting) a small known weight to the others (say 5 mg) and redetermining the resting point with this additional little weight. Call the value thus found *load resting point 2*. By subtracting the two load resting points 1 and 2 we know how much effect the small weight had on the resting point, and consequently the sensitivity can be easily calculated since it is the weight necessary to move the pointer one division on the scale.

Now, using the sensitivity, *calculate the weight* of the object. To do this, it is to be noticed that what has to be calculated is the weight which would have to be added to (or subtracted from) the load at resting point 1, to bring it back to the zero resting point. *Knowing the sensitivity*, and the number of divisions we should like to have the pointer move to get it back to the zero resting point, we get, by multiplying these two quantities together, the weight which would have to be added (or subtracted) to bring the balance to the zero resting point.

Finally, if a rider is available, *check* this calculated value *by using the rider* on the balance arm.

Calculations We see from the data that 0.005 gram moves the pointer $(12.98 - 11.88) = 1.10$ divisions. Therefore

$$\text{Sensitivity} = \frac{0.005}{1.10} = 0.0045 \text{ gram per division.}$$

To bring the pointer back to the zero resting point from position 1, it would have to move $(12.98 - 10.43) = 2.55$ divisions; or, in other words, a mass of $(2.55 \times 0.0045) = 0.0115$ gram would have to be added to the standard masses.

Hence the final mass $= 6.200 + 0.0115 = 6.2115$ grams.

DATA: UNKNOWN ON LEFT PAN

Description of Trial	Trials	MAXIMUM SWING TO			Average Left	Resting Point	Average R.P.
		Left	Right	Left			
Zero resting point	1	3.0	18.0	3.0	3.00	10.50	
	2	1.0	19.5	1.5	1.25	10.38	
	3	5.3	15.3	5.8	5.55	10.42	10.43
Resting point (1) with load of 6.200 g	1	6.0	19.0	7.0	6.50	12.75	
	2	9.0	16.0	9.5	9.25	12.62	
	3	9.0	18.0	9.3	9.15	13.57	12.98
Resting point (2) with load of 6.200 g +0.005 g	1	4.0	19.5	4.5	4.25	11.88	
	2	9.0	14.0	9.5	9.25	11.63	
	3	7.5	16.5	8.0	7.75	12.13	11.88

Sensitivity $= 0.0045$ g/per division.
Mass to be added to standard masses $= 0.0115$ g.
Final calculation of mass $= 6.2115$ g.

For accurate weighing it is well to check on the balance by interchanging the standard masses with the object being weighed. If any difference is found between the two determinations this will probably be due to the fact that the lengths of the balance arms are not the same.

OPTIONAL EXPERIMENT

Repeat part (b) by placing the weight on the left pan and the object on the right pan.

The calculations are made in a manner similar to part (b).

DATA: UNKNOWN ON RIGHT PAN

Description of Trial	Trials	MAXIMUM SWING TO			Average Left	Resting Point	Average R.P.
		Left	Right	Left			
Zero resting point	1	1.3	19.0	2.0	1.65	10.32	
	2	2.0	18.6	2.5	2.25	10.42	
	3	5.9	15.1	6.0	5.95	10.62	10.45
Resting point (1) with load of 6.200 g	1	4.0	11.8	4.2	4.1	7.95	
	2	0.0	15.8	0.3	0.15	7.98	
	3	2.0	14.0	2.4	2.20	8.10	8.01
Resting point (2) with load of 6200 g +0.005 g	1	4.0	14.0	4.3	4.15	9.08	
	2	4.3	14.0	4.7	4.50	9.25	
	3	6.3	12.0	6.6	6.45	9.23	9.19

Sensitivity =
Mass to be added to standard masses =
Final calculation of mass =

Calculation for the true mass, allowing for inequalities in the balance arms. Let m_1 and m_2 be the masses as found on the two sides. Then the true mass (m) is found by the equation

$$m = \sqrt{m_1 m_2}.$$

Questions

(a) If the mass used in this experiment is the same one for which you found the volume in Experiment 1, calculate the density of the mass or masses of the bodies weighed in this experiment. See Chapter X for definition of density.

(b) Did you find the *weight* or *mass* of each body in this experiment?

(c) Would you expect the fine balance to give the same result on a high mountain as at sea level?

(d) Would you expect unequal arm balances, such as fish scales and the more recent triple beam scales, to give the same results on a high mountain as at sea level?

(e) Does the number representing the sensitivity increase in magnitude with increasing sensitivity?

(f) How many divisions would the pointer on the fine balance move if one milligram were added to the load?

(g) If you had done your weighing with the fine balance in a vacuum, do you think your balance was sufficiently sensitive to detect any significant difference in weight over that obtained?

PROBLEMS

Experiment 1

1 Suppose the mass of the object used in the sample data found on pages 34 and 35 weighed 7.237 ± 0.013 g, what are the density of the object and the per cent of error. Use the data obtained with the micrometer screw, page 35. Density is defined as the mass per unit volume. See page 121 for further information on density.

2 You are given a micrometer screw with 20 threads per cm on the scale and with 50 divisions on the revolving sleeve. When the jaws are closed it is found that the micrometer does not come all the way to the zero division by 0.053 mm as read on the scale and revolving head combined. An object is found to measure 3.472 mm with this micrometer. What is the correct reading?

3 Make up a vernier scale such that 5 main scale divisions are equal in distance to 8 on the vernier. Give the order of coincidence of the vernier divisions for successive $\frac{1}{8}$ main scale intervals.

4 Suppose that the mass of the metal cylinder used in the sample data, pages 33, 34 and 35 was intended as a standard mass of 50 g with an average deviation of 50 mg. What will be the density of the object when calculated from the values of the volume found with each instrument? Give complete reasons for the calculated error in the density.

5 A scale is divided into sixteenths of an inch. It is required to read to $\frac{1}{128}$ in. by a suitable vernier. Calculate the number of divisions on the vernier and show by means of a diagram the position of the vernier on the main scale when reading $2\frac{43}{128}$ in.

6 A micrometer gauge has 40 threads per in. There are 25 divisions on the revolving head. Draw a diagram to properly show a reading of $\frac{765}{1000}$ in.

7 A circular scale is constructed so that 59 scale divisions cover 30 vernier divisions. If the scale is divided into $\frac{1}{2}$ degree intervals, what is the least count?

8 A circular scale is divided into $\frac{1}{3}$ degree intervals. It is provided with a vernier of 40 divisions covering 39 scale divisions. What is the least count?

9 A circular scale is divided into $\frac{1}{2}$ degree intervals and is provided with a vernier of 10 divisions covering 21 scale divisions. What is the least count?

PROBLEMS

Experiment 2

1 A balance has a zero resting point of 8.6. A load of 6.430 g is placed on the left pan with the standard weights on the right. The resting point (1) is now found to be 7.1. On addition of a 10-mg weight to the right pan the resting point is found to be 6.2. Calculate the sensitivity of the balance and also the weight of the unknown load.

2 Calculate the resting point, given the following consecutive readings on the scale: 4.2, 13.8, 4.7. Why is this method used for finding the resting point of the balance?

3 Define what is meant by the sensitivity of a balance. Finish the calculations in the optional experiment and find the value of the sensitivity and the unknown mass when placed on the right-hand pan. Determine also the true mass.

4 If the resting point for the load of 6.430 g in problem 1 had been 12.3, and when an additional 10-mg weight had been added it changed to 10.3, what would be the sensitivity of the balance and the weight of the unknown load?

PART 2   MECHANICS

CHAPTER IV

STATICS

The branch of mechanics which deals with the equilibrium of a particle, or of a system of particles distributed at fixed distances relative to each other (i.e., a rigid body), is termed *statics*.

When a body is at rest, it does not necessarily mean that there are no forces acting on it. What more often occurs in practice is that there are forces acting on the body, but they act in such a way that they keep the body in equilibrium. Furthermore, should the particle or body be moving with a constant velocity (either linear or angular or both), then if it keeps on moving with the same velocity and in the same direction, we still speak of the system as being *in equilibrium*, and the same laws are true in this case as were true when the body or particle was being held stationary. In this chapter, we shall study experimentally some of the laws which govern the behavior of these forces which keep a system in equilibrium.

In order to be in equilibrium when a given system of forces is acting, a body must be in equilibrium both as to (1) translation and (2) rotation. Both conditions for equilibrium are necessary when we are dealing with a *rigid* body where the forces are distributed. If the forces are acting at a point or if we are dealing with forces on a *particle*, the translatory condition for equilibrium only is required. In the study of the laws of statics then, it is natural to divide all bodies into two groups, depending upon whether we are dealing with a *particle*, which has mass but no appreciable size, or a *rigid body*, which has both mass and size.

THE EQUILIBRIUM CONDITIONS FOR A RIGID BODY

In this discussion we will simplify the two general conditions by considering all the forces which act on the body to be in one plane, i.e., the XY — coordinate plane. When this is the case, then we can show that if the body is to be in complete equilibrium, *both* the following two laws must be satisfied:

1 *The vector sum of all the external forces acting on the body must be zero.* That is, $\Sigma F = 0$.

Another way of stating this same law is to say that the vector sum of all the components of the external forces parallel to any straight line must add up to zero; i.e., $\Sigma F_x = 0$, $\Sigma F_y = 0$.

2 *The sum of the moments of all the external forces acting on the body must be zero around any axis which we wish to choose perpendicular to the plane in which the forces act.*

Since a moment of force (L) is defined as the product of the force and the perpendicular distance from the axis to the line of action of the force, the rotational equilibrium condition stated mathematically is, $\Sigma L = 0$.

In order to be able to apply these two laws of equilibrium, it is necessary to know how to deal with vectors, since forces fall under the general heading of vectors. The following section applies to vectors generally.

THE GEOMETRY OF VECTORS

Addition of vectors   In order to find the sum, or resultant vector, of the four vectors, proceed graphically as follows: Represent force

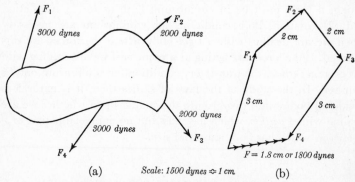

Fig. 20. Addition of vectors (graphically).

F_1 by an arrow of suitable length and proper direction; then, at the tip of the arrow F_1, place the heel of the arrow which represents

F_2, in magnitude and direction; at the tip of F_2, place the arrow representing F_3 in direction and magnitude; and so on. Continue in this way until all the vectors have been drawn (in this case, four). Then finally draw an arrow from the heel of the first arrow to the tip of the last arrow. This vector represents both in magnitude and direction the resultant or sum, shown as F in Figure 20 b.

Resolution of vectors In many cases in which we are dealing with a vector, the problem can be much simplified by splitting a vector up into component parts or vectors, so that the sum of these component vectors together form the original vector. Then for the purposes of the problem in hand, we can neglect the original vector and deal only with the *component vectors* (the so-called "components"). Just as in algebra we can split 5 up into $2 + 3$, $2.5 + 2.5$, $1 + 4$, etc., and do so indefinitely, so we can find many components for a

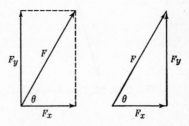

Fig. 21. Resolution of a vector (F) into components.

single vector. For practical purposes we usually *find the components of a vector in two directions at right angles to each other.* For example, in Figure 21 we see that the vector F can be split up into two components, F_x and F_y, at right angles to each other, in such a way that $F_x + F_y = F$ (i.e., when added as vectors). In this case we see that

$$F_x = F \cos \theta$$

and $$F_y = F \cos (90 - \theta) = F \sin \theta.$$

EQUILIBRIUM

The equilibrium of a particle This is the simplest case of equilibrium. Here the forces all meet at a point, because the particle on which they act is negligible in size. Let us also assume, for the time being, negligible mass. *The law of equilibrium of a particle states that when a number of forces F_1, F_2, F_3, F_4, etc., act on a particle and keep it in equilibrium, the resultant force is zero;* or, in other words, when the lines representing the vectors F_1, F_2, F_3, F_4, etc., are placed end to end, they must form a closed figure so that no sum or resultant vector (F above) is possible.

Example 1   Figure 22 represents four forces acting on a particle keeping it in equilibrium. All forces are known. The left diagram

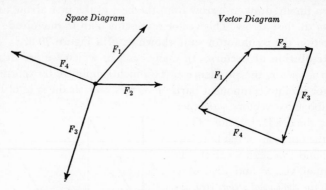

Fig. 22. Four forces keeping a particle in equilibrium.

shows the arrangement of the forces in space, whereas the diagram to the right represents the vector diagram. Note that since equilibrium exists, the four vectors form the sides of a closed figure (the force polygon).

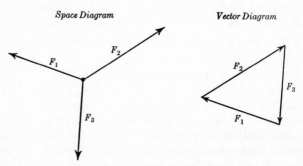

Fig. 23. Three forces producing equilibrium.

Example 2   In this case there are three known forces keeping the particle in equilibrium. The vector diagram becomes a triangle, as shown in Figure 23.

Example 3   Figure 24 represents a particle in equilibrium acted upon by three forces, two of which are known. The problem is to find the unknown force F_u. There are two methods of procedure:

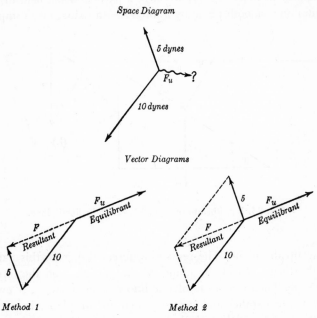

Fig. 24. Graphical method for finding an unknown force.

METHOD 1 Draw the two known forces to scale, with the end of the second placed on the tip of the first, and complete with a third vector F which will be the resultant of the two known vectors. The desired vector, called the equilibrant force, is F_u and is equal in magnitude but opposite in direction to the vector force F.

METHOD 2 Parallelogram of force method. Draw the known vectors from the same point and complete a parallelogram with these two as sides. The diagonal represents the sum F (check these and see that it is the same as by the above method). Then F reversed is the unknown vector F_u, which will give equilibrium (i.e., equilibrant).

Example 4 Another example is to be found by a consideration of the *inclined plane*. It is much easier to solve questions involving motion or equilibrium on an inclined plane, if we resolve each force into components, one along the plane and the other perpendicular to its surface.

Suppose in Figure 25 (a) we have a particle being held in equilibrium on a smooth plane by a force F — a string, for example —

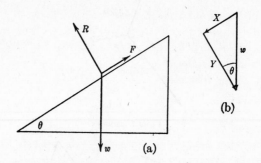

Fig. 25. Equilibrium of a particle on an inclined plane.

acting up the plane. The remaining forces acting on this particle are the thrust (R) of the plane on the particle, and the force of gravity w. Then we can resolve w into two components, X and Y, respectively parallel and perpendicular to the plane, i.e., in the directions of R and F, such that

$$X = w \sin \theta,$$
$$Y = w \cos \theta.$$

Having done this, we need now only work with X and Y and can neglect w. For equilibrium we see that F must balance X, and R must balance Y, hence

$$F = w \sin \theta,$$
$$R = w \cos \theta.$$

There are two other useful trigonometrical relationships, known as the cosine law and the sine law. Consider the three forces F_1, F_2, F_3 in Figure 26 to be in equilibrium. Then the magnitude of force F_1 is related to the other two forces by the cosine formula $F_1^2 = F_2^2 + F_3^2 + 2F_2F_3 \cos \theta$, or the equivalent formula $F_1^2 = F_2^2 + F_3^2 -$

$2F_2F_3 \cos \phi_1$. The sine formula relating forces and angles in the force triangle of Figure 26(b) is

$$\frac{F_1}{\sin \phi_1} = \frac{F_2}{\sin \phi_2} = \frac{F_3}{\sin \phi_3}.$$

The equilibrium of a rigid body   A rigid body has to have an additional test applied to it, to be sure it is in equilibrium. In the

above cases of a particle, the law of equilibrium states that there can be no *translational* acceleration since the resultant force acting on the particle was zero. This same law still holds for a rigid body. This, however, is only half of the test for equilibrium, since a rigid body as a whole might still be in translational equilibrium while rotating around some axis. We need a further test to see if the body is in rotational equilibrium. This test consists in seeing whether it obeys the *law of moments. This law states that*

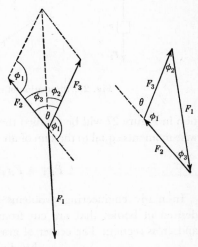

Fig. 26. Three forces acting on a point in equilibrium.

the sum of the moments around any axis must be zero. Remember that the *moment of a force* is the product of the force, and the perpendicular drawn from the axis to the direction in which this force acts. A clockwise moment is usually called positive and a counterclockwise moment is called negative.

The rotary equilibrium condition is illustrated in Figure 27 where a mass m_2 is hung from a massive rod at a distance r_2 from the pivotal point O. The mass is kept in equilibrium by a force F_1 whose perpendicular distance from point O is r_1. Since the rod is heavy, its weight must be considered also. The weight (w) of the rod may be properly accounted for in the moments equation by considering the entire weight of the rod to be concentrated at the *center of gravity*, which may be *defined* as the point where the entire mass may be considered concentrated and be subjected to the same gravitational force as before the concentration. The center of gravity is found by balancing the rod on a fulcrum. Let the center of gravity be d units of distance from point O. The rotary equilibrium condi-

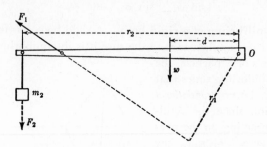

Fig. 27. Illustration of rotary equilibrium.

tion in Figure 27 will be satisfied then if we set the sum of all clockwise moments equal to the sum of all counterclockwise moments, i.e.,

$$F_1 r_1 = F_2 r_2 + wd.$$

In many engineering problems the center of gravity will be desired of bodies that are cut from materials of uniform density and cross section. The center of gravity of the body may be found

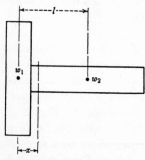

Fig. 28. Location of center of gravity by appropriate geometrical considerations.

by dividing it into parts of such a nature that the center of each part may be found by appropriate geometrical considerations. Then the resultant center of gravity may be calculated. Thus in the T-section of Figure 28, the center of gravity of the left rectangle will be the intersection of its two diagonals, and the weight w_1 of this parallelogram may be considered as located at this intersection. If the weight of the right rectangle is w_2 and is considered as located at its center of gravity (i.e., intersection of its diagonals), then the center of gravity of the whole T-section is found from the equation $w_1 x = w_2(l - x)$ where l is known.

EXPERIMENT 3

THE EQUILIBRIUM OF A PARTICLE

An experimental study of the law of equilibrium of a particle.

Part (a)   *Three forces. To find the resultant graphically. (The resultant should be zero.)*

Part (b)   *Three forces. To use the cosine law to demonstrate equilibrium.*

Part (c)   *Four forces. To show that the sum of the components of all the forces in any two directions is zero (i.e., in the X- and Y-directions, $\Sigma F_x = 0$, $\Sigma F_y = 0$ for equilibrium).*

APPARATUS: Force table, or equivalent, with appropriate hangers; slotted weights and pulleys; string; ruler; triangle.

The experiment refers to a particle only in the sense that the forces are all applied at a single point.   Note that *all forces used are due to the gravitational pull on standard masses*, which in turn are often called weights.

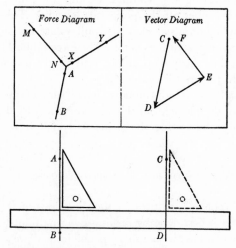

Fig. 29. Constructing a triangle of forces.

Part (a) Three known forces   Draw a thin pencil line across a sheet of paper so as to divide the paper into halves, as shown in Figure 29.   On the one half, construct the space diagram.   This is simply a transfer to this half of the paper of the known forces and their directions from the actual conditions of the experiment The other half can then be used to construct the vector-addition graphically.

*For a force table top of wood.** Pin the paper by means of two or three thumbtacks to the force table in such a way that the center of one half of the paper is approximately in the middle of the force board. Tie three pieces of string, of approximately the same length, together in a small knot, passing the free ends over three pulleys arranged at the edges of the board. On these ends attach the hangers and add known unequal masses until the knot comes to rest approximately at the center of the force table.

In order to obtain good results, two or three precautions must be taken. First, see that the pulleys have as little friction as possible. Second, make sure that the strings are as close to the paper as possible without the knot touching the board. This point is usually taken care of in making the apparatus, but in some instances the height of the pulleys above the plane of the board can be adjusted. Finally, before taking any readings, see that the pulley groove and the string as it comes off the pulley are parallel. This necessitates having the pulley on a swivel. If the pulleys are not on swivels, the knot must come to rest at the center of the force table. This is accomplished by trying the pulley at different places around the force table top until the knot is centered.

Having made these adjustments, make sure of the position of equilibrium of the particle (in this case the knot) by displacing the system slightly and noting the point to which it returns. If, on account of friction, the particle does not always return to the same point, displace the system several times, marking the points to which the particle returns and then set the knot in the center of this region.

The next problem is to transfer the directions of these forces to the paper. This is best done by making two small dots (as far apart as the paper will allow) with a sharp pencil immediately underneath each string. This must be done with care so as not to displace the system, and also to avoid errors of parallax. Having obtained these six points (in the case of the three strings attached to the particle),

* If the force table top is made of steel, omit what follows up to the section "For force table top of steel."

remove the sheet of paper and join the pairs of points. Along these three directions write the corresponding total weight that is pulling on the strings. The accuracy of your results depends largely upon obtaining these directions exactly.

For a force table top of steel. Force tables (Fig. 30) made of steel usually have the circumference divided into degrees. One end of

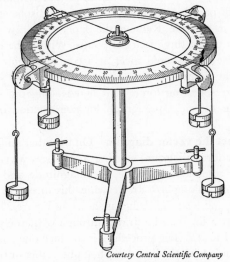

Courtesy Central Scientific Company

Fig. 30. Force table with a steel top.

each string (three strings for part a) is fastened to a ring which goes over a centering pin. Hangers are fastened to the other ends of the strings. The three strings are now placed over pulleys unequally spaced about the circumference of the circle. The centering pin keeps the masses as added from dropping on the table below. Add masses to the hangers until the center of the ring is as nearly centered about the pin as possible. If sufficient masses are not available, the final centering adjustment may be made by moving the pulleys around on the circle as needed. Displace the ring vertically from time to time so that this centering will be obtained as free from the effects of friction as possible.

With the ring centered about the pin, there are now two ways of obtaining the force diagram. One method is to measure the angle between the strings in degrees by means of the graduated circumference. Care should be taken to record properly the magnitude of the force represented by each string. The force diagram may be drawn by means of a protractor. Proceed as in the second paragraph below for construction of the vector diagram.

The other method is to remove the centering pin and place the paper on the force table. Make two small dots (as far apart as the paper will allow) with a sharp pencil immediately underneath each string. Avoid parallax and any accidental displacement of the system as far as possible. Remove the paper and draw straight lines through each of the three pairs of points. Within the experimental error the three lines should meet at a common point which is the position of the centering pin. Along each of these straight lines write the corresponding forces that acted along the strings. Now proceed as in the next paragraph for construction of the vector diagram.

To construct the vector diagram   On the other half of the sheet, adjoining the force diagram, starting at C, draw a vector CD representing, on some suitable scale, the magnitude and direction of the known force along AB. In drawing this direction it is best to use a triangle and a straight edge as shown in Figure 29. This figure illustrates how a line can be drawn through C (namely, CD) accurately parallel to AB. The procedure is to place one edge of the triangle to coincide with the line AB. Then put a ruler or other straight edge along another side of the triangle, being careful to hold the triangle in place with one edge along AB. Now keep the ruler fixed and slide the triangle along the ruler until the side which was parallel to AB now passes through C. Then draw CD, which will be parallel to AB. From the end D, draw DE to represent the second force (along XY). Finally construct EF to represent the force along MN. Now if these forces had been represented correctly, then according to the *law of equilibrium of a particle, the third vector should finish exactly where the first vector began* (viz., at C).

Note the difference in your drawing between the points F and C, and from a measurement of the length of this difference calculate the error. Express the error in per cent (of the last force represented) and note also the error in direction.

It is advisable to use a fairly hard pencil in all graphical constructions. Choose the scale of representation as large as the paper will allow.

Part (b) Change the angles between and magnitudes of the forces so as to obtain a new balance (Fig. 31). Draw the diagonal to the parallelogram made up of two sides F_2 and F_3, representing two of the forces. If the angle between F_2 and F_3 is θ, then the resultant force of the two forces will be $R = \sqrt{F_2^2 + F_3^2 + 2 F_2 F_3 \cos \theta}$, and R should be equal in magnitude to the force F_1 (the equilibrant) but opposite in direction. Determine the error from the mean between the magnitudes of F_1 and R.

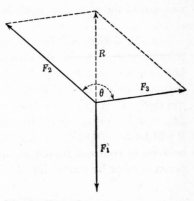

Fig. 31. Three forces acting on a single point in equilibrium.

Part (c) Tie the fourth string to the particle (or ring) and balance the four unequal forces by means of the available weights. We will show that the resultant force is zero by proving that the

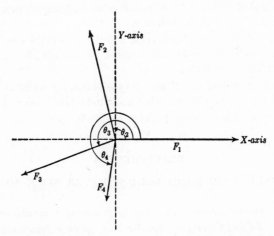

Fig. 32. Four forces acting on a single point in equilibrium.

sum of the components of forces along any two perpendicular axes are zero. If the experiment is confined to a plane, then it will be sufficient to show that the sum of the components along the X-axis ($\Sigma F_x = 0$) and along the Y-axis ($\Sigma F_y = 0$) are equal to zero as stated on page 52. That is, when a particle is in equilibrium, the sum of the components of all forces in *any* direction is equal to zero.

The calculations will be somewhat simplified if we let the X-axis coincide (Fig. 32) with the direction of force F_1; then θ_1, the angle between the force F_1 and the X-axis, will be zero. Let the angles between the X-axis and forces F_2, F_3, and F_4 be θ_2, θ_3, and θ_4 respectively, then $\Sigma F_x = F_1 + F_2 \cos \theta_2 + F_3 \cos \theta_3 + F_4 \cos \theta_4$, and $\Sigma F_y = 0 + F_2 \sin \theta_2 + F_3 \sin \theta_3 + F_4 \sin \theta_4$ and the resultant force R will be $R = \sqrt{(\Sigma F_x)^2 + (\Sigma F_y)^2}$. Since ΣF_x and ΣF_y should each be zero, of course R should theoretically be zero also. Calculate a per cent error by comparing R with the smallest of the four forces.

Questions

(a) Assume that the hangers weigh exactly 50 g each. May they be neglected when the angles between the adjacent strings are (1) equal, (2) unequal? Would the weight of the hangers figure in the per cent of error?

(b) Compare graphically in part (b) the sum of the forces (1) F_2 and F_3 with F_1; (2) F_2 and F_1 with F_3; (3) F_3 and F_1 with F_2. Compare in a direction parallel to the single force in each case.

(c) In part (a), the suggestion is made that the error in per cent be calculated with reference to the last force added. Do you consider this method accurate or a compromise?

(d) What magnitude or magnitudes did you obtain for $\sqrt{(\Sigma F_x)^2 + (\Sigma F_y)^2}$ in part (c) of your experiment? What magnitude should you get?

(e) Repeat question (b) except, *compare by calculation*.

EXPERIMENT 4

EQUILIBRIUM OF RIGID BODIES, METER STICK METHOD

Part (a)   *Determination of the center of gravity of a nonuniform bar.*

Part (b)   *To find the mass of this bar being given a known mass.*

Part (c)   *To show that the sum of the moments of forces equals zero when the bar is balanced.*

Part (d)   *To show that the sum of the forces and the sum of the moments of forces equal zero for equilibrium of a rigid body.*

APPARATUS: A meter bar which is nonuniformly loaded by little metal slugs built into the bar; two spring balances; a knife-edged clamp which can be fixed at any point along the bar; a vertical support for this knife-edged clamp; two movable clamps from which to hang the known masses, a 50-gram mass, and two other standard masses (Fig. 33); some overhead horizontal bar support.

Part (a) The position of the center of gravity of the bar is determined by balancing the bar on a knife edge. The vertical plane

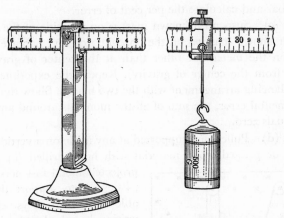

Fig. 33. Arrangement for equilibrium of moments.

through the knife edge passes through the center of gravity. Find the center of gravity by balancing the bar on two opposite sides if the bar is thick. The center of gravity passes through the two vertical intersecting lines.

In the following parts of this experiment when other forces are also applied to the bar, the nonuniform meter bar will be balanced at some point called the fulcrum. This fulcrum point will not coincide in general with the center of gravity of the bar. Hence, the weight of the meter bar can be neglected only when the point of balance (i.e., the fulcrum point) and the center of gravity of the meter bar coincide.

Part (b) Balance the bar on a knife edge (Fig. 33) when a standard mass of 50 grams is hung from some point along the bar.

Measure the distance of the previously mentioned point from the fulcrum and also the distance of center of gravity of the bar from the fulcrum. Write the equation for rotational equilibrium and solve for the mass (or weight) of the meter stick. Note again that the *weight* (*w*) of an object is the pull of gravity on a *mass* and is equal to *mg* in absolute units and is equal numerically to *m* in gravitational units. The hanger and any knife-edged clamp must be included in the calculations.

Repeat using different positions for the 50-gram standard mass. After tabulation of your results, find an average value for the mass of the bar and calculate the per cent of error.

Part (c) Suspend a known mass *m* on one side of the bar and another known mass m_2 on the opposite side and balance at some point on the meter bar other than at the center of gravity (say 10 cm from the center of gravity). Repeat the experiment using any balancing arrangement with the two masses. Show that, within experimental error, the sum of all the moments around any chosen axis equals zero.

Part (d) Pulleys are supported at any angle on a vertical frame, board, or pressed wood material with holes drilled (or properly

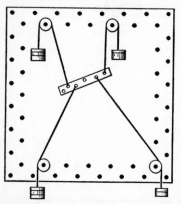

projected metal fasteners placed) as desired to support the available type of pulleys. A raised writing board placed within the drilled periphery with a paper clasp at the top will assist in a more accurate drawing of the directions of the forces and of the angle of the bar. The two objectives are to show: (1) that the sum of the torques about the bar at any point are equal to zero, and (2) that the sum of all forces acting on the bar are zero. Details as to experimental pro-

Fig. 34. Moments of forces about a light aluminum frame.

cedure are left to the individual. If the bar used does not have negligible mass, the torque and force contributions due to its weight must be included in the summation processes for a more exact evaluation respecting equilibrium conditions.

Questions

(a) In part (c), choose a new position about which the sum of the moments can be calculated. What is the resultant moment of force now?

(b) Can you give any reason to indicate why the center of gravity of a rigid nonuniform bar will be located at the point mentioned in the experiment?

(c) What condition or conditions must be fulfilled so that equilibrium is possible for (1) a particle, (2) a rigid body?

OPTIONAL EXPERIMENT, 4–0

EQUILIBRIUM OF A RIGID BODY, FORCE TABLE METHOD

To show that the sum of the forces and the sum of the moments of forces are equal to zero when a body is in equilibrium.

APPARATUS: Force table, or equivalent, with appropriate hangers; slotted weights and pulleys; string; ruler; triangle; 20-gage aluminum square about 8 cm on a side with holes along each edge.

Cut a square of 20-gage aluminum to about 8 cm square and bore holes along each edge so that string or appropriate snaps may be fastened at random positions about the edges. Connect three or more strings as directed by the instructor to the square and tie to hangers placed over pulleys on a horizontal force table. You will have forces now which may be balanced as in Experiment 3 (equilibrium of a particle) but the forces are distributed instead of diverging from a point. Hence, there will be moments of forces, as well as forces, which are balanced. Calculate graphically the sum of the forces after equilibrium has been established.

To show that the moments of forces are zero, you may consider any point you wish as the fulcrum point about which to calculate the magnitude of all moments of forces. The position about which you calculate the moments is optional as long as the system is in equilibrium.

The lightness of aluminum makes this method possible and eliminates frictional difficulties encountered when ball-bearing methods are used to float the plate that is to be balanced.

Question

(a) Calculate the sum of the forces by the method of Experiment 3, part (c).

PROBLEMS

Experiment 3

1 Find by graphical construction the vector sum of the following forces whose directions are indicated in the table below.

PROBLEM	DIRECTION							
	N	NE	E	SE	S	SW	W	NW
(a)	10	0	0	5	0	0	10	0
(b)	10	5	0	7	0	0	5	0
(c)	0	15	10	0	20	0	0	10
(d)	0	0	15	0	0	20	10	5

2 Parts (a) and (b) of our experiment may be done with apparatus as shown in Figure 35. This apparatus consists of two pulleys fastened to a ver-

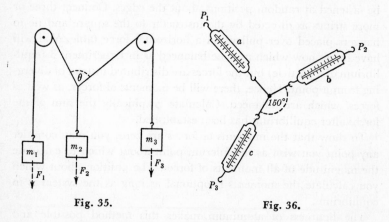

Fig. 35.   **Fig. 36.**

tical board and weights hung so that all strings are parallel to the board. If $F_1 = 100$ g, $F_2 = 150$ g, and $\theta = 80$ degrees, what is the magnitude of F_3?

3 Three spring balances are fastened to a knotted string as shown in Figure 36 and stretched so that each in turn is fastened to pegs P_1, P_2, and P_3. Balances b and c are correctly calibrated and give readings of 350 and 300 g, respectively. The reading on the uncalibrated spring balance is 185 g. What should the balance *a* read? What is the correct angle between the forces represented by the balances *a* and *c*? [*Note.* The angle between the forces *b* and *c* is 150 degrees.]

Experiment 4

1 Without assuming the position of the center of gravity of the bar, how can both this position and the weight of the bar be found by balancing the bar on a knife edge at two positions by means of a 50-g mass (see part b of the experiment)?

2 A meter stick has a small hole drilled in it at point *O* and then fastened loosely to a horizontal board by a nail (see Fig. 37). Another nail is driven

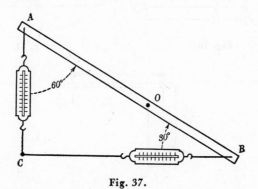

Fig. 37.

into the board at *C*. A spring balance is fastened between point *A* on the meter stick and *C*, and another balance is fastened from point *B* on the meter stick to *C*. The balances are under tension so that the one between *C* and *A* reads 200 g. The angle *CAO* is 60° and angle *OBC* is 30°. What must the balance between *C* and *B* read if *AO* = 60 cm and *OB* = 35 cm? (*Note.* This form of apparatus may be used to perform Experiment 4.)

3 What are the clockwise moments around *O* in Figure 37?

4 Determine graphically the force on the nail at point *O*.

5 A picture weighing 30 lb is hung by a cord that will hold a maximum of 20 lb. The two ends of the cord are connected to the two sides of the picture and hung over a nail. Find graphically the largest possible cord angular opening at the nail.

The following diagrams (Figs. 38 to 42 inclusive) represent flat surfaces of uniform thickness and density. Locate the center of gravity in each figure. The distances are given in arbitrary units.

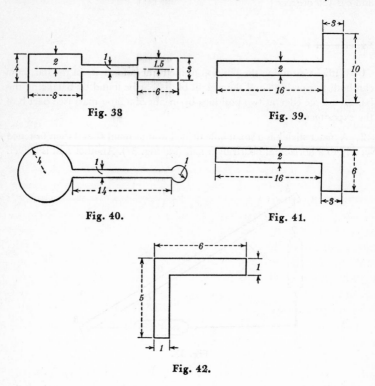

Fig. 38.

Fig. 39.

Fig. 40.

Fig. 41.

Fig. 42.

CHAPTER V

CONSTANT LINEAR ACCELERATION

The simplest type of motion is one in which every particle of a system moves in a straight line with constant speed v. The *velocity* in such cases can be considered to be *constant*, and it is a fairly simple matter to find out how far the object or particle has traveled in a given time. This distance can be represented by the equation:

$$s = vt \tag{1}$$

where v represents the velocity and t represents the elapsed time. In scientific work the units used for velocity are almost always those employing the fundamental units for length and time. Consequently they are the centimeter per second, the meter per second, and the foot per second, depending upon whether the metric or British system of units is being used. Whenever the student is in doubt about units, he should develop the habit of working with the fundamental units.

If the velocity should change during the time under consideration, either in magnitude or direction, then the above relationship (equation 1) can still be used to represent the distance covered. In such cases, however, the velocities* during very short time intervals should be estimated and then some sort of time average calculated such that when this average velocity is multiplied by the total given time, the product will give a correct measure of the distance traversed.

In principle, it is quite simple to measure constant velocities, since it is necessary only to time a given displacement. When the velocities become very great, or the time interval of the motion very small, special and often very ingenious experimental methods have to be undertaken. As an example, consider the problem of measuring

---

* In general, the *velocity at any instant* is defined as the time rate of displacement at that instant. If the time rate is changing, then strictly speaking the time interval and the displacement should be made infinitely small.

71

a bullet's velocity while traveling the length of a gun barrel, assuming the velocity to be constant. One method of measuring the time taken by the bullet in the gun consists in placing contacts known distances apart along the length of the barrel and recording automatically the time of passage of the bullet by means of electric impulses. These leave a permanent record on a photographic film, and by comparing them with standard time markings on the film it is possible to measure the time of flight.

This chapter, however, concerns itself with a rather common type of linear motion in which the velocity changes, but in a very regular way. The motion is known as *uniformly accelerated* motion and is characterized by the fact that the velocity changes by the same amount during consecutive and equal time intervals. As an example of such a motion, consider a sled traveling downhill, which at the end of consecutive half-second intervals has velocities 20, 24, 28, 32 ft per sec. It is seen that the increase in velocity (4 ft per sec) is constant for every half-second. Such motions are called uniformly accelerated motions and are characterized numerically by defining their *acceleration* as the time rate of change of the velocity. In the example just given, the acceleration is

$$\frac{\text{change in velocity}}{\text{time taken for the change}} = \frac{4 \text{ ft per sec}}{\frac{1}{2} \text{ sec}} = 8 \text{ ft per sec per sec.}$$

Note that the fundamental units (ft per sec per sec, or cm per sec per sec) are the proper and usually most convenient units to use. Perhaps the most important examples of linear motion with constant acceleration are to be found in freely falling objects. The earth's attraction for small objects near the surface is such that the object will fall and travel toward the earth's center of gravity with constant acceleration, which is another way of saying that the velocity increases at a uniform rate. Many experiments have been performed in order to measure the acceleration of freely falling objects. When the experiments are carefully performed in a vacuum, in order to eliminate the effects of air resistance, they all verify the conclusion, arrived at by Galileo in his public demonstrations of the laws of falling bodies, that all objects in the same locality fall with the same constant acceleration. This acceleration (g) is known as the gravitational acceleration and has a value of approximately 32 ft per sec per sec or 980 cm per sec per sec, depending upon whether the British or the metric (cgs) system of units has been used in the measurements.

Two experimental methods for determining the gravitational acceleration g will be described in this chapter. A third method involving the simple pendulum is described in Chapter XIII, page 159.

DIRECT DETERMINATION OF g WITH A FREE FALL APPARATUS

These methods involve a freely falling object, such as a tuning fork in Figure 43a or an object O in Figure 43b. The apparatus is so designed that the falling object leaves a record on a chart of its position at known and fixed time intervals.

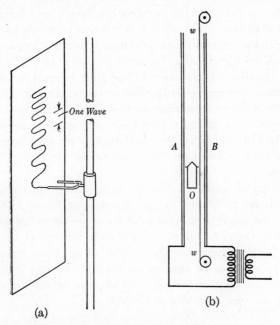

Fig. 43. Free-fall methods for determining g.

In the case of the falling tuning fork (Fig. 43a) if the frequency (f) of the fork is known (e.g., 440 cycles per second — middle A on the musical scale) the stylus attached to one prong will trace one wave (from crest to crest) in $1/f$ second. The distances fallen in consecutive time intervals of duration $1/f$ second can be measured on the record.

Or again, in the case of the free fall apparatus shown in Figure 43b the apparatus is so designed that the metal object (O) falls in front of and very close to a waxed strip of paper (w) placed between two metallic electrical conductors A and B. A motor with contact-making device, or a mechanical interrupter type of mechanism produces sparks that jump between $A-O-B$ at known fixed time intervals $1/f$ second (usually $\frac{1}{30}$ or $\frac{1}{120}$ sec). As the object falls, small dots and holes are left on the wax record, marking the position of O at time intervals $1/f$ second apart. Thus, as in the falling fork method, a record is obtained showing the distance fallen by the object during consecutive time intervals of $1/f$ second.

In order to calculate the acceleration, which is defined as the time rate of change of the velocity, it becomes necessary to measure the velocities at various times. The instantaneous velocities cannot be determined directly, but the *average velocities* can be found by dividing the distance traversed in one time interval by the time $(1/f)$. These average velocities also represent the *true velocities* at the middle of one of these time intervals. The change in the calculated velocities per unit of time will give the required acceleration. The method of calculation for g is essentially the same whether we use the falling tuning fork (Fig. 43a) or the free fall (Fig. 43b) apparatus.

The theory as outlined below will be specific in that it will refer to the two methods used in our experiments 5 and 5–O. Since, however, the theory is general in so far as we use every spot as in Experiment 5 or every other spot as in Experiment 5–O, the symbol f will be used to designate the number of spots per second. The number of spots to be counted in each of the two experiments represents the only remaining part of arbitrariness in order to make the theoretical approach relatively simple.

THEORY BEHR FREE-FALL METHOD

(Every spark spot interval used)

Velocities   Let $\bar{v}_1$ be the average velocity during the time interval $1/f$ to $2/f$ second, where f represents the number of sparks per second (See Fig. 45 where $f = 30$). If the distance covered in this time interval is d_1, then $\bar{v}_1 = fd_1$ by definition of average velocity. Likewise $\bar{v}_2$, $\bar{v}_3$, $\bar{v}_4$, $\cdots \bar{v}_k$ will have velocities* fd_2, fd_3, $fd_4 \cdots fd_k$ where $k = 1, 2, 3$, etc.

Since the time interval between consecutive spot intervals is $1/f$ second and between each numbered interval (i.e., d_1, d_2, etc.) is $2/f$ second, the acceleration may be calculated readily as soon as we specify the time interval through which our change in velocity is to be calculated. Assume as in Experiment 5 that six intervals are to be measured and numbered d_1, d_2, $\cdots d_6$, using twelve consecutive spark spots, as shown in Figure 45.

Calculation for g Divide the data into two equal time interval groups in a manner that will make each calculation independent. This may be done by calculation of the acceleration for the three changes of velocity $(\bar{v}_4 - \bar{v}_1)$, $(\bar{v}_5 - \bar{v}_2)$, and $(\bar{v}_6 - \bar{v}_3)$. Since there are three consecutive numbered distance intervals, that is, six consecutive spot intervals, the time elapsed between each of the above differences in velocity will be $6/f$. By definition, the acceleration of gravity (g) equals the change in velocity divided by the time interval, or

$$g = \frac{f(\bar{v}_4 - \bar{v}_1)}{6} = \frac{f(\bar{v}_5 - \bar{v}_2)}{6} = \frac{f(\bar{v}_6 - \bar{v}_3)}{6}.$$

Hence, if $f = 30$, and 12 consecutive spark intervals are employed as illustrated in Figure 45, the average velocity in the k interval is

$$\bar{v}_k = 30d_k \tag{2}$$

and the acceleration during the time interval of $\frac{6}{30}$ of a second will be

$$g = 5(\bar{v}_{r+3} - \bar{v}_r) \tag{3}$$

where $r = 1, 2$, and 3.

THEORY OF BEHR FREE-FALL METHOD

(Every alternate spark interval used)

For much shorter timing intervals than $\frac{1}{30}$ sec, many additional spark spots may be numbered. In Experiment 5–O, $f = 120$, and

---

* Note that $\bar{v}_1$ is not only the average velocity during the time interval from $1/f$ to $2/f$ sec, but is also the velocity of the body when exactly one-half of this time interval has elapsed, namely, at a time $1/f + (\frac{1}{2})(1/f) = 3/2f$ seconds from O (Fig. 45). Similarly $\bar{v}_2$, $\bar{v}_3$, $\bar{v}_4 \cdots \bar{v}_k$ are the exact velocities from point O at $7/2f$, $11/2f$, $15/2f \cdots (4k-1)/2f$ seconds respectively.

every other spark spot (Fig. 48) has been numbered, as a compromise between accuracy and time available. Note that 24 spark spots are used, so that there will be 12 intervals and 6 independent calculations for the accelerations. Hence, from the theory as developed in the previous section, the average velocity during the kth interval will be

$$\bar{v}_k = 60d_k \qquad (4)$$

where the time interval will be $2/f$ second (i.e., $\frac{2}{120}$ for Experiment 5-O). Since the time interval between 2 adjacent measured distances (i.e., between 4 adjacent spots) is $\frac{4}{120}$ sec, the time interval between 6 consecutive measured distances will be $\frac{24}{120}$ ($=\frac{1}{5}$ sec). Hence the acceleration will be

$$g = 5(\bar{v}_{r+6} - \bar{v}_r) \qquad (5)$$

where $r = 1, 2, \cdots 6$. Although not needed, one may show as in a footnote of the previous section (where $f = 30$) that $\bar{v}_1, \bar{v}_2, \bar{v}_3$, etc. will be the actual velocities at the time interval from 0 of $\frac{3}{120}, \frac{7}{120}, \frac{11}{120}$ sec, respectively, if $f = 120$ and every other spot is counted.

EXPERIMENT 5

THE GRAVITATIONAL ACCELERATION, BEHR FREE-FALL METHOD

Spark time intervals, $\frac{1}{30}$ second

APPARATUS: Free-fall apparatus is shown in Figure 44 and consists of several parts. First there is seen the falling metal object O, so arranged that it is held always in the same position by means of an electromagnet which will release it when the current through the magnet is interrupted. Secondly there is the paper strip in front of which the weight falls freely and on which the distance-time record is made. Finally the timing device can be seen, for producing sparks equally spaced in time. This may take the form of a constant speed motor with a contactor or by an electric interrupter, which is controlled by the constant frequency of the alternating current supply.

If you are to handle the apparatus yourself, be sure to get explicit instructions on the proper adjustment and alignment from the instructor, so that the apparatus will not be damaged. Usually the experiment will be performed and demonstrated by the instructor, who will then make a number of spark recordings and give them to the student for measurement.

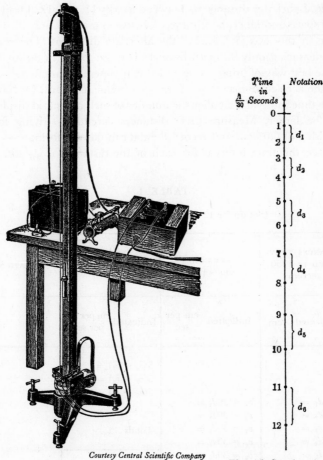

Courtesy Central Scientific Company

Fig. 44. Behr free-fall apparatus.

Fig. 45. Spark points on a paraffined paper strip.

Procedure The sparks occur at intervals of $\frac{1}{30}$ second. Beginning with the last mark made by the spark, label the points from 12 to 0 as in the diagram, Figure 45. These numbers also represent the time in thirtieths of a second since the falling body was at the position marked 0. Notice that the body was already moving at this position.

Make a small pinhole through the paper at the center of each mark. Label the distance d_6 between marks 11 and 12. Omit the next space and label the distance d_5 between marks 9 and 10. Continue in this way, measuring the alternate distances. The reason for measuring only *alternate* distances is to be found in an analysis of the best way of using the recorded experimental data in calculating the acceleration so that *all* the measurements count. Of course, if the time interval is smaller the number of such measured distances will be larger. Measure these distances carefully, striving for a precision of 0.05 cm and record the data in tabular form.

Since the time interval for each of the distances is $\frac{1}{30}$ sec, the

TABLE 1

(Set up for 12 spark spots at $\frac{1}{30}$ sec intervals)

DISTANCES TRAVERSED IN 1/30 SECOND	AVERAGE VELOCITIES	ACCELERATION	DEVIATIONS
Indicated cm	Indicated cm per sec	Indicated cm per sec per sec	
		$5(\bar{v}_4 - \bar{v}_1) =$ $5(\bar{v}_5 - \bar{v}_2) =$ $5(\bar{v}_6 - \bar{v}_3) =$	
$d_1 =$ $d_2 =$ $d_3 =$ $d_4 =$ $d_5 =$ $d_6 =$	$\bar{v}_1 = 30d_1 =$ $\bar{v}_2 = 30d_2 =$ $\bar{v}_3 = 30d_3 =$ $\bar{v}_4 = 30d_4 =$ $\bar{v}_5 = 30d_5 =$ $\bar{v}_6 = 30d_6 =$	Totals	
		Average	
		$\% \, AD =$	

Distance from the original stationary position as scratched on the paraffined sheet to the point marked 0 on the record =

average velocity for each of the measured intervals, d_1, d_2, etc. will be $\bar{v}_1 = 30d_1$, $\bar{v}_2 = 30d_2$, etc., as outlined in the theory (equation 2).

The acceleration will be found by dividing the measured distances into two equal groups as outlined in the theory and calculated by equation 3. Table 1 will be found useful in making the calculations. Note from the table that once the distances d_1, d_2, etc., are measured, the velocities and accelerations may be calculated. For example, note that $\bar{v}_1 = 30d_1$, and $\bar{v}_4 = 30d_4$ hence, $g = 5(\bar{v}_4 - \bar{v}_1)$, since the time interval is $\frac{6}{30}$ ($= \frac{1}{5}$) sec.

GRAPHICAL METHOD OF ANALYSIS

Plot a graph of time and velocity.

Use graph paper having lines one millimeter or $\frac{1}{20}$ inch apart and choose the scales in such a way that the graph occupies most of the sheet. For example, let one millimeter (or $\frac{1}{20}$ inch) represent a velocity of 5 cm per sec and let 5 mm (or $\frac{5}{20}$ inch) represent a time interval of $\frac{1}{60}$ second. If the work has been carefully done the 6 plotted points will fall close to a straight line. With a ruler and a

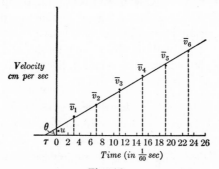

Fig. 46.

sharp pencil draw the best straight line you can among these points. Such a line (Fig. 46) represents the equation:

$$v = u + gt,$$

where u is the initial velocity. Determine the initial velocity u from the intercept on the velocity axis and the initial time interval to position 0 from the intercept on the time axis. Let this initial time interval be τ. Then the distance fallen before reaching position 0 is $gt^2/2$. Note that the *slope* of this velocity-time graph ($\tan \theta$) is equal to g. By measuring this slope determine g and estimate the probable error.

On another sheet plot a graph showing time and the total distance fallen from the point 0 (Fig. 47) which is at the beginning of the recorded time. The actual time elapsed at this point is some un-

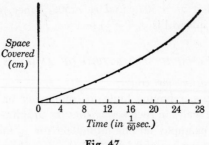

Fig. 47.

known quantity τ. As before, choose the scales to get a suitably large graph. For example, let 1 mm (or $\frac{1}{20}$ inch) represent 1 cm of space covered. Draw a *smooth* curve, similar to the one shown (Fig. 47) among the plotted points. This curve represents the equation, $s - ut = (\frac{1}{2})gt^2$, with the distance ut not shown. A time interval τ had already elapsed up to the point 0. See question (c) below.

Questions

(a) By analyzing the data you have obtained from the spark record, show why the motion has a constant acceleration.

(b) Consider all the possible sources of error in the apparatus as well as the measurements you have taken and discuss quantatively what effect they have on the evaluation of "g."

(c) From your data as used in Figure 46 find the time (in seconds) when the motion started previous to the point marked 0 on the record. Using this value for the time, calculate the original position of rest and mark it on the record.

(d) Write equations for the relations between the variables based on the graphs you have drawn, with all the constants evaluated.

(e) Find the velocity and position of the object, from the graph as well as from the equation, 0.2 seconds after being released.

OPTIONAL EXPERIMENT 5–0

THE GRAVITATIONAL ACCELERATION
BEHR FREE-FALL METHOD

Spark time intervals, $\frac{1}{120}$ second

APPARATUS: Behr fall apparatus, employing a spark jumping mechanism for $\frac{1}{120}$ second intervals, 2-meter rule, cross-ruled graph paper.

The preliminary directions on use of the apparatus is the same as for Experiment 5. The paraffined strip that the instructor gives you will have melted spots every $\frac{1}{120}$ sec.

Procedure Beginning with the last mark made by the spark, label every other mark from 24 to 0 as in Figure 48. The spark intervals so labelled will be for $\frac{1}{60}$ sec.

Make a pinhole through the center of each mark (Fig. 48). Label the distance between marks 23 and 24 as d_{12}. Omit the next space and label the distance between 21 and 22 as d_{11}. Continue in this way, measuring the alternate distances. The reason for measuring only alternate distances is to be found in analysis of the best way of using the recorded experimental data in calculating the acceleration so that all the measurements count. Of course, if the time interval had been smaller the number of such measured distances will be larger. Measure these distances carefully, striving for a precision of 0.05 cm and record the data in tabular form.

Since the time interval for each of the distances (d_1, d_2, etc.) is $\frac{1}{60}$ sec, the average velocity for each of these distances traversed will be $\bar{v}_1 = 60d_1$, $\bar{v}_2 = 60d_2$, etc. as outlined in the theory (equation 4).

The acceleration will be found, in accordance with the theory, by first dividing the measured distances into two equal time interval

Fig. 48. Reproduction of an experimental set of points. Before reduction the distance between points 23 and 24 was 6.56 cms.

groups (i.e., d_1 to d_6 inc., d_7 to d_{12} inc., etc.). Equation 5 is used to calculate the acceleration. Consult Table 2 for a useful form to tabulate the data. Note that once the distance intervals d_1, d_2, d_3, etc. are measured, velocities and accelerations may be calculated. For example, note that $\bar{v}_1 = 60d_1$, $\bar{v}_7 = 60d_7$, and $g = 5(v_7 - v_1)$, since the time interval is $\frac{24}{120}$ ($= \frac{1}{5}$) sec.

TABLE 2

(Set up for 24 spark spots at $\frac{1}{60}$ sec. intervals,
every alternate spot (Fig. 48) numbered.)

DISTANCES TRAVERSED IN $1/60$ SECOND	AVERAGE VELOCITIES	ACCELERATION	DEVIATIONS
Indicated $\quad$ cm	Indicated $\quad \frac{cm\ per}{sec}$	Indicated $\quad \frac{cm\ per\ sec}{per\ sec}$	
$d_1 =$	$\bar{v}_1 = 60d_1 =$	$g = 5(\bar{v}_7 - \bar{v}_1) =$	
$d_2 =$	$\bar{v}_2 = 60d_2 =$	$g = 5(\bar{v}_8 - \bar{v}_2) =$	
$d_3 =$	$\bar{v}_3 = 60d_3 =$	$g = 5(\bar{v}_9 - \bar{v}_3) =$	
$d_4 =$	$\bar{v}_4 = 60d_4 =$	$g = 5(\bar{v}_{10} - \bar{v}_4) =$	
$d_5 =$	$\bar{v}_5 = 60d_5 =$	$g = 5(\bar{v}_{11} - \bar{v}_5) =$	
$d_6 =$	$\bar{v}_6 = 60d_6 =$	$g = 5(\bar{v}_{12} - \bar{v}_6) =$	
$d_7 =$	$\bar{v}_7 = 60d_7 =$		
.	.	Totals	
.	.		
.	.	Average	
.	.		
$d_{12} =$	$\bar{v}_{12} = 60d_{12} =$	$\%\ AD =$	

Distance from the original position of rest as scratched on the paraffined sheet to the point marked 0 on the record =

The above experiment may be repeated using the intervals designated by capital letters if greater accuracy is desired. A table similar to the above may be used.

GRAPHICAL METHOD OF ANALYSIS

Plot graphs of (1) time versus velocity (Fig. 46) and (2) time versus distance fallen from the point O (Fig. 47). Detailed suggestions for drawing these graphs are the same as in the previous experiment and will be found on pages 79 and 80.

Questions

The same as those used for Experiment 5.

EXPERIMENT 6

GRAVITATIONAL ACCELERATION — TOTAL TIME OF FALL

To determine the gravitational acceleration.

APPARATUS: Release switch, a-c operated interval timer, transformer, stop switch, rheostat, meter rule.

Introduction Let a body fall different distances, $s_1, s_2 \cdots s_k$. If the square of the corresponding times of fall are plotted as abscissas

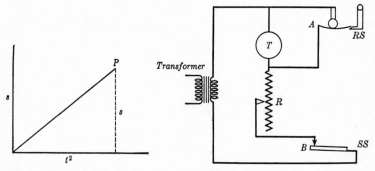

Fig. 49. For free-fall, the distance from rest is proportional to t^2.

Fig. 50. Single time-interval free-fall apparatus.

against distances as ordinates, a straight line (Fig. 49) will result, since $s = (\frac{1}{2})gt^2$ when the initial velocity is zero. The slope (i.e., $\tan \theta = s/t^2$) of this line will give twice the acceleration due to gravity.

The apparatus is set up as shown in Figure 53. The step-down transformer is connected to the timer (T) in series with a rheostat so that the timer will operate satisfactorily when the release switch (*RS*) is open and will prevent excessive current from flowing when *RS* is closed.

Procedure   A brass or copper sphere is held at *A* (Fig. 50) by means of the special release switch *RS*. When the sphere is in position *A* and *RS* is closed as shown, the electrical current from the transformer goes through the switch *RS*, rather than through the timer *T*. When the ball is released by opening *RS*, then the electric current is forced to go through *T* and thus sets the timer in operation. As soon as the falling ball strikes the stop switch (*SS*) at *B* the circuit is opened and the timer is stopped. The timer is operated by the 60-cycle alternating current and its indicator hand moves twice for each cycle so that it reads each $\frac{1}{120}$ second.

Start with the distance *AB* equal to about 25 cm and measure the average times of free fall for distances up to 200 cm. (A good procedure is to measure the time for some given distance and then slowly increase the distance until the timer begins to show an increase in time; thus obtaining the *maximum* distance for a given time.)

Plot the distances against the squares of the times of fall. A straight line will be obtained similar to the one shown in Figure 49. Obtain the acceleration *g* from the slope of this curve (i.e., $g = 2s/t^2$).

Questions

(a) Assuming that the timer records time in steps of $\frac{1}{120}$ sec, how large an error did you note on the account for distances of fall of the order of (1) 25 cm, (2) 50 cm, (3) 100 cm, (4) 200 cm?

(b) If you did Experiment 5 or 5–O, compare the accuracy of the resulting value of *g* in the two experiments.

(c) How would you go about to estimate the accuracy in this method for the determination of *g*, the acceleration due to gravity.

(d) In what relative way will the friction due to the air affect the magnitude of the resulting acceleration when the body falls (1) 25 cm, (2) 200 cm?

PROBLEMS

Experiment 5

1   A bicyclist has a uniform velocity of 12 mph, how long does he take in passing two telephone posts spaced 50 yards apart? Work this problem using the fundamental units of length and time and express your answer in seconds.

2 If the bicyclist of the previous problem had a velocity of 12 mph at the first pole and by speeding up uniformly his speed at the second pole is 15 mph calculate his average speed and the time taken to pass the poles.

3 Convert:

(a) A velocity of 60 mph into fps.

(b) A velocity of 22 mph into fps.

(c) A velocity of 30 mph into kmph.

(d) An acceleration of 3 mph per min into fps per sec.

(e) An acceleration of 32 fps per sec into cm per sec per sec.

4 What restriction, if any, is necessary in the acceleration when the average velocity $(\bar{v})$ is defined mathematically as (a) $\bar{v} = (v_1 + v_2)/2$, (b) $\bar{v} = s/t$?

5 Calculate the positions and velocities of a freely falling object, starting from rest, after 1, 2, 3, 4, 5, 6, 7, and 8 seconds. Tabulate your results (use the mks system, g = 9.8 m per sec per sec) and plot graphs to show the positions and velocities which you have calculated.

6 If an object is thrown vertically downwards from a cliff of height 500 ft and it takes 4 sec to reach the base, what initial velocity did it have (g = 32.0 fps per sec)?

7 A parachute trooper who dropped from a plane pulled the rip cord 3 sec after jumping. What downward velocity did he have when the parachute opened?

8 Calculate the answer to problem 6 above, using the mks system of units in all the calculations.

Experiment 6

1 What time interval would be required for a body to fall 25 cm, if starting from rest?

2 How accurately would a timer have to read to obtain a value of g to 1 per cent for a fall of (a) 0.25 m, (b) 2.0 m?

3 Assume that one-eighth cycle is lost on a certain reading in problem 9 before the timer actually starts operating. What per cent error in the time interval will be found? Assume that timer operates on a 60-cycle a-c line.

4 A bomb is dropped from an airplane traveling horizontally at a speed of 250 mph. If the airplane is at a height of 30,000 ft, how many seconds will elapse before the bomb strikes the ground? What horizontal distance does the airplane travel in the time interval required for the bomb to fall?

5 Repeat the above problem for a height of 10,000 ft.

CHAPTER VI

THE CONSERVATION OF MOMENTUM

Whenever two bodies collide, forces come into play which depend upon the respective velocities and masses of the objects. In such cases each object exerts a force on the other which usually lasts only for a very short time. Newton's third law states that the two forces involved, when only two bodies collide, are equal in amount and opposite in direction. If we now add the further fact, that the time during which each of these forces acts is the same, then this law can be stated in the form that the *impulses* (force × time) given to each object during the collision are the same in magnitude, but opposite in direction.

Introduction of the second law of Newton, that the impulse given to a body is equal to the change of momentum produced in it, leads to the *law of conservation of momentum* which applies to all collisions, whether they are elastic or not. The law states that the total momentum possessed by a system of particles or objects before they collide is equal to the total momentum of the same system after the collision, provided no outside forces have acted on this system during the collision. Stated simply, it means that when two bodies collide, the total momentum before the impact equals the total momentum after the impact. If a gun fires a bullet the total momentum before the firing (zero) must equal the total momentum after the firing (again zero).

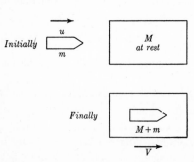

Fig. 51. Conservation of momentum.

We shall study in this chapter only the case of inelastic impacts, in which the two colliding bodies stick together and move with the same velocity after the impact. This forms the basic idea underlying a common procedure for determining the velocity of a bullet fired from a gun.

Let an object of mass m having a velocity u collide with another object of mass M, initially at rest, in such a way that they stick together and move off with the same velocity V after the impact (see Fig. 51). According to the law of conservation of momentum the total momentum before the impact must equal the total momentum after the impact, i.e.,

$$mu = (M + m)V. \quad (6)$$

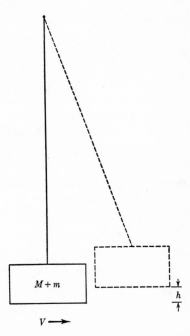

If the purpose of the experiment is to find U, the velocity of a bullet, then according to the above equation a knowledge of V becomes necessary. Velocity V may be found by arranging the block M in such a way that it can swing freely (see Fig. 52) like a pendulum, in which case the *kinetic energy* $[(\frac{1}{2})(M + m)V^2]$ acquired by the block of mass M with the bullet embedded in it, will be changed into potential energy of position* by moving along an arc of a circle

Fig. 52. Change from kinetic to potential energy.

* A small amount of the initial kinetic energy goes into rotational kinetic energy, since the block rotates around the centre of suspension. Bifilar suspensions have been designed in order to eliminate this rotation. When rotation has to be considered, the velocity V becomes $V = \sqrt{\dfrac{gh}{\dfrac{1}{2} + \dfrac{k^2}{2l^2}}}$ where k is the radius of gyration and l is the distance between the center of mass and the axis of suspension. In the apparatus described above this rotational correction will make a difference of approximately 3 per cent in the value of u.

until the potential energy $[(M + m)gh]$ is just equal to the kinetic energy.

$$\text{Hence } (\tfrac{1}{2})(M + m)V^2 = (M + m)gh$$
$$V^2 = 2gh$$
$$V = \sqrt{2gh} \tag{7}$$

which gives V in terms of g and h. The value of g can be assumed to be 980 cm per sec per sec in the cgs system of units, and h can be measured as outlined in Experiments 7 and 8. Finally, in order to find the unknown velocity u of the bullet it is necessary only to combine equations (6) and (7) in such a way as to eliminate V.

$$\text{Hence, } u = \left(\frac{M + m}{m}\right) \sqrt{2\,gh} \tag{8}$$

EXPERIMENT 7

THE BLACKWOOD BALLISTIC PENDULUM

Part (a)   *To find the velocity of a projectile using the law of conservation of momentum.*

Part (b)   *To find the initial velocity of a projectile by measuring the range and vertical displacement.*

APPARATUS: Blackwood ballistic pendulum (Cenco or similar type), platform balance, triangle, meter rule, level.

The apparatus (see Fig. 53) consists of a gun that, by means of a spring, projects a brass ball into the block of a ballistic pendulum in such a way that the ball gets stuck in the suspended block. The block is supported from a pivot by means of a light rod, and the center of gravity of this pendulum with the ball caught in it is marked by the point of a small brass pointer mounted on this block. When the ball is shot into the block they both swing upwards until the kinetic energy has been changed into an equivalent potential energy, at which point the block is held by engaging a tooth on a curved rack placed next to the swinging pendulum. This holds the pendulum in its highest position and thus allows measurements of h to be made.

The same apparatus can be used for the second part of this experiment, but instead of shooting the brass ball into the block the gun shoots the ball horizontally over the edge of the table, so that the horizontal range and the vertical height can be measured and thus the velocity once more can be calculated.* The value of u determined in part (b) can then be compared with the velocity as found in part (a).

Part (a) Place the apparatus near one end and along the front edge of the laboratory table, using the level to test whether the base of the apparatus is level (see Fig. 53). If necessary use some small paper or cardboard shims to make it level.

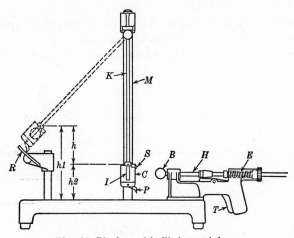

Fig. 53. Blackwood ballistic pendulum.

To prepare the gun for firing first pull the pendulum over and let it rest on the rack R. Then having placed the brass ball at the end of the firing rod, pull back on the ball until the compressed spring is caught by the trigger. This will compress the spring a given amount and thus always give the same velocity to the projectile. Replace the pendulum into the vertical position and fire the gun. The block will receive the projectile and be propelled along the rack, where it is caught in the highest position. Record this reading

---

* In this chapter we have described the use of the Blackwood type of pendulum. For other excellent types which are adapted for the use of an actual rifle see Hansen and Richtmyer — *Am. Phys. Teacher*, 5, 112 (1937), and McLeod — *Am. Phys. Teacher*, 3, 37 (1935).

on the scale along the rack. Repeat this procedure at least five times and calculate the average position of rest on the rack. Having calculated this average position, place the block in the ratchet tooth nearest to this average and measure the vertical distance (h_1) of the center of gravity above the base of the instrument. In measuring this distance use the triangle and meter rule. Next also measure the distance (h_2) from the base to the center of gravity of the block when hanging straight down. The difference $(h_1 - h_2)$ gives the actual vertical displacement (h) produced by the impact energy. Express the value of h in centimeters and estimate the possible error in this value.

In order to find M and m, the masses of the block and bullet respectively, they can be removed and weighed on a platform balance. These data, together with the known value of g, will enable

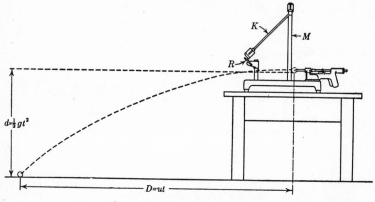

Fig. 54. Projectile path.

a calculation of u to be made from equation (8). Do not forget to include the estimated error in your answer.

Part (b)   For this part of the experiment the pendulum is placed out of the way on the rack R and the gun is loaded as before. On being fired the ball will have an initial horizontal velocity u and thereafter a downward parabolic path, striking the floor at a horizontal distance D cm from the gun (see Fig. 54). The point where the ball strikes the ground can be determined by allowing the ball to fall on a piece of waxed paper placed on the floor. The initial position of the ball, measured horizontally along the floor, can be measured by means of a plumb bob suspended from the center of the ball in its initial position of rest. In this way the distance D (Fig. 54) can be measured. The vertical distance d also needs to be found. Then for the horizontal part of the motion we have

$$D = ut \qquad (9)$$

where t is the time of flight, and for the vertical motion

$$d = \tfrac{1}{2} g t^2. \qquad (10)$$

Eliminating t and solving for u we get

$$u = D\sqrt{\frac{g}{2\,d}} \qquad (11)$$

Take several determinations for D in order to find an average value and estimate also the error in your measurement of it. Finally, calculate u with the "error" and compare this value with that determined in part (a).

Questions

(a) Do the two values for u as obtained in part (a) and part (b) agree within their experimental errors? If not, what possible precautions or corrections have been neglected or what inaccuracies are inherent in the methods used?

(b) Calculate the kinetic energy of the bullet before impact.

(c) Calculate from your data the velocity of the bullet and block after impact.

(d) Calculate the kinetic energy of the block and bullet just after the impact. Is it the same as the kinetic energy of the projectile before the impact? Is kinetic energy conserved?

(e) Does the law of conservation of energy hold in this case?

(f) Calculate the time of flight in part (b).

EXPERIMENT 8

SPEED OF A BASEBALL

To determine the speed of a baseball as ordinarily thrown.

APPARATUS:* Box suspended from ceiling at an average shoulder height, baseball, platform balance and weights, two pillows for padding the inside of the box, meter stick, sliding index on a meter stick.

* One box will be sufficient for several students.

The baseball may be thrown into a light barrel or a box may be made up for the experiment. The opening should be fairly large, because of the inaccuracies in the direction of throw, and should taper toward the rear. The box is suspended from the ceiling by four wires as shown in Figure 55. This type of suspension will do

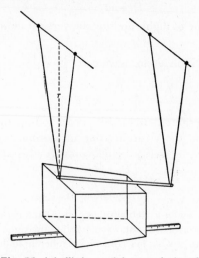

Fig. 55. A ballistic pendulum—velocity of a baseball.

away with any necessity to consider rotational energy, which must be considered in the previous experiment for greater accuracy.

The velocity of the baseball is found by use of equation 8, where M is the mass of the box and accessories, including pillows, and m is the mass of the baseball. The height h, however, is not observed directly but may be calculated by noting the horizontal distance d that the box moves. Note that a horizontal meter stick is placed under but not quite in contact with the box. A light slider is provided which moves along the meter stick to indicate the horizontal distance that the box moves after the baseball is thrown. Let r be the perpendicular distance from the line of supports at the ceiling to the support on the top of the barrel. From Figure 56, the similar triangles ADC and CDB yield the ratio

$$\frac{2r - h}{d} = \frac{d}{h}$$

on the assumption that the side BC represents a small enough portion of an arc to be essentially straight. Hence, we find that h has the value for all practical purposes of $h = d^2/2\,r$, where h^2 is negligible compared to $2\,rh$. Hence our working equation becomes

$$u = \frac{(M+m)d}{m}\sqrt{\frac{g}{r}} \qquad (12)$$

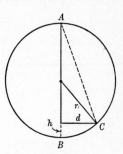

Fig. 56.

Procedure Before each throw, the box must be stationary and the sliding index must be placed in contact with the box. Stand three or four feet from the box and throw the baseball into the box several times and record each time the distance d that the barrel (or box) swings back. This measurement is made by noting the distance the slider moves. Weigh the baseball on a platform balance. Obtain from the instructor the mass of the box and accessories. He may wish also to give you the distance r, especially if the ceiling is high.

CONSTANTS OF APPARATUS

Mass of box and accessories (M) =
Mass of baseball (m) =
Mass of box, accessories and
   baseball $(M+m)$ =
Distance from support to top
   of box (r) =

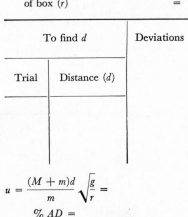

To find d		Deviations
Trial	Distance (d)	

$$u = \frac{(M+m)d}{m}\sqrt{\frac{g}{r}} =$$
$$\% \ AD =$$

Questions

(a) Why are four supports (Fig. 55) provided for the barrel instead of a single rope?

(b) Calculate the average speed of the baseball in fps, if the experimental value was given in cm per sec. Compare with a fast automobile speed, say 60 mph (i.e., 88 fps).

(c) What is the momentum of the baseball before collision?

(d) What is the momentum of the baseball, box, and accessories after collision?

(e) What is the impulse in the collision?

(f) What is the kinetic energy of the baseball before impact?

(g) What is the kinetic energy of the baseball, box, and accessories after collision?

PROBLEMS

Experiment 7

1   A bullet having a mass of 20 g is fired into a wood block initially at rest and suspended like a pendulum. The bullet had a velocity of 300 kmps when it struck the block of mass 4 kg and became embedded in it. Calculate:

    (a) the kinetic energy of the bullet before impact,
    (b) the momentum of the bullet before impact,
    (c) the velocity of the block just after the impact,
    (d) the kinetic energy of the block and the bullet just after the impact,
    (e) the energy lost in the form of heat, and
    (f) the height to which the block will rise.

2   A bullet of mass 50 g is fired into a stationary block in which it remains. If the block has a mass of 10 kg and is found to have a velocity after impact of 250 cm per sec calculate the velocity of the bullet.

3   If the block of problem 2 had been arranged as a pendulum to what height would the pendulum swing?

4   A projectile of mass 500 lb is fired from a gun having a mass of 40 tons with a velocity of 2000 fps. Calculate the velocity of recoil of the gun and the energy of recoil which has to be dissipated.

5   A projectile is fired horizontally with an initial velocity of 500 cm per sec from a height of 5 m. Calculate the horizontal distance traveled and the time of flight.

6   A 2000-lb bomb is released from an aeroplane traveling horizontally 250 mph when at a height of 4 miles above ground. Neglecting the effects of

air resistance, where will the bomb land and how far will the aeroplane be from its target when the bomb strikes?

Experiment 8

1   A bullet weighing $\frac{1}{2}$ oz is fired into a block of wood weighing 30 lb. If the block moves back 20 in., what is the initial velocity of the bullet provided that $r = 10$ ft?

2   A bullet weighing 1 oz is fired into a block of wood weighing 50 lb. The block is suspended, as in the experiment, by 4 wires the distance from the point of suspension to the top of the box being 12 ft. What horizontal distance will the block move if the bullet has an initial velocity of 2500 fps?

3   A bullet weighing 30 g is fired into a block of wood suspended from a 4-meter support and is forced back a distance 40 cm. If the block weighs 18 kg, what is the velocity of the bullet?

4   Assume that the box and padding used for the baseball experiment, has a mass of 34 lb and that $r = 10.1$ ft. If the baseball weighs 0.33 lb, how many inches will the box move if the initial velocity of the baseball towards the box is 65 mph?

CHAPTER VII

FRICTION

Sliding friction is probably due either to adhesion or to roughness of the solid surfaces. If due to roughness of the solid surfaces, the friction is due to the lifting of the surfaces of contact up some common slope and then dropping again. This will account for the usual independence of the coefficient of friction with moderate loads. The above explanation agrees with the tendency for a slightly higher value of μ_s (coefficient of static friction) to occur for very light and for very heavy loads. For very light loads, the climbing slope will tend to be a little greater since the deformations of the hills will be smaller. At very great loads, the frictional force is used more to bend and tear away the hills. In the roughness theory which is due to Coulomb, a lubricant fills the valleys so as to present a smooth sliding surface and at the same time prevents the hills from penetrating into the valleys. The liquid film should be such as not to prevent flow of the fluid along the surface even though the hills otherwise would prevent a free flow of the fluid. The effect of friction is to decrease efficiency of machines.

Consider a body at rest on a rough horizontal surface, and let us try to slide it along the surface. The force which the plane will

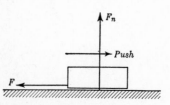

Fig. 57. The force of friction.

exert on the body will be in some unknown direction (not necessarily perpendicular to the surface). We can think of this force as having two components, (1) a thrust F_n normal to the surface, and (2) a frictional force F acting horizontally, which comes into play when we try to move the body (Fig. 57). This frictional force becomes larger and larger the more we push, and finally reaches a limiting value just before the body starts to slide. It is found experimentally that the limiting frictional force F depends upon the thrust F_n.

The ratio F/F_n is a constant and is called the coefficient of friction μ.

In practice the force of friction is found to decrease slightly once the body has started moving, and then to remain constant while the body is sliding along slowly without accelerating. This fact leads us to be more specific and define:

        (1) the coefficient of static friction, μ_s

        (2) the coefficient of dynamic friction, μ_k

depending upon whether we are dealing respectively with the frictional force F_s necessary to start the body moving, or with the force F_k required to move it slowly at constant velocity. Thus the coefficient of kinetic friction is the ratio of the force parallel to the surface of contact sufficient to cause constant slow velocity, to the force normal to the area of contact that presses the two surfaces together.

Automobile tires   The ratio of the frictional force by *rubber tires* in contact with road surfaces to the normal thrust force does not give a coefficient of friction that is independent of the area of contact,* contrary to general treatment for elementary purposes. Thus for the same load smooth tires may offer more friction than treaded tires when the surfaces are dry. The friction is found also to be less at high speeds. Thus, a coefficient of friction of 0.79 between automobile tires and a concrete road at 40 mph may be reduced to 0.70 at 60 mph because of heat developed. The friction, moreover, is reported to be more nearly proportional to the area of contact, instead of being independent of the area of contact as is usually assumed for fairly rigid surfaces in contact with each other. The treaded tire offers traction advantages when roads are wet. Experiments with rubber on concrete indicate that the coefficient of friction may vary from about 1.2 to 0.1, or less, depending upon the surfaces of contact and degree of dryness. Apparently glass gives about the same traction as a concrete slab. In any case, the experiments on traction are quite variable depending upon conditions noted above.

Skidding on a horizontal and curved road**   The wide variability of coefficient of friction between rubber and a road surface,

---

* E. R. Fountain, *Am. J. Phys.*, 10, 322 (1942).

** The mathematics of this section and part of the following requires an understanding of Newton's laws of motion and of acceleration. It is inserted for those having had this subject matter in lecture work by this time.

depending upon the weather, speed, and condition of the tires, imposes considerable responsibility upon a driver of a fast car. A car that is to be stopped in the minimum distance should have the largest braking force applied that will just keep the wheels moving. Applying Newton's second law of motion ($F_s = ma$) to this situation shows that the maximum negative acceleration a will be,

$$a = \mu_s g \qquad (13)$$

since $\mu_s = F_s/F_n = F_s/mg$ for a horizontal surface.

If the body is skidding as shown in Figure 58, the negative acceleration will be $a = \mu_k g$ where $\mu_k < \mu_s$.

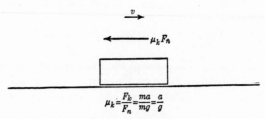

$$\mu_k = \frac{F_k}{F_n} = \frac{ma}{mg} = \frac{a}{g}$$

Fig. 58. A skidding block.

Equation (13) may be combined with the equation of accelerated motion, $v^2 = u^2 + 2\,as$ (not derived here), to show that the minimum stopping distance without skidding will be

$$s = \frac{u^2}{2\,\mu_s g}. \qquad (14)$$

This does not take into account the time of about 0.7 second required to get the foot from the accelerator to the brake pedal. The maximum velocity v at which a car can go around a curve of radius r is found by combining equation (13) with equation (25) (Note: $a = v^2/r$) of Chapter IX. The resulting maximum velocity around the curve without skidding is

$$\hat{v} = \sqrt{\mu_s g r}. \qquad (15)$$

Once skidding starts, it tends to continue, since the kinetic coefficient of friction μ_k is less than the static coefficient of friction μ_s.

Friction on an inclined plane If a body is dragged with constant velocity up an inclined plane (Fig. 59) the parallel force F'

required must be sufficient to overcome the force component of the weight down the incline F_p and the force of friction $\mu_k F_n$, namely,

$$F' = F_p + \mu_k F_n.$$

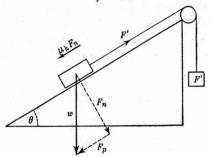

Fig. 59. Motion on an inclined plane, with friction.

We may use this equation to find the coefficient of kinetic friction, since

$$\mu_k = \frac{F' - F_p}{F_n} = \frac{F' - w \sin \theta}{w \cos \theta}. \tag{16}$$

If there is no upward force F' on the body, then the only force acting (Fig. 60) is the downward component F_p due to the weight of the body. This results in an acceleration a provided θ, the angle between the inclined plane and the horizontal, is sufficiently large. Hence if the mass of the body is m, then our equation of motion becomes

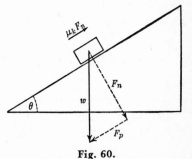

$$F_p - \mu_k F_n = ma \tag{17}$$

where a is taken as positive downward, and F_p and F_n are expressed in absolute units. With a

Fig. 60.

proper timing device the above equation furnishes an excellent method for calculating μ_k.

If the block slides down the inclined plane with constant speed, the acceleration a is zero and our equation becomes

$$F_p - \mu_k F_n = 0, \tag{18}$$

or

$$\mu_k = F_p/F_n = \frac{mg \sin \theta_r}{mg \cos \theta_r} = \tan \theta_r, \qquad (19)$$

and F_p becomes equal in magnitude to F_k. The angle θ_r is called the limiting angle of repose. Since $\tan \theta_r$ can be measured directly or in terms of the height h and length s of the inclined plane, the co-efficient of friction is easily measured by this method.

EXPERIMENT 9

COEFFICIENT OF FRICTION *
CONSTANT VELOCITY METHODS

Part (a)   *Determination of the coefficient of dynamic and of static friction between two surfaces.*

Part (b)* *Determination of the coefficient of friction of a rubber surface.*

Part (c)   *Determination of the coefficient of friction by pulling up an inclined plane.*

Part (d)   *Determination of the coefficient of friction by finding the limiting angle of repose.*

APPARATUS: Inclined plane apparatus, two sets of slotted weights (10–500 g), string, hanger, friction block, platform balance. Also, rubber-surfaced block or mounted miniature tires, glass or concrete slab, if the coefficient of friction of rubber is determined.

Part (a) Determination of the dynamic coefficient of friction consists in measuring the force of friction on a level surface. This force of friction is measured by applying the force F' horizontally until the block just slides with a slow and constant velocity. Hang the string, which is attached to the friction block and the hanger, over the pulley, and add

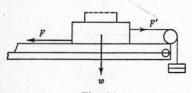

Fig. 61.

weights until the block just slides slowly on the horizontal plane surface (Fig. 61). This might necessitate interpolation if the slotted weights which are put on the hanger are not provided in small

* For a shorter experiment, omit part b.

enough steps. Make three to five trials, adding standard masses to the block and redetermine F'. Enter your results in tabular form. Calculate μ_k, the kinetic coefficient of friction, and state the accuracy and reproducibility of your result. Compare your result with values given in tables of physical constants for these two kinds of surfaces. Repeat for the block turned on its side, with and without a load.

Repeat the above experiments for static coefficient of friction. Since static friction is much greater than dynamic friction, the weights will quickly accelerate to the floor once the friction block is started. Arrange the apparatus so that the distance the weights fall is short.

Part (b) Repeat the above experiment with a rubber surfaced friction block, and include some tests to find the effect of a change in area with constant load. A spring balance may be substituted for the hanger, weights, and pulley, since the frictional force will be found quite variable and large.

Part (c) Adjust your apparatus (Fig. 59) so that the plane is inclined to the horizontal by an angle θ. Adjust the value of the force F' so that the body will move up the inclined plane with constant velocity. Repeat two or three times to obtain an average value for F' and then solve for the kinetic coefficient of friction by use of equation (16). Repeat for two or more values of the angle θ. Repeat for values of the static coefficient of friction.

Part (d) Increase the angle θ (Fig. 60) starting with a small angle, until by light tapping, the block slides down the inclined plane with constant velocity. Repeat two or more times and calculate the average tangent from the sum of the tangents of the angles obtained. If a load may be placed in the block, repeat for one more load. Repeat for values of the static coefficient of friction. Arrange your results in tabular form and calculate both μ_k and μ_s. Find the per cent of deviation from the mean result.

Questions

(a) What was the approximate ratio of the static to the dynamic coefficient of friction for the surfaces used in your experiment?

(b) Which frictional force (static or kinetic) probably governs skidding hazards with automobiles? Explain.

(c) How far would an automobile, with four-wheel brakes and going 60 mph, skid after applying the brakes if the coefficient of friction between wheels and road proved to be the maximum found in your experiment under the following two conditions: (a) braking force sufficient to lock the wheels; i.e., the four wheels skid; (b) brakes applied to all four wheels for maximum braking force without skidding?

(d) How fast could an automobile make a right-angled bend in a road of 30 ft radius assuming maximum coefficient of friction found in your experiment? Assume that the road is horizontal and not banked.

(e) Did you find the coefficient of friction to vary with load on the friction block?

(f) Compute the value of the coefficient of kinetic friction, using all values obtained in the experiment above for the same surfaces and calculate the per cent of error by the method found on page 11 of Chapter II. Compare your mean value with values from tables, if values are listed. Repeat the calculations for the coefficient of static friction.

PROBLEMS

Experiment 9

1   Prove that the coefficient of friction (dynamic or static) is equal to the tangent of the limiting angle of repose.

2   A body of mass 500 g is held in equilibrium on a smooth incline by a tension of 300 g force acting upwards along the plane. Show that the angle of the plane must be nearly 37° and also that the sum of the component forces, in any direction you wish to choose, must be zero.

3   Define *coefficient of friction* and distinguish between static and dynamic coefficients. Discuss practical conditions under which either one or the other is used.

4   A body is moving up an incline of 30° with a velocity of 20 fps. What are the components of this velocity horizontally and vertically?

5   Assume that the coefficient of dynamic friction in the previous problem is 0.4. How much force parallel to the inclined plane will be required to move the body (a) up the incline at 20 fps; (b) down the incline plane at 20 fps? Assume that the body weighs 200 g.

6   A block is skidded along a floor for a distance of 25 ft before coming to rest. If the time interval in which the block skidded was 2.5 sec, what is the coefficient of friction of the block? Assume that $g = 32$ fps per sec.

CHAPTER VIII

An understanding of (1) the meaning of concepts of work and power, (2) the differences between work and power, and (3) the differences between power and machines will help considerably to appreciate how the power age came about and why people can have so many conveniences today that were not known even to kings of past ages.

WORK

If a certain force produces a displacement in the same direction, then the *work* (w) is defined as the product of a force by the distance through which the force acts; i.e.,

$$W = Fs. \tag{20}$$

If the force and displacement are not in line, then the component of the force in line with the displacement must be taken. Some of the common units of work are: dyne-centimeters (ergs), newton-meters (joules), foot-pounds (ft-lb), ton-miles.

ENERGY

A body in motion can do work because of its energy of motion. Likewise, a body at the top of a hill can do work by rolling down the hill. A body is said to possess *energy* if it can do a certain amount of work. *Energy* is the total work a body can do. For example, a boy throws a baseball. The baseball has gained a certain amount of energy at the expense of the boy and can do work in the process of giving up the energy.

There are two kinds of energy; namely, potential and kinetic. A body will possess potential energy if (1) it is taken up a hill (i.e., energy due to position), (2) wound as in a clock spring (i.e., due to configuration), (3) it can be made to change its molecular constitu-

103

tion (i.e., chemical energy). In the case of a body lifted a height h, the potential energy PE is, in accordance with equation 20, in

$$PE = mgh, \tag{21}$$

in absolute units (i.e., ergs or joules in the metric system).

Kinetic energy KE is stored up energy due to speed v. The formula may be derived from equation (20), by noting that if a body possesses a velocity v_0 and is acted upon by a force F over a distance s, then in accordance with Newton's second law of motion,

$$W = KE = Fs = mas$$

and since $v^2 = v_0^2 + 2\ as$, we have

$$KE = \frac{m}{2} (v^2 - v_0^2) \tag{22}$$

in absolute units.

If the initial speed (v_0) is zero, then

$$KE = \tfrac{1}{2}mv^2. \tag{23}$$

Whether the initial speed is zero or otherwise, the total kinetic energy the body of speed v possesses at any instant of time is expressed by equation (23).

A body raised to a height h will possess a potential energy expressed by equation (21). When the body falls the height h, its energy just before contact with ground will be all kinetic and will be expressed by equation (23). If the body, raised to a height h, is the hammer of a pile driver, then the pile will be driven into the ground a distance s with an average force F which may be calculated from the equation.

$$Fs = mgh \tag{24}$$

where F will be in absolute units.

POWER

The time rate at which work is done is called the power. Two machines which exert equal forces can have very different power ratings depending upon the rapidity with which the force moves and consequently the rate at which the machine does work. If power is represented by the symbol P, then

$$P = \frac{Fs}{t} = Fv$$

where v is the velocity. An electric mixer used in the house may be stopped with a relatively small torque, but since its rotational velocity is high, its power output over any time interval, in excess of a few minutes, is much greater than can be put out by an individual.

The fundamental units of power are:

(1) in the cgs system $\backsimeq$ 1 erg per second (dyne-cm per sec)
(2) in the mks system $\backsimeq$ 1 joule per second (watt)

In addition to these, two common units found in practice are:

1 ft-lb per sec $\backsimeq$ 32 ft-poundals per sec
1 horsepower $\backsimeq$ 33,000 ft-lb per min $\backsimeq$ 550 ft-lb per sec
1 watt $\backsimeq$ 10^7 ergs/sec $\backsimeq$ 1 joule per sec
1 horsepower $\backsimeq$ 746 watts

MACHINES

A machine is a device, or mechanism, which will transfer a force from one point of application to another for some useful advantage. The pulley system, the jackscrew, and the lever are everyday illustrations of machines. The pulley is commonly used to hoist heavy loads, such as steel girders, through great distances, while the jackscrew and lever are employed to lift massive objects through short distances. The primary object of these machines is utilization of a great force by application of a small force.

There are many cases, however, where a change in direction of the force is the primary object of a machine, but not a change in magnitude. Illustrations are supplied by a single pulley, reversing belts, and reversing gear wheels. More generally, however, the machine is arranged to change both the magnitude and direction. These characteristics are demonstrated by a study of the block and tackle, the differential pulley, the transmission gear, the wedge (i.e., double inclined plane), and the wheel and axle.

Mechanical advantage and efficiency While machines enable us to do work in an easier and more advantageous way, one should not be misled into thinking that the total work put into the machine (i.e., input) to accomplish the task is any less than that obtained from the machine (i.e., output). In fact, it is generally greater than that obtained from the machine because of frictional losses.

In sum, the useful advantage of a machine depends, theoretically, upon a knowledge of the resultant and applied forces, and consequently the frictional losses. *The ratio of the force exerted by the machine to the force applied by the operator is called the mechanical advantage,* while *the ratio of the work obtained from the machine (output) to that put into the machine (input) is called the efficiency.* To express the efficiency in percent, the ratio is multiplied by 100. Notice that the mechanical advantage is a ratio of forces, while the efficiency is a ratio of work. The latter determines the frictional losses.

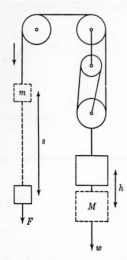

Fig. 62. A pulley system —ideal case.

Two possibilities are to be considered in the development of the theory of machines, namely, (1) the *ideal case,* (2) the *actual case.*

The ideal case The ideal case is thought of as a machine having no frictional losses. No such machines exist, bu, a few approach the ideal condition (such as, for example, the lever). The ideal case is useful to consider, however, since it gives us a limiting minimum force and is found to be related to the actual efficiency of the machine.

The ideal mechanical advantage (I. M. A.) is (Fig. 62) by definition

$$\text{I. M. A.} = \frac{w}{F},$$

and since, by the theory of conservation of energy,

$$Fs = wh,$$

provided there are no frictional losses in the machine where s and h are the respective distances through which F and w operate, we have

$$\text{I. M. A.} = \frac{w}{F} = \frac{s}{h}.$$

It will be seen that in the pulley system pictured in Figure 62 and Figure 63 when M goes up 1 cm, F will go down 3 cm. Hence the ideal mechanical advantage equals 3, since

$$\text{I. M. A.} = \frac{s}{h} = 3.$$

The ratio, s/h is often called the velocity ratio since the force must go a distance s in the same time that the resistance is going a distance h.

The ideal mechanical advantage, or its equivalent (the velocity ratio), may be figured from the dimensions of the machine as noted above. It should be noticed, however, that whatever is saved in force by the ideal machine is lost in distance through which the force oper- ates, so that the work done is the same whether the machine is used or not. Consequently, the efficiency in the ideal case is

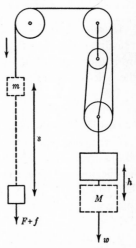

$$\text{Eff.} = \frac{wh}{Fs} = 100\%.$$

The actual case   Frictional losses are always encountered in practice. To il- lustrate, Figure 63 represents a mass M being lifted where the frictional force is found to be of the magnitude f, while

Fig. 63. A pulley system— actual case.

the ideal force (i.e., force as found when there is no friction) is F. The frictional force f is found by experiment. By definition the mechanical advantage is

$$\text{M. A.} = \frac{w}{F+f}.$$

It is to be seen that in this case the work $[(F+f)s]$ put into the machine is greater than that (wh) obtained from the machine, the difference being dissipated by friction inside the machine. The efficiency is given by:

$$\text{Eff.} = \frac{\text{output}}{\text{input}} = \frac{wh}{(F+f)s}$$

and since $wh = Fs$,

$$\text{Eff.} = \frac{Fs}{(F+f)s} = \frac{F}{F+f}.$$

Note that we may write

$$\frac{F}{F+f} = \frac{\dfrac{w}{F+f}}{\dfrac{w}{F}},$$

so that the efficiency may be written as

$$\text{Eff.} = \frac{\text{actual mechanical advantage}}{\text{ideal mechanical advantage}}.$$

In some belt systems, it may be easier actually to obtain the velocity ratio instead of figuring the ideal mechanical advantage from the mechanical dimensions, since the actual radius used by the belt is not easily figured, especially if the belt fits tightly in a groove as in **V**-type belts. When in doubt as to the correct ideal mechanical advantage, obtain the velocity ratio, which will be the correct ideal mechanical advantage.

When f is greater than F, the work to overcome the friction becomes greater than the output work of the machine. This gives us a self-locking machine, the efficiency of which is less than 50 per cent. The jackscrew, wedge, and the differential pulley are examples of this type. The large mechanical advantage usually associated with these machines makes them very useful for transfer or dislodgment of very massive objects.

Jacks are operated commonly by the lever, screw, or hydraulic principle. In any case, the velocity ratio, or ideal mechanical advantage, may be found by noting through what distance the input force must be exerted to raise the weight through some unit distance, such as the pitch of the screw.

EXPERIMENT 10

PILE DRIVER

Part (a)   *To determine the depth a nail is driven in with varying heights of the hammer.*

Part (b)   *To determine the variation of resistance with depth of nail.*

Part (c)   *To determine the variation of resistance with kind of wood; i.e., pine, spruce, oak, etc.*

Part (d)   *To determine the variation of resistance with cross-sectional size of the nail.*

APPARATUS: Pile driver,* meter stick, vernier caliper; eight 10-penny nails;†
one 30-penny nail, one 60-penny nail; hammer; one 2 in. by
4 in. by 8 in. piece of pine, of spruce, of oak, or other available
wood.

The apparatus, shown opposite Figure 64 consists of a 4-kg mass,
which may fall a distance of about 1 meter in a pair of guides. When
the mass is raised a distance of h cm, the potential energy is given
by equation (21). If the nail is driven into the board a distance
s the average force F required to force the nail into the block of
wood will be given by equation (24). Nails to
be driven into the block are started sufficiently
with the hammer so that they will not fall over
before being hit with the falling mass (i.e.,
driver).

Part (a) Start a 10-penny nail into a block
of wood just sufficiently to stand up. Measure,
with the vernier caliper, the distance from block
to the top of the nail. Raise the driver as high
as it will go and drop on the nail. Measure again

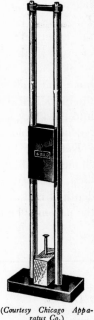

(*Courtesy Chicago Appa-
ratus Co.*)

Fig. 64. Model pile
driver.

TABLE I

Distance the Driver Falls (cm)	DISTANCE FROM BLOCK TO TOP OF NAIL	
	initial	final

* Our pile drivers are equipped with a wooden base placed on top of the
iron base.
† A few common nail lengths are as follows: 4-penny, $1\frac{1}{4}$ in.; 6-penny,
2 in.; 8-penny, $2\frac{1}{2}$ in.; 10-penny, 3 in.; 20-penny, 4 in.; 30-penny, $4\frac{1}{2}$ in.;
60-penny, 6 in.

the distance from the block to the top of the nail. Measure also the total distance the driver fell. Repeat with another 10-penny nail but raise the driver only about two-thirds the former distance. Finally repeat with a third 10-penny nail but raise the driver only about one-third the first distance. The data may be compiled as in Table I. *Plot a curve* with distance the driver falls as ordinates and with distance the nail is driven as abscissas. Do not attempt to use the same scale on the abscissa axis as on the ordinate axis. If the nature of the curve is uncertain, increase the data by allowing the driver to fall from other distances.

Part (b)   Start a 10-penny nail in a block of wood. Measure the height of the top of the nail from the block with a vernier caliper. Raise the driver to the top of the guides and allow to fall. Measure the exact falling distance of the driver with a meter stick, and measure again the height of the nail top from the block with the vernier. Raise the driver again to the top and allow to fall on the same nail and repeat the measurements on the height of nail with the block and the distance the driver fell. Continue driving the nail into the block and repeating the measurements until the nail head reaches the block.

Determine by use of equation (24) how, if any, the resistance changed with depth. Table II will be useful for tabulating the data. *Plot a curve* with the resistances as ordinates and with the initial depth of nail at each trial as abscissas. The depth required to start the nail may be neglected for our purpose.

TABLE II

Distance Driver Falls (cm)	DISTANCE FROM BLOCK TO TOP OF NAIL		Differences (s)	Resistance (dynes) mgh/s
	Initial	Final		

Part (c)   Start a 10-penny nail in a block of pine and measure the depth the nail sinks in the block when the driver is allowed to fall the maximum distance. Repeat with two or more different kinds of wood. Set up a table of data that will show how the resistance to motion in the block varies with the kind of wood.

Part (d)   Start a 10-penny nail in a block of wood and measure the depth the nail sinks in the block when the driver is allowed to fall the maximum distance. Repeat with two or more nails of widely different cross section such as 30- and 60-penny nails. Set up your own table of data. *Plot a graph* with the resistances as ordinates and with the cross-sections as abscissas.

Questions

(a) Should the distance the driver falls be given as the starting distance to (1) the initial height of the nail, or (2) the final height of the nail after being driven to its resting place?

(b) Does the energy imparted to the nail vary directly (1) with the height, (2) with the square of the height, or (3) with the square root of the height?

(c) To what height would the driver have to be raised to compare favorably with the force a carpenter can use on a nail with the usual carpenter's hammer?

(d) Approximately, what is the kinetic energy of the driver just before hitting the nail if raised initially to the maximum height? Upon what height is your answer based?

(e) What will be the velocity of the driver just before striking the nail in question (d)?

(f) If h is the distance the driver falls, the distance the nail is driven into the wood is more nearly proportional to (1) h, (2) h^2, or (3) $\sqrt{h}$.

EXPERIMENT 11

MACHINES,   PULLEYS

Part (a)   *To find the mechanical advantages, efficiency, and force of friction in a pulley system.*

Part (b)   *To find the mechanical advantage, efficiency, and force of friction in a jack. Optional.*

APPARATUS: A mounted double and a single pulley, a single pulley, strong twine, two sets of slotted weights (10–500 g), two hangers, meter stick, automobile jack, heavy mass for load on jack, spring balance. *Note.* 5-g masses are available in slotted weights for finer adjustments.

Part (a)   Set up the apparatus as shown in Figure 63. Place a standard mass (say 200 g) in the pan meant for the load w. This mass, together with the hanger and movable pulley (neglect weight of string), constitutes the total load of weight w which the machine exerts. On the other pan, which is to supply the force applied to the machine, add a number of standard masses until this side of the pulley system *falls without acceleration*. To offset the effect of static friction, give the system a slight push to start it moving. These

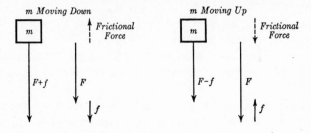

Fig. 65. Vector representation of forces applied by the operator.

masses, together with the hanger, give the force $(F + f)$ necessary to raise the weight w. The two separate forces, the ideal force F and the force f opposite and equal to the force of friction, are pictured in Figure 65. Then take off masses on the side at which the force is applied until it will go up without acceleration. This force is $F - f$. Notice that the direction of f has changed. In this case the frictional force, which is acting equal and opposite to f, is directed downward. If the 10-gram mass is not sufficiently small for adjustments of mass to secure constant velocity for rise and fall, estimation of the correct mass should be made.

Repeat the experiment with standard masses of 400, 600, 800, 1000, and 1200 grams placed in succession on the weight pan. The following table will be found useful for recording the results.

DATA

Velocity ratio, or ideal mechanical advantage, $s/h =$

w Including hanger, pulley	FORCE			$(F+f)-F$	$\dfrac{w}{F+f}$	$\dfrac{F}{F+f}$
	Down $(F+f)$	Up $(F-f)$	F			

The ideal force F is one-half the sum of the down and up forces while the frictional force f is one-half the difference between the down and up forces. The ideal force F is given in column 4, while the frictional force f is found in column 5. Calculate from the data the ideal force applied to the machine (i.e., F), the frictional force $[f = (F+f) - F]$, the actual mechanical advantage $\left(\dfrac{w}{F+f}\right)$ and the efficiency $\left(\dfrac{F}{F+f}\right)$ for the various loads.

OPTIONAL

Part (b)   Examine the jack carefully and determine its velocity ratio by measurement of the distance the input force moves while the output force is raised some unit distance. Now measure the force actually required to lift a given load. From these two measurements, calculate the efficiency and actual mechanical advantage. Repeat the measurements and calculations for two additional loads.

Questions

(a) In the pulley experiment of part (a), let D be the force down, and U be the force up to maintain constant velocity in each direction for a load w. Write, using these symbols, (1) the force of friction, (2) the mechanical advantage, (3) the efficiency. What are the values of D and U for the lightest load used?

(b) To what would the expression wh/s correspond in the suggested data table of part (a). What is the value of wh/s for each of the loads in part (a)?

(c) Does h/s correspond to the number of strings supporting the load w in part (a)? Draw a pulley system where h/s does not correspond to the number of strings supporting the load.

(d) Plot on a single coördinate paper the loads as abscissas against the efficiency, actual mechanical advantage, and friction, respectively, as ordinates. The curves are more easily observed if a different colored ink is used to trace each curve. The ordinates for each curve should be inked in corresponding colors. If colored ink is not available, the curves can be distinguished by use of broken lines, dots and dashes, following some systematic scheme, such as dot-dash, long dash-short dash, etc.

(e) If you raise a load of 800 lb with the jack you experimented with in part (b), what force will have to be exerted on your part? How much work will be done by lifting the load 6 in.?

(f) What was the average frictional force, expressed as a per cent of the total input force in your experiment, part (b).

(g) Repeat question (d) above for the jack.

PROBLEMS

Experiment 10

1 A boy walks up a 150-ft hill. How much work must he do to gain this additional potential energy if he weighs 150 lb? What average power is developed if he walks up the hill in 12 min?

2 A boy runs 100 m in 12 sec. What is his kinetic energy if he weighs 70 kg?

3 Convert the energy in problem 2 into (a) joules, (b) kg-m.

4 Which has the most energy; a 10-lb ball moving at 5 fps or a 5-lb ball moving with a velocity of 10 fps?

5 Which has the most energy; a 10-lb mass raised 10 ft or a 10-lb mass moving with a velocity of 10 fps?

6 A 5-kg mass is dropped on a nail from a height of 0.7 m. What is the average force on the nail if it sinks into a block 1.5 cm?

7 A pile is driven into the mud 1.5 ft when a mass of 2 tons strikes the pile after falling a total distance of 15 ft. What is the resistance offered by the mud?

8 Assume one-fourth of the energy in the driver of problem 7 goes into wasted heat energy. What is now the average resistance due to the mud if the pile is driven 1.5 ft into the mud?

9 A 4-kg driver falling 92 cm drives a 10-penny nail into a block of soft pine 3 cm. How far would you expect a 30-penny nail to be driven if the resistance is proportional to the cross-section of the nail? A 60-penny nail? (*Note.* As-

sume that the cross-sections of the 60-penny, 30-penny, and 10-penny nails are 0.36 cm², 0.29 cm², and 0.11 cm², respectively.)

Experiment 11

1 Suppose that in a pulley system, as shown in Figure 63, $M = 900$ g, while the mass m necessary to pull it up without acceleration is 333 g. Find the following: (1) ideal force F, (2) frictional force due to the pulley system, (3) the actual mechanical advantage, (4) the efficiency. (*Note.* Assume that the ideal mechanical advantage is given by the number of cords supporting the mass of 900 g.)

2 A painter is suspended to the side of a house by the pulley system in Figure 63. The upper block of the pulley system is fastened by a hook to the cornice of the building. The painter may fasten the free or hoisting end of the rope either to his staging or to the side of the building. If the weight of the man and pulley system is 450 lb, examine the force exerted on the cornice of the building in each case.

3 Make a schematic drawing of a pulley system that has a velocity ratio of 5. (*Note.* The ratio s/h is called often the velocity ratio since the force must go a distance s in the same time that the resistance is going a distance h.)

4 Is the mechanical advantage of a watch system (a) less than 1, (b) 0, or (c) grater than 1?

5 You are given a tackle 75 per cent efficient, consisting of two 2-sheave blocks with appropriate rope. You must pull a load of 400 lb with this tackle. Draw a diagram showing the most efficient arrangement and state the force required to pull the load.

6 A hydraulic jack has pistons with diameters in ratio of 1 : 3 and a connecting handle with velocity ratio of 9. What is the over-all ideal mechanical advantage. If the efficiency is 90 per cent, what load could be lifted with an input force of 150 lb?

CHAPTER IX

CENTRIPETAL FORCE

If a body has rotational motion only, the accompanying equations of motion under the influence of torque-producing forces will be simplified if we substitute angular displacements for linear displacements.

An angular displacement is measured in radians, and is defined as the arc divided by the radius. Suppose that the disk in Figure 66

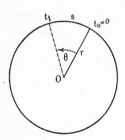

Fig. 66. Disk rotating at constant velocity.

is rotating about axis O and sweeps out angle θ in t seconds, when $t = t_1 - t_0$. The displacement θ will be the ratio s/r radians. Of course, angular displacements may be figured in degrees and revolutions also, but such terminology will not fit directly into the equation of rotary motion.

The angular velocity is defined as the time rate of change of angular displacement. In Figure 66, the angular velocity (ω) will be $\omega = \theta/t$. Since, in the present experiment, only constant angular velocities

are considered, we do not need to concern ourselves with the problems of variable angular velocity. Note that since $s = r\theta$, if the left and the right side are each divided by the time interval t, the resulting equation gives the relation between linear and angular velocity, namely, $v = r\omega$.

A rotating body is subjected always to an inward force even though it may be rotating at constant angular velocity. For simplicity, assume that a mass m is rotating in a circular path of constant radius r with a constant angular velocity ω (Fig. 67a). We assume that the mass m is at point A at the beginning of our calculations and after a short time interval (t) has traversed the arc distance AB. The velocities at points A and B are v_1 and v_2, respectively. By definition, the speed is constant. Hence, the magnitudes of v_1 and v_2 are the same and will be designated as v. The vector triangle of velocities in Figure 67b indicates that the change in velocity may be seen to be perpendicular to the circular path when

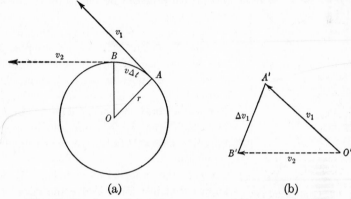

(a) (b)

Fig. 67. Circular motion with constant speed has an acceleration.

the time interval (Δt) is taken sufficiently small, and is directed towards the center of rotation. For very small time intervals then, we may write

$$\frac{\Delta v}{v} = \frac{v\Delta t}{r}$$

or

$$a = \frac{\Delta v}{\Delta t} = \frac{v^2}{r} = \omega^2 r. \tag{25}$$

This acceleration is directed towards the center of rotation as indicated in the vector diagram showing the change in velocity. The centripetal force will be

$$F = ma = m\frac{v^2}{r} \tag{26}$$

EXPERIMENT 12

CENTRIPETAL FORCE

An experimental study of Newton's law of force as applied to centripetal force.

APPARATUS: Equal arm balance mechanism with appropriate stops, 0.2–0.3 kg mass with one eye fastener, slotted weights.

A 0.2 kilogram mass is fastened (Fig. 68) to one end of a string of about 100 cm in length. The other end of the string is fastened to one end of a lever arm about 23 cm in length. A hanger, carrying standard masses, is hung from the other arm of the equal arm balance. The mass m is raised a vertical height (h) of about 60 cm from its lowest free position and is allowed to swing through the arc formed by its downward motion. Sufficient masses (M) are placed on the balance so that it will be raised from the support nearest M and be stopped by the other support, making a low sound intensity click. The height h_2 at which the click from the support opposite masses M fails to be heard should be measured.

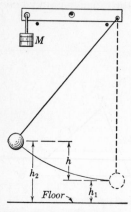

Fig. 68. Centripetal force. Pendulum method. Not drawn to scale.

Once the approximate height h_2 is known that just fails to give the click on the up swing, the more exact desired height may be measured with increased accuracy by use of a string loop. The loop is placed around a diameter of the pendulum bob that is perpendicular to the string length while the two ends of the string are held with your fingers. Once the height h_2 is measured, the mass is allowed to fall by releasing either end of the string. Other ways to obtain the height h_2 will suggest themselves.

The mass required to raise the balance from the support nearest to the hanger without touching the other support is used to measure the total force (F) on the string at the bottom of the swing. Since the swing may be made through a wide arc, **reasonable safety precautions** for others in the room are desirable. The distance (h) fallen is measured more easily by obtaining the height (h_2) at the start and height (h_1) at the lowest point of swing. The floor is used as a reference position for making both measurements (i.e. $h = h_2 - h_1$). The centripetal force (F_c) is found experimentally by taking the difference between F and w, where w is the weight of mass m.

This difference is compared then with the centrifugal force equation, namely

$$F_c = F - w = \frac{mv^2}{r},$$

which is obtained from the equations of motion and from Newton's second law. The details are left as an exercise in collection and analysis of pertinent data. Note that the above equation is in absolute units.

A calculation of the velocity v of mass m at the bottom of the swing may be made directly from the equation used to express the law of conservation of energy, namely

$$\tfrac{1}{2}mv^2 + mgh = \text{constant},$$

where the kinetic energy (KE) is $KE = \tfrac{1}{2}mv^2$ and the potential energy (PE) is $PE = mgh$. Our reference position is so chosen that $\tfrac{1}{2}mv^2$ at the bottom of the swing is numerically equal to mgh at the beginning of the swing, or that

$$v^2 = 2gh.$$

The table below may be useful in organization of the data. Distinction between forces and masses will be necessary. Note that the length of the pendulum (r) is the length of the string plus the radius (r_0) of the spherical pendulum bob.

Mass (m) with estimated error =

F	h_2	h_1	$h_2 - h_1$	$F - w$	v^2	r	$\dfrac{mv^2}{r}$	$F - w$ minus mv^2/r	% error

Questions

(a) Many texts describe a centrifugal force. Is there a centrifugal force associated with this experiment?

(b) Consider any one pendulum length used in your experiments. What was the maximum angular velocity when the mass (m) was swung from the highest position used in this series of experiments?

(c) The effective length (r) of the pendulum was taken as the length (l) of the string plus the radius (r_0) of the sphere. The length (r_0) is not quite correct for the sphere. Why?

(d) From what height (h) must the mass fall so that the centripetal acceleration towards the center of rotation will have the same magnitude as the acceleration due to gravity?

(e) Suppose the mass were to be rotated in a vertical circle at a speed which is just sufficient to keep the mass from falling towards the center when at the top of swing. What is the speed of the mass?

PROBLEMS

Experiment 12

In apparatus shown in Figure 69, a shaft AB can be made to rotate about its own axis. A crosspiece, having suspended from it a metal ball m, is rigidly

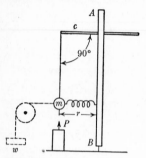

attached to this shaft. When the shaft rotates, the ball will tend to fly outwards, but is prevented from doing this by the spring. When the proper speed is attained and kept constant, the wire supporting the ball will be vertical, and its position is marked by a fixed pointer P below. A string passing down the center of the spring acts as a safeguard in case the spring is stretched too much. This equipment may be used to study centrifugal forces. Suppose that mass in Figure 69 revolves 60 times in 80 seconds. Questions 1 to 3 inclusive.

Fig. 69. Centripetal force apparatus.

1 What will be the tension in the spring if $m = 600$ g and radius $r = 25$ cm?

2 What would be the period T if $m = 1$ kg?

3 What will be the period in problem 1, if the tension of the spring and the mass remains unchanged, but the radius $r = 0.5$ meters?

4 Suppose a mass of the same magnitude as used in your experiment is hung from a 4-meter cord which has the other end fastened to the ceiling. The mass swings in a circular path 1 m in diameter. What will be the gravitational acceleration if the experimental period is found to be 3.999 sec? (*Note:* This is another method for the determination of the constant g, the gravitational acceleration, and uses the centripetal force equation in addition. Tan $\theta = m\omega^2 r/mg$.) In what way, if any, does the resulting value of g, (or the experimental value of T) depend upon the magnitude of m?

CHAPTER X

DENSITY AND SPECIFIC GRAVITY OF BODIES

The *density* of a body is defined as the mass per unit volume. Consequently, if ρ represents the density, v the volume and m the mass, then

$$\rho = \frac{m}{v}$$

In fundamental units the density is expressed in grams per cubic centimeter, pounds per cubic foot, or kilograms per cubic meter. Thus in the English (fps) system the densities of water, mercury at 20 C, and gold (cast) are 62.4, 845.6, and 1204.6 pounds per cubic foot, respectively, whereas in the metric (cgs) system these densities become 1, 13.56, and 19.3 grams per cubic centimeter.

It is very common, especially in the case of liquids, to compare the weight of a given volume of it to the weight of the same volume of some standard substance. The standard substance generally taken is water. *This ratio is called the specific gravity (s) of the substance.* Specific gravity can also be expressed as the ratio of two densities, i.e.,

$$\text{sp gr} = s = \frac{\rho_u}{\rho_k}$$

where ρ_u and ρ_k are the densities of the unknown and known substances, respectively. Referring to the above figures for water and mercury, it will be seen that in either system of units the specific gravity of water is 1 and that of mercury is 13.56, if water is chosen as the standard.

Density is a concrete number with dimensions dependent on the system of units used; while *specific gravity* is an abstract number and hence without dimensions. The value of the specific gravity of a liquid, therefore, does not depend on the system of units.

Because of the fact, that in the metric system a unit volume (one cubic centimeter) of water was meant to have a mass of 1 gram, specific gravity and density in this system have equal numerical magnitudes. For reasons of convenience, plus the fact that it is fairly simple to obtain it in pure form, water is used as a reference substance. It should be pointed out that its change in density with temperature is important (the maximum density occurs at 4° C) and if the volume at 4° C is 1 cu cm, then at 20° C the volume will be about 1.0018 cu cm. Furthermore, since the fundamental standards of length and mass are defined in terms of the standard meter and the standard kilogram kept in Paris, accurate measurements have shown that 1 kg of water at 4° C and at normal atmospheric pressure occupies a volume of 1000.027 cu cm. The volume of 1 kg of water under such conditions is often termed a liter and the

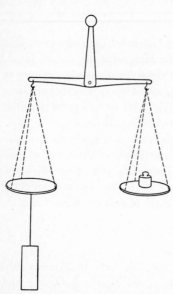

1/1000 part of this a milliliter (ml). If the mks system of units is used, the density is expressed in kilograms per cubic meter. Thus the density of water becomes 1000 kg per cu m. The densities of mercury and gold would be 13,560 and 19,300 kg per cu m, respectively. The numerical values of the specific gravity are not affected by the units used.

DENSITY DETERMINATION BY ARCHIMEDES PRINCIPLE

Archimedes' principle is very commonly used in some manner in measurements of densities and specific gravities, since the volume of the body must be determined by some convenient means in measure-

Fig. 70. Principle of comparing masses with the aid of a balance.

ments of density, and may be useful in specific gravity measurements. Use of Archimedes' principle to find the volume will be applied to an unknown which is insoluble in water and sinks.

For a body that sinks, Archimedes' principle states that the loss of weight of the body in the fluid is equal to the weight of the fluid displaced. The fluid in the present instance is water. We will assume, to be specific, that the weighing is accomplished by some form of balance that uses standard masses as illustrated in Figure 70. The standard masses are placed in the right pan and the unknown mass is placed in the left-hand pan. Since the unknown mass is determined by use of the pull of the earth on both bodies, the process is known as weighing.* Let the mass of the unknown be m. Its weight w when expressed in absolute units (dynes or poundals) will be mg. This weight will be recorded by corresponding masses on the other scale pan. The object is next arranged to hang immersed in water (Fig. 71b). It will be found that the effective weight w_1 is less than before, as shown by the fact that masses can be removed from the right-hand pan in order to bal-

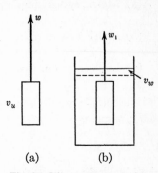

Fig. 71. When measured with a balance the weight of mass m is w in air and w_1 in water.

ance the system. Now, according to Archimedes' principle this difference in the weight of the object should be equal to the weight of the displaced water. A volume of water v_w will be displaced equal to the volume v_u of the unknown. The weight of this displaced water in absolute units will be $v_u \rho_w g$, where ρ_w represents the density of water. Hence we have $w - w_1 = v_u \rho_w g$ according to Archimedes' principle.

We wish to find the density ρ_u of the object. By the definition of density as the mass per unit volume, and the fact that the volume of the block must be equal to the volume of the displaced water we have:

$$\rho_u = \frac{\text{mass of object}}{\text{volume of object}} = \frac{m}{v_u}$$

$$= \frac{m}{\dfrac{w - w_1}{\rho_w g}} = \rho_w \frac{w}{w - w_1} = \rho_w \frac{m}{m - m_1} \qquad (27)$$

The above use of Archimedes' principle neglects the very small buoyancy effect of air.

* A. G. Worthing has proposed the term *massing* for this process. *Am. J. Phys.*, 12, 111 (April, 1944).

Application of Archimedes' principle to the following three systems of units yields formulas for densities as follows:

(a) Metric system (cgs); $\rho = \dfrac{m}{m - m_1}$ g per cu cm

(b) Metric system (mks); $\rho = 1000 \left(\dfrac{m}{m - m_1}\right)$ kg per cu m

(c) English system (fps); $\rho = 62.4 \left(\dfrac{m}{m - m_1}\right)$ lb per cu ft

The specific gravity may be obtained by definition from equation (27); namely,

$$s = \frac{\rho}{\rho_w} = \frac{m}{m - m_1}. \tag{28}$$

Archimedes' principle, therefore, may be used to determine specific gravities. Note that this ratio has the same value in all systems of units.

EXPERIMENT 13

ARCHIMEDES' PRINCIPLE, DENSITY, AND SPECIFIC GRAVITY

Part (a)   *To find the density of solids which sink in water.*
Part (b)   *To find the density of solids which float in water.*
Part (c)   *To find the specific gravity of a liquid using Archimedes' principle.*
Part (d)   *Use of a specific gravity bottle to find the specific gravity of a liquid.*
Part (e)   *Specific gravity by the U-tube method. Optional.*

APPARATUS:

Part (a)   Solids insoluble in water, platform or other type of balance, standard weights, beaker, thread.

Part (b)   Solids lighter than water (e.g., paraffin wax, non-absorbent wood, etc.), a sinker, balance, beaker, thread.

Part (c)   Such liquids as carbon tetrachloride, methyl alcohol, ethyl alcohol, toluol, glycerin, or oil are suitable, balance as in part (a), beaker or ungraduated cylinder, thread.

Part (d)   Specific gravity bottle, balance, and liquid as in part (c).

Part (e)   U-tube, two nonmiscible or nonsoluble liquids, meter rule. Optional.

Part (a) Weigh the solid in air and let its weight in absolute metric units be w ($=mg$). Then weigh the solid (Fig. 72) in water. If the weight in water is w_1 its loss of weight is $(w - w_1)$. According

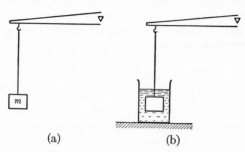

(a)　　　　　　　　(b)

Fig. 72. Solid denser than water.

to Archimedes' principle this loss in weight is equal to the weight of the displaced water, thereby enabling us to determine the volume of the unknown body. Reference to equation (27) shows that the unknown density is

$$\rho_u = \rho_w \frac{m}{m - m_1},$$

the dimensions depending upon those used for water, ρ_w. Note that if the cgs system is used, $\rho_u = m/(m - m_1)$, and $(m - m_1)$ becomes equal numerically to the volume of the displaced water.

Part (b) First find the mass M of the solid which is less dense than water. Next attach a sinker to the solid so that only the former

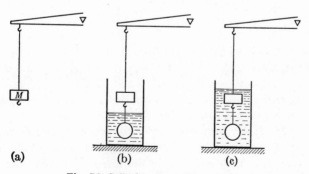

(a)　　　　　　(b)　　　　　　(c)

Fig. 73. Solid less dense than water.

hangs immersed in water in a beaker a few inches below the solid. The solid should not be immersed (Fig. 73b). Let the observed mass under these conditions be M_1. Finally the water level in the beaker is raised so that both are now immersed and once more the apparent mass M_2 is determined (Fig. 73c). Then as in part (a) the volume of the solid can be found from the apparent loss in mass of the solid $(M_1 - M_2)$ and the density is

$$\rho = \rho_w \frac{M}{M_1 - M_2}.$$

Part (c)   Weigh a solid (insoluble in water or in the liquid whose specific gravity is desired) in air and call its mass m'. Next weigh

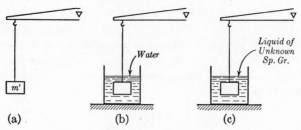

(a)   **(b)**   **(c)**

Fig. 74. Specific gravity of a liquid.

the same solid immersed in water (Fig. 74b), and then in the liquid whose specific gravity is being determined (Fig. 74c). Let these apparent masses be (in water and in the liquid) m'_1, and m'_2, respectively. Then the specific gravity of the liquid is

$$s = \frac{m' - m'_2}{m' - m'_1}$$

This equation has its origin (1) from Archimedes' principle, which states that the loss in weight of a body immersed in a fluid is equal to the weight of the fluid displaced; and (2) from the definition of specific gravity, which is the ratio of the masses of the two liquids when the volumes are the same.

Part (d)   If the specific gravity bottle is not dry and clean, rinse with water and then dry by blowing heated compressed air into the bottle. It is then weighed on the fine balance. Fill the bottle with water and weigh again. Next, having emptied and dried the

specific gravity bottle, it is again weighed when filled with the liquid the specific gravity of which is desired. The bottle should always be exactly full when at room temperature.
If m, m_1, and m_2, in the order given, represent the mass of the empty bottle, the mass of the bottle when filled with water, and the mass of the bottle when filled with the liquid, the specific gravity is

$$s = \frac{m_2 - m}{m_1 - m}.$$

Fig. 75. Specific gravity bottle.

Note that there is a hole of capillary size along the axis of the ground stopper (Fig. 75). This hole is provided to allow excess liquid to escape from the bottle upon sealing with the stopper. The bottle should be wiped after closing with the stopper. *To prevent the formation of bubbles within the bottle*, insert the stopper in such a fashion as to have one side touching the neck of the bottle and the bottle tipped slightly.

Repeat your experiment one or more times and calculate the per cent of error. Compare the value found by experiment with the value as given in tables.

OPTIONAL

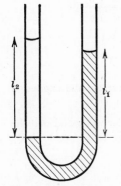

Fig. 76. Specific gravity by U-tube method.

Part (e) Fill the **U**-tube (Fig. 76) about one-third to one-half full of the liquid, then add water to one side until the tube is filled to a desired height. In Figure 76, the shaded portion represents the liquid of which the specific gravity is desired, while the unshaded portion is water. The water column of length l_2 is balanced by the column of liquid of length l_1. Hence, in accordance with Pascal's principle,

$$l_2\rho_2 = l_1\rho_1$$

and therefore we have

$$s = \frac{\rho_1}{\rho_2} = \frac{l_2}{l_1}.$$

Questions

(a) Why is the body in part (a) immersed in water? Can the experiment be performed if the solid were immersed in alcohol? Give reasons.

(b) Why does the weight of the sinker in part (b) not enter into the calculations?

(c) How could you determine the specific gravity of the solids in parts (a) and (b)?

(d) Compare your values with those found in tables. Can you make some estimate of the reliability of your determinations of density?

(e) If a specific gravity bottle, calibrated by means of water of 20° C, is filled with the unknown liquid at 40° C, how would the value of the specific gravity determined in this way and at this temperature compare with the actual value?

(f) Suggest a method for finding the density of a powder.

(g) Give the details of a method for finding the density of a solid which is soluble in water.

(h) Discuss, in terms of accuracy, the use of an overflow can to measure the volume of water displaced by the body whose density is desired.

PROBLEMS

Experiment 13

1 If a solid weighs w_1 in air and w_2 in water, explain the expression $w_1 - w_2 = V\rho g$, as well as the units involved.

2 Assume that a liquid of density ρ_l is substituted for water and that the body weighs w in air and w_2 in the liquid. Prove that the density ρ of the body may be found by the relationship $\rho = \rho_l \dfrac{w}{w - w_2} = \rho_l \dfrac{m}{m - m_2}.$

3 Show that $s = \dfrac{m' - m_2'}{m' - m_1'}$, found in part (c), can be obtained from the definition $s = \dfrac{\rho}{\rho_w}$, where ρ and ρ_w are the densities of the body and water, respectively.

4 How much will a block of aluminum of mass 60 g weigh in water if the density of aluminum is 2.6 g per cm^3?

5 A spherical mass of cast gold weighing 166 g is thought to have a hollow center. When weighed in water, it is found to weigh 142 g. What is the volume of the enclosed air space. (Density of gold = 19.3 g per cm^3.)

6   A stone weighs 343 g in air, 208 g in water, and 242 g in a liquid. Calculate (a) the volume of the stone, (b) the density of the stone, (c) the specific gravity of the liquid, (d) the buoyant force on the solid when immersed in the liquid (in dynes).

7   Work example 4, using the mks system of units.

8   A specific gravity bottle weighs 24.6 g when empty. Then a small amount of sand is put in the bottle and it weighs 34.3 g, with the sand. The remaining space in the bottle is filled with water and the combination weighs 80.6 g. The bottle is next emptied and filled only with water and the total weight is 74.6 g. Calculate the density of the sand.

CHAPTER XI

ELASTICITY

All bodies are deformed in some way by application of a force, no matter how small that force may be. A perfectly elastic body will return to its original shape, or position, when the applied forces are removed. In any actual case, there is a limit to the magnitude of the force which may be applied, if the body is to return to its original state. This is called the *elastic limit*. A greater force would cause permanent distortion and finally fracture. Applications of the laws of elastic bodies may be seen in watch springs, automobile springs, spring balances, etc.

One of the most important properties of an elastic body is that, when it is bent, twisted, compressed, or stretched, *the ratio of the magnitude of the applied force to the deformation is constant*. In order that we may obtain the same constant for bodies, made of the same material, no matter what the dimensions of the object may be, we state that, within the elastic limit, the ratio of the stress to the strain is a constant e,

i.e.,
$$e = \frac{\text{stress}}{\text{strain}} \tag{29}$$

(This is *Hooke's Law*, discovered by Robert Hooke in 1660.) The constant e is called the *modulus of elasticity*. Stress is measured by the magnitude of the force per unit area causing distortion. Actually, the term *stress* refers to the internal forces per unit area set up to oppose the external force. These forces are, however, equal and opposite for all cases which we shall consider.

The deformations may be, essentially, a change of shape, length, or volume. In practice, the most important deformation, resulting from a pulling or compressing force, is the change in length. For our purposes, then, we will consider only deformations which are essentially changes of length. In such cases the strain would be defined as the change in length per unit length.

STRETCHING OF MATERIALS

Consider a wire of length l and of cross section A (Fig. 77) to be stretched by a force F so that the new length is $(l + \Delta l)$. Application of Hooke's law gives

$$\frac{\text{stress}}{\text{strain}} = \frac{\dfrac{F}{A}}{\dfrac{\Delta l}{l}} = \text{constant.}$$

Instead of calling the constant e, we substitute for it the letter Υ (and call this Young's modulus, in honor of Thomas Young, who first gave physical meaning to this constant), which expresses the relation between stress and strain.

Consequently,

$$\Upsilon = \frac{Fl}{A\Delta l}. \tag{30}$$

BENDING BEAMS

In engineering practice, considerably less material is needed if girders are placed so that the thin side is vertical, for bending is usually inversely proportional to the cube of the depth but only to the first power of thickness. The **H** type steel girder and the steel rail are examples of useful applications of the law of bending beams. Theory and experiment show that the bend B in a beam of rectangular cross section is proportional to the force F and to the cube of its length l; and inversely proportional to its breadth b and to the cube of its depth d; that is:

$$B \propto \frac{Fl^3}{bd^3}$$

or

$$B = C\frac{Fl^3}{bd^3}, \tag{31}$$

where C is a constant, depending upon the mode of support and the material of the rod. When the rod is supported by a fulcrum

Fig. 77. Wire stretched by a force F.

at either end and the force is applied midway between them, then

$$C = \frac{1}{4\,\Upsilon},\tag{32}$$

where Υ represents Young's modulus, and

$$B = \frac{Fl^3}{4\Upsilon bd^3}.\tag{33}$$

Notice that bending is essentially a combination of stretching and

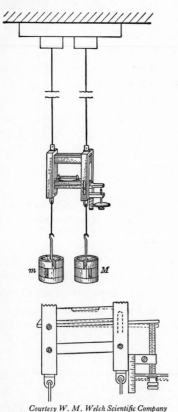

compression. This explains why Young's modulus appears in our equation. The top half of the beam is compressed, while the lower half is stretched.

EXPERIMENT 14

YOUNG'S MODULUS

A determination of Young's modulus for materials in the form of long wires*

APPARATUS: Young's modulus apparatus, meter stick, weights, micrometer caliper.

The apparatus consists of two wires of equal length, each having one end fastened to a rigid support or beam in the ceiling, while the other end is attached to a rectangular frame, as shown in Figure 78. The frame is loaded under each wire with masses m and M. A level with micrometer screw attachment tells us how much the wire is stretched for a given load. The mass m is used to keep the

Courtesy W. M. Welch Scientific Company

Fig. 78. Young's Modulus Apparatus.

---

* Other suitable methods for measuring small linear displacements are given in Chapter XXXIV, page 407.

wire at a constant tension and, in particular, to eliminate any kinks in the wire. This mass m should be one or two kilograms, depending upon the size of the wire. The other mass M is variable and is used to vary the tension on the second wire.

The wire supporting the mass m may be replaced by a rigid wall support.

The procedure is to adjust the micrometer screw so that the bubble in the spirit level is in the center when an initial load M of one of two kilograms is applied. Then increase the value of M by two kilograms† and bring the bubble to its zero position by adjustment of the micrometer screw. Repeat until 10 or 12 kilograms have been added. Now since Young's modulus is given by the equation

$$Y = \frac{\text{stress}}{\text{strain}} = \frac{Fl}{A\Delta l},$$

we can find Y by substituting our measured values of F, A, Δl, and l in equation (30). In order to test Hooke's law we shall plot the stress (i.e., force per unit area) as ordinates and strain (i.e., change of length per unit length) as abscissas. If Hooke's law is valid, a straight line should result (Fig. 79). Provided the elastic limit has not been exceeded, draw the best straight line through the plotted points. If the line does not pass through the origin, draw a parallel line that does. For large loads (i.e., when the elastic limit is exceeded), the curve bends towards the horizontal.

Calculate Y from your straight line, which passes through the origin, by taking the ratio of any ordinate to the corresponding abscissa. Choose an ordinate of reasonably large value in order to minimize the error in reading your graph. The unit of Y will, of course, depend upon the units in which the stress is measured.

† The values of this incremental load as well as the maximum load should be obtained from the instructor, since they depend upon the size and kind of wire used in this test.

YOUNG'S MODULUS

Value of M for initial load = ...kg.

Initial micrometer reading =

Total Force (F) Added	Force per Unit Area, F/A = stress	Micrometer Readings	Total Stretch Δl	Change in Length per Unit Length, $\frac{\Delta l}{l}$ = strain

To find area of the wire

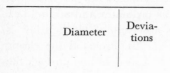

	Diameter	Deviations
Total =		
Av. dia. =		

Area of wire,

$$A = \frac{\pi d^2}{4} =$$

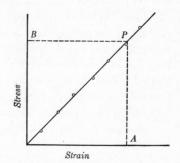

Fig. 79.

$$Y = \frac{\text{stress}}{\text{strain}} = \frac{OB}{OA} = \frac{AP}{OA}$$
$$=$$

Questions

(a) How far does the screw of the micrometer screw move vertically for one revolution? What is the least count of the micrometer screw in your experiment?

(b) Consider the several quantities to be measured in finding Young's modulus and discuss the per cent error involved in each when using the measuring instruments provided. Estimate the per cent error of the result.

(c) Suppose you had made an error in your experiment of 0.5 cm in measuring the length l. Would this error be serious when compared to the errors accumulated in the other measurements?

(d) If the micrometer screw which raises or lowers the level is not located immediately under the wire to be stretched, will any correction be necessary for this extra lever arm? Explain your answer.

(e) Express your value of Young's modulus (metric units) in terms of the engineering units (lb per in.²).

(f) Look up in a table of elastic constants the modulus of elasticity of the material you used and calculate the per cent error in your experiment, using the constant found from the table as standard.

(g) Look up in tables the elastic limit and the breaking stress for the wire you used.

$$y = \frac{\pm l}{ae} = \frac{Fl}{12l} - \frac{F}{2}$$

PROBLEMS

Experiment 14

1 Assume that a wire of unit cross section could be stretched to twice its original length, and still remain within its elastic limit and that the change in its cross section is negligible. What expression would you obtain for Young's modulus?

2 From an examination of the equation representing Young's modulus, what relation exists between the distorting force and stretch for any given wire?

3 What is the object of the initial load of 2 kg suspended from each wire before measurements are taken? Is an initial load required if a single wire is used in the experiment?

4 Are any corrections, due to the stretch of the initial load of two kilograms on each wire, to be made in the calculations for Young's modulus? State reasons for your answer.

5 A flat brass rod and a flat copper rod, each 4 m long and 0.3 cm² in cross section, are suspended vertically and rigidly connected all along their lengths. If a mass of 20 kg is suspended from the lower end of the combined rods, what will be the resultant stretch of the bar and the restoring force exerted by each bar? Assume Young's modulus for brass to be 9.2×10^{10} newtons per m²; for copper, 10×10^{10} newtons per m².

6 What will be the length of a brass rod which stretches one-half the distance of a 3-m steel rod when subjected to the same stretching force, assuming that the steel rod is one-half the diameter of the brass rod. If the stretching force is 13 kg and the diameter of the steel rod is 0.5 mm, what will be the stretch in this rod? Young's modulus for steel is 22×10^{11} dynes per cm^2, and for brass as given in problem 5.

7   A 40-ft steel rod of diameter 2 in. changes in length 0.8 in. due to the difference between summer and winter temperatures. Calculate the mechanical force necessary to stretch the rod this amount. Assume Young's modulus for steel to be 3×10^7 lb per in.^{2}

8   Assuming Young's modulus for brass to be 13.4×10^6 lb per in.^{2}, what minimum diameter of brass wire (length 5 ft) will be necessary to sustain a load of 75 lb and not stretch more than one-tenth inch?

Express your result in terms of the B & S gage as well as in centimeters.

9   From the results of problem 8, calculate the minimum thickness of a brass wire that will be necessary to support a 150-lb weight.

CHAPTER XII

SURFACE TENSION

Surface tension is a molecular phenomenon. We know that strong forces must exist between the molecules since fairly large drops can be made to fall through space without breaking up. A molecule within the liquid at A in Figure 80 will have molecular forces acting upon it from all directions, statistically distributed so that the resultant force on the molecule will have no fixed resultant direction. However, the molecule at the point B on the surface will have a resultant force downward normal to the surface. The surface molecules came to this surface position because of favorable molecular action and therefore possess excess potential energy and have a resultant force on them which is normal to the surface. This potential energy manifestation will be seen when a soap bubble bursts. The potential energy changes to kinetic energy and the liquid drops fly in many directions.

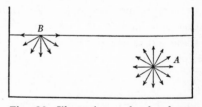

Fig. 80. Illustrating molecular forces that act on a molecule—sphere of action.

If the surface is disturbed by addition of another liquid of different surface energy, the former normal components are temporarily at an angle to the normal until balanced again. Here the surface tension manifests itself as a phenomenon parallel to the surface instead of normal to the surface. The normality of forces here is somewhat similar to the normal electric field radiating from a charged metal sphere except that the forces do not obey the inverse square law, so that the size of the container has no effect on the surface energy. The resulting force, no doubt, depends upon forces varying to a much higher power with distance. This will be seen when we note that a clean wire frame dipped into a liquid and removed will bring a liquid film with it. The film will always be such as to present a minimum possible new surface, since the potential energy always tends to a minimum value.

In Figure 81 a film forms in the plane of the frame and will continue to form as the frame is raised until there is insufficient liquid between the two film layers on each side of the frame. Since the

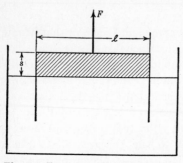

Fig. 81. Formation of a film as the frame is raised out of the water.

force due to the surface energy is normal to the surface, the force F is constant, for all practical purposes, until the film breaks. In Figure 81 the surface energy acts as if it had a tension along the surface so that if we define surface tension T as the *normal force per linear distance on the surface film*, a useful relation may be established for use in connection with surface tension phenomena. The surface acts elastically but not like a rubber membrane since an increase in the stretching distance s (Fig. 81) does not increase the tension. Let the work done in moving the frame a distance s be W; then $W = Fs$. Defining the surface tensions T as the force per linear distance,

$$W = Fs = T2ls = TA, \tag{34}$$

where $F = T2l$ since there is a film on both sides of the frame of length l, and where A is the total area of the two films. The film breaks when the excess water is too depleted to fill the surface needs. The cross section of the wire must be small also, since a large excess of water will give a force F too large to account for the surface tension alone.

Equation (34) indicates well the true nature of surface tension, in that we may define it as the *excess free surface energy per unit area*, i.e. $T = W/A$.

The energy relationships, as related to forces connected with surface tension, may be studied by making a sample calculation of the work required to increase the size of a water drop, and relating this work to our concept of surface tension. A calculation* shows that the surface tension of the water drop is $T = Pr/2$, where P is the excess pressure due to surface tension. This surface tension acts as if it were a force per unit distance acting tangentially to the sphere on both sides of any diameter of the water drop, but perpendicular to the diameter, and may also be so regarded in calculations.

The two definitions of surface tension prove to be equivalent, so that either definition may be used, depending upon convenience of the occasion. In our experiments, surface tension defined as the

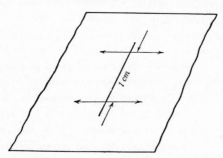

Fig. 82. Unit length of the surface of a liquid.

tension acting on both sides of an imaginary unit length in the surface, has proven very useful. In the cgs system, the surface tension so defined will be given in dynes per centimeter (Fig. 82).

Another point which must be mentioned in connection with our definition is that, when we speak of the surface tension, we must specify the media on both sides of the surface. Usually when we

* The surface energy W in a water drop of volume V is $W = PV$, where P is the excess pressure due to surface tension. If the volume is increased by a small increment, the increment of work ΔW required and the corresponding increment of volume ΔV and of surface area ΔS are outlined below

$$W + \Delta W = P(V + \Delta V); \qquad\qquad V + \Delta V = 4/3\pi \, (r + \Delta r)^3;$$
$$\Delta W = P\Delta V; \qquad\qquad\qquad \Delta V = 4\pi r^2 \Delta r \text{ approximately};$$
$$= P \, 4\pi r^2 \Delta r \text{ approximately};$$

$$S + \Delta S = 4\pi(r + \Delta r)^2$$
$$\Delta S = 8\pi r \Delta r \text{ approximately}$$
$$= \frac{2a}{r} \, \Delta r \text{ approximately}$$

Therefore, since ΔS is the new surface area exposed, the surface tension is defined as the energy expended per unit increment of surface, or

$$T = \frac{\Delta W}{\Delta S} = \frac{P \, 4\pi r^2 \Delta r}{8\pi r \Delta r} = \frac{Pr}{2} \tag{35}$$

refer to a water surface, we assume water below and air above. The value of T, i.e., the surface tension, will be different if we have some other gas or liquid above the water.

METHODS OF MEASUREMENT

There are several indirect methods, based generally on the effects produced by surface tension, which may be used for its measurement. Such measurement may involve an increase of the exposed surface as in the use of ripple waves, the formation of a film on a rectangular frame or circle, or the use of bubble methods. With practice and skill, all the above methods will lead to accurate determinations of surface tension.

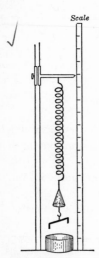

Fig. 83. A Jolly balance of simple construction.

In all surface tension measurements the main requirement for accurate and reproducible results is cleanliness. The slightest amount of foreign substance on the surface will cause large errors in the value of T. This is especially true for small amounts of grease. Hence the liquids or solids that are going to be in contact should not be touched with the fingers. Unless this precaution is observed, the value as found may vary by as much as 10 per cent or more.

Two methods will be described. The first method using the so-called *Jolly balance* is straightforward in principle, but does not give such accurate results. The other method, making use of the effect of surface tension in producing so-called *capillary action*, will give very good results, although a large amount of skill and technique are required. It is included here, therefore, as an experiment designed to test and develop the student's technique in experimental procedure. If enough time is available, there is no reason why accurate results are not possible.

Direct determination of surface tension (Jolly balance). A Jolly balance of simple construction may be made from a long spiral spring which hangs vertically and is fixed above to a crosspiece. This crosspiece can be moved up or down very slowly and the amount of motion measured by some suitable means. Such means are the observation of the motion of a certain point of the spring on a scale engraved on a mirror surface which remains stationary, or, by having a scale and vernier engraved on the telescope tube which moves up or down (Figs. 83 and 86).

At the end of the spiral is attached a carefully cleaned platinum or aluminum frame, usually rectangular (Fig. 84) or circular. This frame is allowed to sink right into the liquid, and then the force F necessary to pull this frame through the surface is measured in dynes.

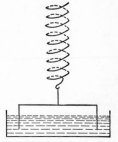

Fig. 84. Frame in the liquid without film.

Now the force F has to be applied against a film on each side of the frame. Hence this force has to be exerted against a length of film $2\,l$ (Fig. 81). Therefore by definition $T = F/2\,l$ dynes per centimeter. If a circular frame is used, replace $2\,l$ by $4\,\pi r$, where r is the radius of the circle.

Effect of surface tension in capillarity The forces of adhesion between glass and water molecules, being larger than the forces of cohesion between the water molecules themselves, cause the surface of water to rise whenever it comes in contact with the glass. Although these forces are small, they can be readily shown to be appreciable if we make use of a capillary tube. The adhesive forces will make the water rise in the tube until these forces acting upwards just balance the force of gravity acting downwards on the column of water. The adhesive forces however will not cause the water to rise in the tube with any determinable angle of contact unless the tube is clean and the liquid wets the tube much higher than the water will rise.

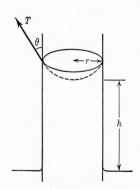

Fig. 85. Capillarity.

The force due to the surface tension of any liquid will act upward in a direction tangent to the liquid surface at the point of contact between the liquid and the capillary. Let the radius of the tube be r and let the surface of the liquid (i.e., also the direction of T) make an angle θ with the surface of the tube (Fig. 85). Then, by definition T is the force acting on the surface on every centimeter and hence at the edge the total vertical force acting will be $T \cos \theta \times 2 \pi r$ dynes. This is, therefore, the resultant force which the adhesive forces exert upwards.

The mass of liquid elevated in the capillary tube exerts a downward force $V \rho g$, where V is the volume of liquid in the capillary and ρ is the density. Hence, noting that the upward forces are equal to the downward forces, we obtain the equation

$$2 \pi r T \cos \theta = V \rho g.$$

The volume of liquid in the capillary tube will consist of a column of area πr^2 and of height h (the height from the free surface of the liquid in the vessel to the base of the meniscus) plus a volume of liquid which is the difference between a cylinder of height r and a hemisphere of radius r. That is,

$$V = \pi r^2 h + (\pi r^2 \cdot r - \tfrac{2}{3} \pi r^3)$$
$$= \pi r^2 h + (\tfrac{1}{3}) \pi r^3 = \pi r^2 [h + (\tfrac{1}{3})r] = \pi r^2 l,$$

where

$$l = h + \tfrac{1}{3} r$$

Extensive experiments[*] on a number of metallic and glass surfaces that are wet by liquids indicate that the cosines of the angle θ are unity to a few parts in a thousand. Material is of less importance than cleanness. Hence, for all cases in which the liquid wets the surface, assume that $\theta = 0$, then

$$T = \frac{r l \rho g}{2} \text{ dynes per cm.}$$

It is often quite accurate enough to measure the distance h from the surface of the liquid to the bottom of the meniscus and, neglecting r, call this distance l.

EXPERIMENT 15

SURFACE TENSION.   JOLLY BALANCE METHOD

Part (a)   *Calibration of the spring balance.*
Part (b)   *Measurement of the force due to surface tension either by use of (1) the Jolly balance, or (2) simple spring balance.*

[*] *J. of Science*, **34**, 614 (1943).

APPARATUS: Jolly balance or similar spring balance, movable platform, several platinum or other metallic frames (approximately #24 B & S gage), a few weights for calibration purposes (1 up to 10 grams), a meter rule, pair of tweezers, distilled water, bunsen burner to clean the platinum wire by heating to a dull red color, cleaning solution (page 424), thermometer, micrometer caliper (if questions (c) and (d) are answered).

Part (a)   To calibrate the spring balance, hang a very light pan on the bottom of the spring and make a note of the position of a convenient mark or pointer on the lower end of the spring and read the scale. (This reading can be in arbitrary spring balance units.) Next, place the known mass on the scale pan (say m grams). This of course will stretch the spring. The balance is restored by moving the upper support of the spring upwards until the point on the lower part of the spring, that was observed before, comes to rest in the same position. The amount of motion of the upper support is measured on the scale. Table I gives a convenient method for recording the results.

Having measured the elongation e for m grams mass added to the spring, the force constant k, which is the force necessary to give a stretch or elongation of one scale division, is $k = mg/e$. Make several trials with two or more masses and calculate the mean. Express the force constant k in dynes per division elongation.

Part (b 1)   *When Jolly balance is used.* A refined form of Jolly balance consists of a long sensitive helical coil attached at the upper end to the telescoping tube which may be raised or lowered by means of a knurled wheel at the base (Fig. 86). There is a vernier at the upper end for more accurate readings. An index is attached to the lower end, between the spring and the pan, which may be used to obtain coincidences with an etched line on a small glass cylinder which surrounds it. The platform on which the liquid container rests is often made adjustable in height by means of a screw located under the platform. Heat the platinum wire to a dull red heat to burn off dirt accumulations. Care must be taken never to touch the frame with the fingers once it has been cleaned by heating. Hang this frame on the hook at the bottom of the spring and place a clean dish of distilled water on the movable platform, so that the frame hangs centrally in the dish. Turn the adjusting screw A (Fig. 86) until the pin p is held up against the lower part of the glass cylinder g as shown in the figure. Hold a beaker of water in the hand and bring it up under the ring r until the ring is well under the surface of the water. Then lower the beaker to the platform to see if the indexed pin p can be pulled away from the cylinder

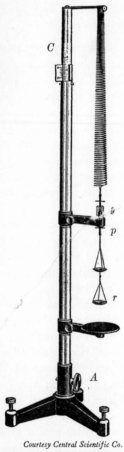

Fig. 86. A sensitive Jolly balance with vernier at the upper end.

before the surface film breaks. If it is possible to pull the pin down with the surface film raise the inner cylinder C by means of the adjusting screw A. Repeat this procedure until the *maximum* pull which the surface film can exert will just barely break the pin loose from the glass cylinder. After this adjustment has been made read the position on the vernier scale. Then without the surface film present, carefully lower the inner cylinder C until the pin is just released from the glass cylinder. Again read the position on the vernier. The difference in the readings of course is the stretch of the spring which is necessary to balance the pull of the surface film. We will call this difference in the two readings d. See Table II for recording the data.

Alternate procedure The Jolly balance is provided with a moving index which allows an equally good, or better, procedure for the experienced manipulator. The beaker, containing the liquid under test, may be raised to obtain a film and then rested back on the platform. Now raise the spring by use of the knurled wheel at the base. Note, by observing coincidences of the movable index with one of the indices on the glass cylinder, when the film breaks. Take the reading and then take another reading when the moving index is returned with film to the same position as when the film was attached. Repeat several times. The under side of the platform of some Jolly balances has a screw device with knurled head for adjusting the height within small distances.

OPTIONAL METHOD

Part (b 2) *When simple spring balance is used.* If a spring only is provided as in Figure 83, the upper support is moved down slowly until the whole frame is immersed. Then stretch the spring slowly until the frame is pulled out of the water. Note approximately how much the film can be stretched just before it breaks. (Sometimes an adjustable marker is provided which can be used to mark this point.) Now bring the legs of the frame back slowly into the liquid up to the position which the frame had when the film broke (being careful to see that there is no film formed on the frame). Read this position on the scale. The frame is now lowered into the liquid and pulled up again, this time with the film formed on the frame tending to keep the frame in the liquid. Raise the spring slowly until the film breaks. Take the reading on the scale when the film just breaks. The difference gives the number of scale divisions that the spring is stretched due to the surface tension. Repeat several times. Calculation of results by any of the above methods is indicated in Table I.

TABLE I

CALIBRATION OF SPRING BALANCE

Trials	Length of Frame (l) $2\pi r$	Deviations	Trials	Zero Reading	Reading After Addition of m Grams	Elongation e	Spring Constant (k)	Deviations
1.	$2\pi r$	c	1.)	19.7	25.8g			
2.	$2\pi r$	c	(2.)	19.7	26.9			
Averages					Averages			

The constant k will be $k = mg/e$ while the force F due to the surface tension is $F = kd$. The surface tension (T) will be

$$T = \frac{F}{2\,l} \text{ dynes per cm.}$$

TABLE II

Temperature of water =

Determination of the force of tension produced by the film

Final Reading With Film	Corresponding Reading Without Film	Difference in the Two Readings (d)	Force Due to the Film (F)	Deviations
		Averages		

$$T =$$
$$\% \, AD =$$

Note   There are two correction factors to be considered in the equation, $T = F/2\,l$, for accurate work. One of the correction factors, i.e., excess liquid lifted, was mentioned earlier. Another type of correction occurs when a circular frame is used. The film, instead of being vertical, has a component inward which tends to give a value for T which is a little small (Fig. 87). The two types of corrections are opposite each other. The resulting correction factor depends upon the size of the wire, the liquid (such as density), and circumference of the wire (if a circular wire is used). We will assume the correction is not sufficiently serious for the experiment above.

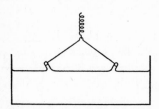

Fig. 87. Circular frame.

Questions

(a) On the assumption that the surface tension of water between the temperatures of 10° C and 60° C can be represented by the formula, $T = 75.796 - 0.145\,t - 0.00024\,t^2$, what value for the surface tension should you have obtained?

(b) What value is given for the surface tension in your handbook?

(c) About what was the diameter of the wire used in your experiment?

(d) If two wires of considerable difference in diameter was used, were the results reasonably in agreement. If not, which wire gives the larger value for the surface tension?

(e) Does the surface tension depend upon the type of wire used, i.e., platinum, nickel, or aluminum?

EXPERIMENT 16

SURFACE TENSION BY CAPILLARY TUBES

Determination of surface tension by the method of capillarity.

APPARATUS: Small glass evaporating dish, transparent glass scale with millimeter divisions, a thermometer, a burner, glass tubing of less than a millimeter diameter (if capillaries are made by students), a microscope with either a micrometer eyepiece or else a finely divided scale placed in the focal plane of the eyepiece.

Part (a) *Making the capillary tubes. Consult the instructor.*
Part (b) *Measuring the height of rise in the tubes.*
Part (c) *Measuring the diameter of the bore of these tubes.*

Part (a) The glass tubes which you are given have been well cleaned inside by rinsing with caustic soda solution, then water, then 10 per cent nitric acid, and finally washed out with water again, and dried. Heat the glass about 5 cm from the end until it is soft (rotating the tube during the process of heating). Then remove the heated glass tube from the flame and draw it out until a capillary tube about 1 mm (or less) external diameter has been obtained. If the drawn-out section is long enough, cut or break it off into pieces about 15 cm in length. Using the remaining sections of the original glass tube and holding by the drawn-out end, make some finer capillaries until about five have been obtained of varying sizes, each of length 10 to 15 cm. Handle the capillaries as little as possible.

Part (b) Fill the thin evaporating glass dish about half full of clean water from the faucet. It is understood of course that the glass dish itself has first been cleaned and is thoroughly free from grease or dirt. Stand the glass scale up in the water and next to it one of the fine capillaries. Usually the capillary will adhere to the scale if the latter has been wet a little. The water will rise in the tube. In order to be sure that the tube is wet inside (i.e., $\theta = 0$) for the whole length of the capillary, lean the tube over, still keeping the lower end in the water, until the water fills the whole tube. Then tilt the capillary tube up again to see whether the water comes back to the same height as before. If this is not the case, reject this capillary and use another. If the capillary and water are both clean, the water will always rise to the same height.

Measure the height of the water column in the capillary, taking the measurement from the outside water surface to the bottom of the meniscus (the correction $\frac{1}{3}$ can be added here if the tube has a large radius, but in most cases this is negligible). Stick a small piece of gummed paper to the tube about 2 mm above the highest point of the column of water. Draw the capillary tube up about 5 mm and measure the height again, sticking a small piece of paper 2 mm above this latter height. If the tube is uniform, these two heights should agree. If there should be a large difference between these heights, use a tube of more uniform bore.

Repeat for two other sizes of capillary tubes. Be sure to mark them so as to know which tube was used in finding the measured elevations!

Part (c)   Break the capillaries off halfway between the gummed paper marks and mount in a **V**-groove, or stick upright in some soft material, so that the micrometer microscope can be properly focused on the broken tip. Measure the inside diameter several times in accordance with the technique described for the micrometer microscope in Chapter XXXIV.

If the capillary tubing is too large to break without preparation, scratch first with a fine file or a rough knife.

Optional technique to determine the diameter   The following method is very satisfactory but requires considerable skill. Introduce a thread of mercury into the capillary (Fig. 88a), measure the length of the thread, and find its mass on a balance. From these data, knowing the density of mercury, the diameter of the tube can be found. By this method the uniformity of the bore can also be tested.

Let r represent the radius to be determined, s the length of the mercury column, m the mass of the mercury column, and ρ the density of the mercury.

Then $$m = \pi r^2 s \rho$$

and $$r = \sqrt{\frac{m}{\pi s \rho}}.$$

Test the uniformity of bore by moving the mercury column along the capillary tube and measuring the length l of the mercury column.

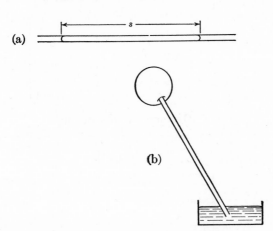

Fig. 88. Drawing mercury into a capillary tube.

In order to get a thread of mercury into the tube it is possible to insert the end of the tube into a small globule of mercury and suck a little into the tube. However, if this is not done carefully, the method is dangerous since mercury is a poison. A cheap rubber ball (Fig. 88b) will serve the purpose just as well if a small hole is made in the ball and the capillary inserted.

Record your results as follows:

Liquid _____, Temperature of liquid =
(For calibration of micrometer microscope)
1 division on standard scale =   cm
1 division on standard scale $\approx$ divisions on microscope scale
1 division on microscope scale =   cm

TABLES

Part (b)

Capillary No.	READING IN CENTIMETERS AT		Height of Column
	Outside Level	Meniscus	
1			
2			
3			

Part (c) Micrometer microscope

DIAMETER IN		Radius	T	Deviations
Micrometer Scale Div.	Cm.			
1				
2				
3				

Av. $T =$
% $AD =$

Part (c) Mercury

$\rho = 13.55$ g per cm³ at 18 C

Capillary No.	m	s	$r = \sqrt{m/\pi s \rho}$

Repeat, if time allows the use of a different liquid.

Questions

(a) Compare the radii obtained by use of the mercury method with those obtained with the micrometer microscope method. From your data, which set of data for the radius of each capillary tube seems to be most reliable?

(b) Compare the value of the surface tension obtained here with that obtained by the Jolly balance method.

(c) Which of the above measurements, r or l, will cause the largest error in the result for T? Why? What is approximately the per cent of error in each of the quantities measured?

(d) If the angle of contact is not zero, what additional test would have to be carried out?

(e) Why may the method of weighing (in order to find the diameter) be more accurate?

(f) Do your results show what relation exists between the rise of a liquid in a capillary and the radius of the capillary? What is the relationship?

(g) Would it be better, as far as accuracy is concerned, to take a very long tube of extremely fine bore or a short tube of fairly large bore?

PROBLEMS

Experiment 15

1 Define surface tension.

2 Does surface tension obey Hooke's law? Give reasons for your answer.

3 A toothpick-shaped sliver of wood 3 cm long is dropped into water which has a surface tension of 73 dynes per cm. If alcohol is poured on one side of the sliver of wood, what will be the resulting differential pull on the wood provided the surface tension of the alcohol is 55 dynes per cm?

4 A rectangular frame made of platinum has one edge cut away and is so mounted that the two legs dip into a liquid. When the frame is immersed and pulled out again, it is found that a spring attached to the frame is stretched 6 cm before the frame actually breaks through the surface. The horizontal length of the rectangular frame (i.e., the length of the platinum wire immersed, neglecting the legs) is 8 cm. Find the surface tension if an elongation of 11 cm is produced when a mass of 2 g is placed on the spring.

5 Find the surface tension of a liquid if a rectangular frame with horizontal length of 9 cm immersed in the liquid requires a stretch of 5 cm in a spring. It is known that a mass of 2 g will stretch the spring 13 cm.

Experiment 16

1 Prove the expression for capillary rise in a tube, namely, $l = \dfrac{2\,T\cos\theta}{r\rho g}$, giving full reasons for each step.

2 How would you prove experimentally the relation between:
  (a) l and r?
  (b) l and d?

3 The surface tensions of two liquids A and B are 350 dynes per cm and 465 dynes per cm, respectively, whereas the angle of contact for glass and liquid A is 140° and for glass and B is 135°. Using the same capillary tube in both liquids, what is the ratio between the heights of the liquids A and B in this tube? (Given that the ratio of the density of liquid A to density of liquid B = 4 : 5.)

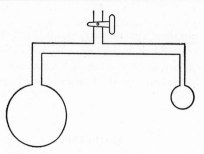

Fig. 89. Two soap bubbles.

4 Find the surface tension of a liquid which wets a capillary tube and rises in this tube of 1 mm diameter to a height of 3.8 cm. The density of the liquid is 0.8 g per cm³.

5 Two soap bubbles are blown (Fig. 89) so that the one has a momentary radius of 10 cm while the other has a radius of 5 cm. What will be the subsequent changes in size, before either bubble bursts.

From Hooke's Law we have seen (Chapter XI) that a distortion is proportional to the distorting force. Hence in Figure 90 if a force F displaces a mass m a distance x, against the restoring force due to the springs, then $F \propto x$, and our equation of motion becomes

$$F = kx, \tag{36}$$

where k is a constant to be determined. The oscillatory motion of the mass m is called simple harmonic motion. The equation tells us

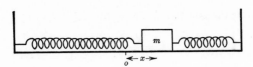

Fig. 90. Simple harmonic motion on a frictionless table.

that *simple harmonic motion is a linear motion such that the magnitude of the restoring force is proportional to the displacement.* In addition, the restoring force and displacement are opposite in direction. This latter point is not indicated in the equation for simple harmonic motion and is omitted to add simplicity in the later development which may be accomplished without use of the negative sign for the displacement x. One of the most important characteristics of simple harmonic motion is its period, or the inverse, which is the frequency. Either of these could be obtained readily from equation (36) by the use of the calculus. Since the use of calculus is beyond the scope of the present work, we shall study the uniform speed of a point on the circumference of a circle, projected on any diameter. This projected motion is an example of simple harmonic motion.

Consider the motion (Fig. 91) of a point P on the circumference of the circle of radius r and having a velocity v. We have from the figure that:

$$v = r\omega,$$

153

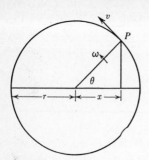

Fig. 91. Circular motion of point P.

where ω is the angular velocity; also that

$$a = \frac{v^2}{r} = \omega^2 r \cdot$$

The acceleration along the x axis is

$$a_x = a \cos \theta = \omega^2 r \cos \theta = \omega^2 x$$

and the force in the x direction is

$$F = ma_x = m\omega^2 x.$$

Since by definition,

$$\omega = \frac{2\pi}{T},$$

we have that:

$$F = \frac{4\pi^2 m}{T^2} \cdot x. \tag{37}$$

This shows that the constant k for equation 36 has the value,

$$k = \frac{4\pi^2 m}{T^2}.$$

Our equation 37 gives us the expression

$$T = 2\pi \sqrt{\frac{m}{\left(\frac{F}{x}\right)}} \tag{38}$$

for the period. It is the time interval taken by the object to pass any point (e.g., the origin, Fig. 90) of reference two consecutive times in the same direction while making its to-and-fro excursions. In the case of a simple harmonic motion r is often called the amplitude.

The motion of a *simple pendulum* may be treated as simple harmonic if the oscillation occurs through a sufficiently small angle. Referring to Figure 92, if the initial angle θ is less than 10 degrees, the oscillation of mass m will be approximately simple harmonic motion and the period of oscillation (a complete to-and-fro motion) will be a constant quantity.

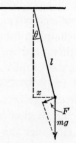

Fig. 92. Simple pendulum.

In the figure a small but massive spherical ball is fastened to a cord of negligible weight. When the spherical ball is small, we may consider the length of the pendulum as the distance from the upper support to the center of the spherical mass. When the pendulum is displaced a slight distance, the restoring force F, due to gravity, is related to the displacement x by the equation

$$\frac{F}{mg} = \frac{x}{l}$$

and from equation (38), we obtain

$$T = 2 \pi \sqrt{\frac{l}{g}} \tag{39}$$

as the approximate period of a simple pendulum. The inexactness of the equation is due to the fact that x is not actually the displacement as required in simple harmonic motion. However, the error for $\theta = 10°$ is only of the order of 0.2 per cent, and correspondingly less for smaller angles. Hence, the pendulum may be made a fairly accurate instrument for the determination of the acceleration of gravity, provided the period (T) can be measured with accuracy.

TORSION PENDULUM

Moment of inertia (I) is defined as the summation

$$I = \sum_{k=1}^{k=n} m_k r_k^2,$$

where there are n distinct particles. The mass in each case may be considered as concentrated at a point the distance of which from the center of rotation is r. The moments of inertia about any axis are usually found by the methods of calculus. Even by these methods the procedure is very difficult, and sometimes impossible when irregularly shaped bodies have to be considered. The moment of inertia of any body can, however, be readily found by experimental methods.

The student will probably have observed in his studies concerning the dynamics of rotation that this quantity I, which has been called the moment of inertia, plays about the same role there that mass does in the dynamics of translation.

Consequently, it can easily be shown that the general expression for the period of a simple harmonic motion of rotation has exactly the same form as the general expression for the period in the case of linear simple harmonic motion. For the linear case, $T = 2\pi\sqrt{\dfrac{mx}{F}}$, where x is the linear displacement produced by a force F, whereas for angular simple harmonic motion, $T = 2\pi\sqrt{\dfrac{I\theta}{L}}$, where θ is the angular displacement produced by a torque L, and I represents the moment of inertia of the rotating body around the axis of rotation.

A very convenient way of determining experimentally the moment of inertia of a body of any shape (around an axis of rotation) is to attach it to the end of a wire, clamped so that the wire hangs vertically, and then allow it to perform rotational simple harmonic motion. The period of oscillation is carefully observed. Next a body of known moment of inertia is added and the period of the combination redetermined. From these two periods and the known moment of inertia of the body which was added, it is possible to calculate the unknown moment of inertia of the first original body.

For the first condition (unknown body only),

$$T_1 = 2\pi\sqrt{\frac{I\theta}{L}}, \tag{40}$$

where I is the unknown moment of inertia.

In the second case (unknown + known),

$$T_2 = 2\pi\sqrt{\frac{(I + I_1)\theta}{L}}, \tag{41}$$

where I_1 is the known moment of inertia.

Dividing (40) by (41), we get

$$\frac{T_1}{T_2} = \sqrt{\frac{I}{I + I_1}},$$

or

$$I = \frac{T_1^2}{T_2^2 - T_1^2} I_1,$$

from which I can be calculated.

In the apparatus used, the body added is in the form of a thin ring of mass m and average radius r, whose moment of inertia I around an axis through the center is known to be $I = mr^2$.

Note. If the ring cannot be assumed to be thin, but if instead it has a thickness which is appreciable compared to the radius, then the more exact formula should be used in calculating the moment of inertia of the ring, *viz.*, $I = \frac{1}{2} m(r_1^2 + r_2^2)$.

EXPERIMENT 17

THE PERIOD OF OSCILLATION AND FORCE CONSTANT OF A SPRING

Part (a) *To determine the force constant of the spring.*

Part (b) *To determine experimentally the period of oscillation of the system for several masses.*

Part (c) *To check on the experimental period found in (b), by calculation from the formula using the force constant found in (a).*

APPARATUS: Spiral spring mounted on rods and clamped rigidly to the table (Fig. 93), slotted weights (up to 1000 grams), hanger, stop clock, meter rule, small platform balance.

Part (a) Consult the instructor as to the maximum load that should be placed on the spring. Then plan your spring loadings in successive equal increments of about one-sixth to one-eighth, preferably one-eighth, the total permissible load in keeping with the type of spring and any specific directions. Place the meter rule vertically and take readings from the table to a certain point on the hanger before any mass is added and after the addition of each mass. Tabulate your results for stretch as shown in Table I.

TABLE I

Initial reading =

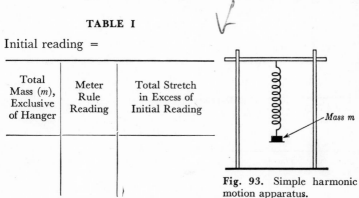

Total Mass (m), Exclusive of Hanger	Meter Rule Reading	Total Stretch in Excess of Initial Reading

Fig. 93. Simple harmonic motion apparatus.

Examine the successive values found for the stretch x, when additional loads are added. The value of x, of course, should be constant, since Hooke's law is assumed to hold. For the smaller loads it is quite possible that x is not constant. This, however, is due to negative tension in the spring which must be overcome before the spring really becomes stretched. Omit initial readings needed to overcome negative tension and then divide the remaining readings into two groups to determine the force constant. Thus if there are eight readings and the last six are useful readings, subtract the mass and stretch in the (a) sixth row from the third row, (b) seventh from the fourth, (c) eighth from the fifth. Add the three stretches above and divide by 3. This will give an average stretch $\bar{x}$ caused by a mass m_3 which is three times the magnitude of the incremental mass m_1 in each succeeding row. The force constant is found by the relationship

$$\text{Force constant} = \frac{F}{\bar{x}} = \frac{m_3 g}{\bar{x}}.$$

Any other grouping of data will necessitate a change in the method for calculation of the result. The force constant in all cases will be the force required to cause unit displacement.

Part (b)   Determine the periods of three masses experimentally by taking the average of one hundred oscillations for each mass. Each of the three masses should be in excess of that required to overcome any negative tension of the spring.

TABLE II

Mass of the spring =

m Includes Hanger and $\frac{1}{3}$ Mass of Spring	Time for 100 Oscillations	PERIOD OF MASS m		% Difference from the Mean
		By Theory Part (c)	By Exp.	

Part (c) Calculate from equation (38) the theoretical period for each of the three masses in part (b), using the value of $F/\bar{x}$ found in part (a). The mass m must include the weight of the hanger as well as one-third the mass of the spring if the latter mass is appreciable compared to the other masses. (The reason for adding one-third the mass of the spring appears in more extended treatises.)

Questions

(a) What is the average residual in readings for the displacements in part (a)? What is the (a) % ad and (b) % AD?

(b) This experiment may be used for the measurement of masses (i.e., is a form of inertial balance). How? (*Note.* We assume only here the existence of some standard mass.)

(c) Is there any dependence of the period upon amplitude of swing?

(d) What will be the error in the period of the smallest mass used in part (b) if the mass of the spring is neglected?

(e) How does Hooke's law enter into this experiment?

EXPERIMENT 18

THE SIMPLE PENDULUM

To find the period of a simple pendulum of different lengths and to determine the value of the acceleration due to gravity.

APPARATUS: A spherical pendulum bob of lead or brass about 2 to 2.5 cm in diameter, flexible string 1.5 to 2 meters long, meter stick, mounting clamp, stop clock, vernier caliper for question (d).

Fig. 94. Clamping arrangement for a simple pendulum.

Start your experiment with the longest possible pendulum length, making sure that the pendulum is secured to the support (Fig. 94) in such a way that the string swings always with a definite and fixed length. *The amplitude of swing of the pendulum should not exceed 5 degrees each side of the equilibrium position.*

Since the time available for this experiment is decidedly limited, we shall have to content ourselves with allowing the total period of each observation to be about one minute. Time these swings as accurately as possible with the stop watch available, remembering that the time for *one complete to-and-fro swing* of the pendulum is called T.

Record the time for two sets of oscillations for each length of the pendulum and let your partner do likewise for two more. Record the results in the tabular form as shown below. Calculate the per cent of error in your timing.

Measure the length of the pendulum from the point of the support to the center of the bob. Next make the length about one-half, one-fourth, one-eighth, and one-sixteenth of the original and carry out the same procedure for each of these lengths, timing the pendulum always for about one minute.

Repeat your time measurements for the other pendulum bob for one length of pendulum only. This second pendulum has a bob made of different material. The diameter and mass of the bob are also different from those of the first. Since none of these factors influence the period, provided of course we still have a simple pendulum, these data for the period of the second should fit the curves for the period of the first.

Calculate T, the time for one complete oscillation, as well as T^2. Then draw a graph showing the relation between (1) the length and T, and (2) the length and T^2. (Refer to Chapter II for procedure in plotting graphs.) The two curves should be plotted on the same sheet with T and T^2 as ordinates.

The period of the pendulum is given in equation (39), page (155), and therefore the acceleration is

$$ g = \frac{4\pi^2 l}{T^2}. \tag{42} $$

The effective length l of the pendulum is the distance from the point of support to the center of the spherical bob plus a correction factor $2\,r^2/5l$ where r is the radius of the sphere. The correction factor is due to an angular displacement of the bob as it swings through the angle θ. However, the correction factor is unimportant, except for very small lengths l or for more accurate work.

SAMPLE DATA FOR ONE PENDULUM BOB

(1)

Total Time (sec)		Deviation
	63.3	−0.20
	63.6	+0.10
	63.5	0.00
	63.6	+0.10
Total	254.0	0.40
Average	63.50	±0.10

Length = 159.6 ± 0.2 cm

No. of swings = 25

$T = 2.540$ sec ± 0.08%
$T^2 = 6.452$ sec^2 ± 0.16%

$ad = 0.10\%$

(2)

Total Time (sec)		Deviation
	73.4	−0.08
	73.7	+0.22
	73.5	+0.02
	73.3	−0.18
Total	293.9	0.50
Average	73.48	±0.13

Length = 83.7 ± 0.2 cm

No. of swings = 40

$T = 1.837$ sec ± 0.09%
$T^2 = 3.375$ sec^2 ± 0.18%

$ad = 0.13\%$

(3)

Total Time (sec)		Deviation
	66.9	+0.10
	66.7	−0.10
	66.8	0.00
	66.8	0.00
Total	267.2	0.20
Average	66.80	±0.05

Length = 44.3 ± 0.2 cm

No. of swings = 50

$T = 1.336$ sec ± 0.037%
$T^2 = 1.785$ sec^2 ± 0.075%

$ad = 0.05\%$

(4)

Total Time (sec)   Deviation

66.1	+0.3	
65.8	0.0	
65.8	0.0	
65.5	−0.3	

Length = 22.0 ± 0.2 cm

No. of swings = 70

$T = 0.9400$ sec ± 0.11%
$T^2 = 0.8836$ sec^2 ± 0.22%

Total	263.2	0.6
Average	65.80	±0.15

$ad = 0.15\%$

(5)

Total Time (sec)   Deviation

69.9	−0.05	
70.1	+0.15	
70.0	+0.05	
69.8	−0.15	

Length = 12.4 ± 0.2 cm

No. of swings = 100

$T = 0.6995$ sec ± 0.07%
$T^2 = 0.4893$ sec^2 ± 0.14%

Total	279.80	±0.40
Average	69.95	±0.10

$ad = 0.10\%$

Calculate the value of g either from the curve (i.e., l plotted as abscissas against T^2 as ordinates) or from the average of g calculated from the individual data.

Questions

(a) What must be the length of a simple pendulum where your experiment was done in order that (1) the period may be one second? (2) the half period may be one second?

(b) The slope of your straight line curve with T^2 as ordinates and l as abscissas will be $4\pi^2/g$. Why? What was the slope for the curve obtained from your experiment?

(c) The more correct formula for the period T of a simple pendulum is

$$T = 2\pi \sqrt{l/g} \left[1 + \frac{\sin^2 \frac{\theta}{2}}{4} + \frac{9 \sin^4 \frac{\theta}{2}}{64} + \cdots \right],$$

where the terms in brackets are a part of an infinite series in increasing powers of θ. What error in the formula is introduced when the angular displacement for the simple pendulum bob is (1) $\theta = 5°$, (2) $\theta = 10°$, (3) $\theta = 20°$?

(d) What error, due to the neglect of the correction factor $\frac{2 r^2}{5 l}$, is introduced into your results?

(e) What is the magnitude of the acceleration due to gravity in your locality according to the published values? What is the per cent difference between your value and the published value, using the published value as standard?

EXPERIMENT 19

THE TORSION PENDULUM

Part (a)   *To find the moment of inertia of a disk.*

Part (b)   *To find the moment of inertia of a ring. Optional.*

APPARATUS: Torsion pendulum with rod, table clamp and test tube holder inertia ring, stop clock, meter stick, micrometer gage for question (c), knife edge if part (b) is performed.

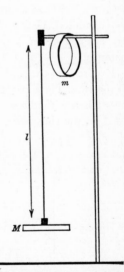

Fig. 95. Torsion pendulum.

Part (a) The apparatus consists essentially of a disk rigidly attached to a wire of length l. The upper end of the wire (in Fig. 95) is attached to a cylindrical block, which, in turn, is held rigidly by a clamp. The upper end of the wire may be secured in a wall support. If the disk of mass M is given a small twist, say a half-turn, it will oscillate back and forth with a given period. If the ring of mass m is now placed on top of the disk so that the wire is at the center of the ring, the period will be longer. From these two values of the periods it is possible to obtain the moment of inertia of the disk of mass M. This, therefore, is *an experimental method for finding the moment of inertia of a disk. The method is applicable no matter what the shape of M*, the only requirement is that the body added have a shape for which one can readily calculate the moment of inertia from its dimensions and mass. In order to check the experimental determination, the body M is given a shape such that it is also possible to calculate, by methods of calculus, the moment of inertia. When M has the shape of a disk as shown in the figure, then the calculation by calculus gives I (central axis perpendicular to the disk) = $\frac{1}{2} Mr^2$, where M is the mass of the disk and r is its radius. Consequently in performing this experiment find the time, first without and then with the ring, of 25 or more complete angular oscillations. Make a number of observations of this same quantity, recording each one in a table or form shown below. By averaging each set of readings and then dividing by the number of oscillations, the period of a single oscillation can be calculated. Unless the mass of the disk and the mass of the ring are already given, it will now be necessary to weigh them on a balance.

Record also the radius of the disk and the inner and outer radius of the ring. These can all be found by averaging a number of readings taken with the vernier caliper. If the approximate formula is used for the ring $(m\bar{r}^2)$, then $\bar{r}$ must be the mean radius.

TO FIND THE PERIOD (Seconds)

Trial	TIME FOR 25 VIBRATIONS			
	Without Ring		With Ring	
	$25\ T_1$	Deviations	$25\ T_2$	Deviations
1				
2				
3				
Total				
Average				

TO FIND THE RADII (cm)

	Diam. of Disk	Deviations	Diam. (Inside) Ring	Deviations	Diam. (Outside) Ring	Deviations
Total						
Average						
Radius						

$$
\begin{aligned}
\text{Mass of the ring} &= \quad \text{grams} \\
\text{Mass of the disk} &= \quad \text{grams} \\
\text{Experimental value of } T_1 &= \quad \text{seconds} \\
\text{Experimental value of } T_2 &= \quad \text{seconds} \\
\text{also} \qquad I_1(\text{ring}) &= \quad \text{g. cm}^2 \\
\text{hence} \qquad I(\text{disc}) &= \quad \text{g. cm}^2 \\
\text{and} \qquad I(\text{calc}) &= \quad \text{g. cm}^2
\end{aligned}
$$

Note: Measurements of the length and diameter of the wire will be required for question (c).

OPTIONAL

Part (b) The moment of inertia of the ring may be found by swinging the ring from some knife edge K (Fig. 96). The knife edge should be leveled carefully. Better success may be had by making the ring rest on two points only by use of a slightly concave knife edge.

The period T, for the ring, is found by oscillating the ring, with an amplitude of 5 degrees or less, from the knife edge (K) as shown in Figure 96. The plane in which the oscillation occurs must be in the plane of the disk and perpendicular to the axis formed by the knife edge. Take the time for about 25 oscillations and repeat at two or more positions about the ring. From these results an average

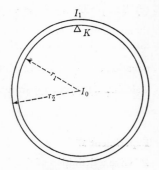

Fig. 96. Ring.

value of T is obtained. The equation for a physical pendulum is

$$T = 2\pi \sqrt{\frac{I_1}{mgr_1}}$$

where I_1 is the moment of inertia about the axis through K. The terms m and r_1 are the mass and inner radius of the ring respectively. From this equation, the moment of inertia I_1 is calculated. The moment of inertia (I_0) at the center about an axis parallel to the axis at K is related to I_1 by the very useful equation

$$I_1 = I_0 + mr_1^2, \tag{43}$$

where m is the mass of the ring.

Hence knowing the value of both I_1 and mr_1^2, I_0 may be determined. Compare this value (I_0) of the moment of inertia with the value assumed in the earlier part of the experiment by calculation.

Questions

(a) From the dimensions of the ring used, calculate the error introduced in the moment of inertia of the ring by use of the mean radius rather than the more exact formula.

(b) Your working equation in part (a) was $I = \dfrac{T_1^2}{T_2^2 - T_1^2} I_1$. From your experimental data for T_1 and T_2, and from the calculation on the magnitude of I_1, what may you conclude as to the magnitude of the resulting error in I?

(c) The period of the torsion pendulum is given by $T = 2\pi \sqrt{\dfrac{I}{L'}}$ where I is the moment of inertia of the disk and L' is the torque required to twist the disk through one radian. Also, the coefficient of rigidity n is given by the equation $n = \dfrac{2\,lL'}{\pi r^4}$ where r is the radius of the supporting wire of length l. Calculate n for your apparatus.

PROBLEMS

Experiment 17

1 Give a definition of simple harmonic motion.

2 What is the amplitude of a simple harmonic motion?

3 If the period of your spring, with a mass m, should be obtained in another locality with a different value of g (the gravitational acceleration), would you expect the period to be altered? Explain your answer.

4 If a mass of 100 g stretches a given spring 8 cm, what would be the period of the spring if 600 g were placed on the spring?

5 Assume that the restoring force in a given spring is 14,000 dynes per cm and that the amplitude of swing is 4 cm. If there is a mass of 500 g on the spring what will be the (a) maximum velocity of the mass, (b) maximum acceleration of the mass, (c) maximum restoring force of the spring?

6 A standard mass of 1 kg oscillates a spring at the rate of 80 vibrations in 100 sec. What will be the mass of a piece of metal that will vibrate the spring at the rate of 120 vibrations in 100 sec.

7 Assume that you are given two springs with force constants k_1 and k_2. Prove that the resultant force constant, if both are used to oscillate a mass m, is $k_1 k_2/(k_1 + k_2)$ if hung in series (i.e. same force through the springs), and $k_1 + k_2$ if hung in parallel (i.e. same displacement through the springs).

Experiment 18

1 What is a simple pendulum and what is its use?

2 Would you expect a meter stick hung from one end to have the same period as a simple pendulum of the same length as the meter stick? Explain.

3 Plot on graph paper the displacements of a seconds pendulum as ordinates and time as abscissas for a single to-and-fro oscillation. Plot on the same graph paper the corresponding displacement velocities as ordinates and time as abscissas for a single oscillation. Choose a displacement amplitude of 3 cm. (*Note.* $v_x = \dfrac{2\pi}{T} \sqrt{r^2 - x^2}$ where x is the displacement and r is the amplitude.)

4 How does the period of a simple pendulum vary with (1) the length, (2) the mass of the bob?

5 What will be the length of a seconds pendulum at a place where $g = 980.2$ cm per sec per sec?

6 A certain clock is correct at a place where $g = 980.1$ cm per sec per sec. If the clock is taken to a place where $g = 979.9$ cm per sec per sec, will it lose or gain time? How much, per day?

7 A certain clock has a pendulum length of 25 cm and is keeping correct time. A heat wave causes an expansion of 0.1 cm in the length of the pendulum? Does the clock gain or lose time? How much, per day?

8 What must be the length of a simple pendulum where $g = 980.1$ in order that (a) the period may be one second? (b) the half period may be one second?

Experiment 19

1   Does the period of a torsion pendulum vary with the angular displacement?

2   Calculate the moment of inertia of a disk with an axis perpendicular to the plane of the disk and through the center, given that the mass is 1000 g and the radius is 15 cm.

3   Find the moment of inertia of a ring around a central axis if its mass is 1000 g and the inside and outside diameters are 13 and 15 cm, respectively.

4   Verify the equation $I = I_1 \left(\dfrac{T_1^2}{T_2^2 - T_1^2} \right)$ for a torsion pendulum.

5   Look up in some handbook, or textbook, the moment of inertia for each of the following bodies: (1) uniform thin rod of length l and mass m with axis normal to the length and at one end, (2) uniform thin rod of mass m and length l with axis normal to the length and at the center, (3) thin circular sheet of mass m and of radius r with axis along any diameter, (4) sphere of mass m and of radius r with axis tangent to surface element.

6   Compare the moment of inertia of a disk of mass 500 g and of radius 15 cm (a) when the axis is central and perpendicular to the plane of the disk, and (b) when the axis is along any diameter. What is the moment of inertia of the disk with axis as in (a)?

PART 3 SOUND

CHAPTER XIV

WAVE MOTIONS AND FREQUENCY OF VIBRATING SYSTEMS

Waves are a means of transfer of energy from one point to another. This transfer, when occurring in material media, is brought about by some elastic property of the media.

Thus, when a wave travels along a rope as shown in Figure 97, the elastic property is determined by the tension. In sound waves, however, it is determined by the bulk modulus. These two types of waves have one important difference, as to propagation characteristics, namely: in rope waves the vibrations of all portions of the rope are at right angles to the direction of propagation of the

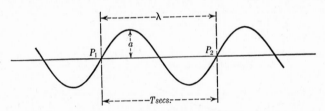

Fig. 97. Wave along a rope.

wave, while in sound waves the vibrations of the medium are back and forth in the direction of propagation of the wave. The former is representative of a class called *transverse waves* because the vibrations are perpendicular to the direction of motion. The latter type are representative of *longitudinal waves* because the vibrations are parallel to the direction of propagation.

Consider now a long train of sine waves, proceeding in one direction, known commonly as progressive waves. Such a series of waves might exist, for example, along a rope (Fig. 97) of very great length. Figure 97 represents a portion of the series of waves traveling to the right with neither the beginning nor end of the train shown.

The distance from a point P_1 in the vibrating rope to another point P_2, the displacement and direction of vibration of which is the same as that at P_1, is called a wave length (λ). The time it takes a wave to travel the distance λ is called the period (T) of the wave, so that the velocity is, by definition,

$$v = \frac{\lambda}{T} = f\lambda,$$

where f is the frequency with which the waves pass a given point per second. Again, the maximum displacement of the segments of the rope from their neutral positions is called the amplitude (a).

While transverse waves are easily represented as in Figure 97, sound waves may be represented by such a simple diagram only if we represent the forward longitudinal displacements upwards on the y-axis when the waves are considered as proceeding to the right on the x-axis. Reference to Figure 98 shows one method of

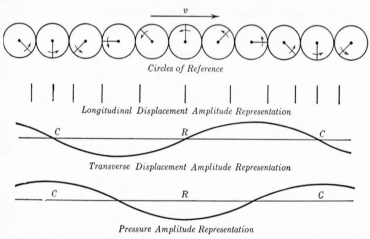

Fig. 98. Representations of a wave proceeding to the right with a velocity v.

using this transverse representation of sound waves. At the points where the particles pass through their equilibrium positions, we have alternately condensations and rarefactions. At the condensation, the particles are moving with the wave, while at a rarefaction the particles are moving in the opposite direction. It should be noted, however, that both the condensation and the rarefaction as such are moving to the right each with velocity v, and what the ear hears depends upon the magnitude (i.e., pressure changes) and frequency of the condensations and rarefactions, rather than upon the velocity of the gas particles. In Figure 98 the circles are con-

structed so that a point in each circle is in constant motion. The
point in each succeeding circle represents an earlier moment of
time. The series of straight lines below the circles represent the
corresponding simple harmonic motions (i.e., longitudinal wave)
and the curve is the transverse representation of the longitudinal
wave.

Consider now a rope of finite length with one end fastened to a
wall (Fig. 99) and the other end P subjected to a vertical simple

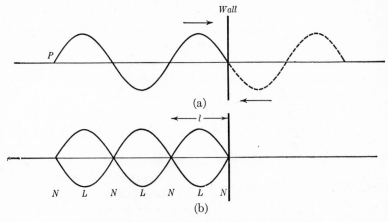

Fig. 99. Reflection of waves.

harmonic force. This simple harmonic force may be produced by
attaching the string to one prong of a vibrating tuning fork. This
is an example of forced oscillation, and if the tension of the rope is
properly adjusted, stationary waves will be produced as shown in
Figure 99 (b). When this happens, the frequency of the fork and
string will be found to be the same, a special case of forced vibrations, called resonance. These stationary waves have *places where
there are no motions of the rope, called nodes* (N), *and places of maximum
displacements of the rope, called loops* (L) *or antinodes.* The presence of
these nodes and loops may be explained if we consider a wave
coming in from behind the wall with a displacement equal in
magnitude but opposite in direction, as shown in Figure 99 (a).
If you draw the resultant amplitude for such a reflected wave and
the approaching wave, at intervals of one-eighth period over eight
such intervals, for example, you will find that the transverse displacements of the rope at a given point will assume at the proper

time intervals all values between the extreme displacement of each point as shown in Figure 99 (b) and zero displacement, for all points along the rope. If we call the distance from one node to the next, l, then from the definition of wave length, we have that $\lambda = 2\,l$, also that $v = f\lambda$, or

$$f = \frac{v}{2\,l}.$$

It is known that the velocity of a transverse wave along a flexible stretched wire, having a tension $\mathfrak{I}$, is

$$v = \sqrt{\frac{\mathfrak{I}}{\sigma}},$$

where σ is the mass per unit length. Hence, the frequency f of the string represented in Figure 99 (b) will be

$$f = \frac{1}{2\,l}\sqrt{\frac{\mathfrak{I}}{\sigma}}. \tag{44}$$

If a sound wave is being considered, then in order to have standing waves produced we must confine the waves in some manner, as in a hollow tube the diameter of which is small compared to a wave length. We shall use as our applied simple harmonic force, a tuning fork. Hit the tuning fork with a rubber hammer (or tap the tuning fork against a rubber block or cork stopper) and hold it over a hollow tube as shown in Figure 100. If the tube is of the proper length, standing waves will be produced in the air column. Figure 100 (a), (b), (c) represents waves set up in three tubes of lengths d, $3\,d$, $5\,d$, etc., when the same fork is used, where d is the distance from node to loop.

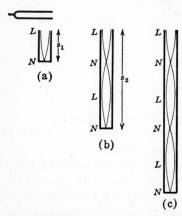

Fig. 100. Resonance in an air column.

In order to tell when these standing waves are set up, listen for the reinforcement of the sound of the tuning fork, which is due to the resonant vibration of the air column. The frequency of the vibrating air column will be the same as that of the fork. This is a well-known example of resonance in the study of sound waves. The closed end represents the place of greatest change in pressure, yet here there is no motion of the molecules if the walls are rigid, and thus represents a node. The open end of such a tube will be found to be a place of greatest change in velocity of the air molecules with but little (if any) change in pressure because the medium is less confined here of all positions which have anything to do with the vibrating air column. Hence the open end represents an anti-node, or a loop. With these restrictions in mind as to nodes and loops, the representation of nodes and loops in Figure 100 (a), (b), and (c) should be clear.

Unfortunately, the loop L is not located exactly at the open end of the tube but is a little beyond. It takes a short distance for the equalization of the pressures to take place. This additional distance is a function of the radius r and is usually between 0.6 r and 0.8 r. One way to find the correction factor c is to find the resonance length as in Figure 100 (a), (b), with a tube of adjustable length. Call the length of the pipe for first resonance s_1, and the length for second resonance s_2. Then $(c + s_1)$ will be a quarter-wave length or

$$\lambda = 4(c + s_1), \tag{45}$$

also

$$\lambda = 2(s_2 - s_1), \tag{46}$$

so that, eliminating λ from the above equations, we have the correction factor

$$c = \frac{s_2 - 3 s_1}{2}. \tag{47}$$

While the wave length of a fork of unknown frequency may be determined by use of equation (45), assuming a value for c, the determination of the wave length by the use of equation (46) is more accurate because the correction factor does not enter. In any case the frequency of the fork is determined from the equation $v = f\lambda$, where the velocity at $t°$ C is

$$v = 331.5 + 0.6 \, t \text{ meters per second.}$$

EXPERIMENT 20

STATIONARY WAVES IN A SPRING

To determine the pitch of a tuning fork by means of stationary waves set up in a string.

APPARATUS: Electrically driven tuning fork (or vibrator), flexible twine (fish cord), hanger to hold lead shot, platform balance and weights, meter stick.

The apparatus consists (Fig. 101) of an electrically driven tuning fork (or vibrator) mounted on a board so that it may be secured vertically to rods and clamps or to an "arm" which may extend from the wall. One end of a string is fastened to one prong of the fork and a hanger (made from an aluminum tea ball) is fastened to the other end of the string.

The procedure is to start the fork into vibration and pour shot into the basket until stationary waves of one or more loops are formed. Use different masses so that segments from one up to four (or more), if possible, are obtained. Find the distance l between two nodes. This is

Fig. 101. Standing waves in a string.

best done by taking an average of all the nodes, remembering that the node formed at or near the vibrating fork is not usually very definitely defined. It is better to omit this node when possible. Then weigh the basket with shot to find the tension, $\mathfrak{J} = mg$. The frequency f of the fork will be

$$f = \frac{1}{2\,l}\sqrt{\frac{\mathfrak{J}}{\sigma}},$$

where σ is the mass per unit length. Obtain this constant from your instructor, or weigh the string and divide the mass obtained by the length.

It will be observed experimentally that fewer loops are obtained when the tension is increased. Add weights carefully so that the string does not break.

Repeat two or more times, obtaining each time a different number of segments (i.e., nodes and loops) by changing the load on the string.

Length of string (L) from   Frequency marked
prong of fork to hanger =   on the tuning fork =

σ =

No. of Segments	LENGTH OF SEGMENTS (l)				Average l	m	$\mathfrak{J}$	$\dfrac{1}{2\,l}\sqrt{\dfrac{\mathfrak{J}}{\sigma}}$	Deviations
	1st	2nd	3rd	etc.					

Questions

(a) Calculate the per cent of error (i.e., % AD).

(b) Assuming that your result is correct, calculate the per cent of error in the frequency as stamped on the fork.

(c) How much larger is the tension for one segment on the string than for two segments?

(d) The equation for the frequency f is, $f = (k/2\,L)\sqrt{\mathfrak{J}_k/\sigma}$ where $\mathfrak{J}_k$ is the tension for k segments, i.e., $k = 1, 2, 3$, etc. What magnitudes do you get for the tension ratios (1) $\mathfrak{J}_2/\mathfrak{J}_1$, (2) $\mathfrak{J}_3/\mathfrak{J}_1$, (3) $\mathfrak{J}_4/\mathfrak{J}_1$, (4) $\mathfrak{J}_3/\mathfrak{J}_2$?

EXPERIMENT 21

THE SONOMETER

To determine the frequencies of tuning forks.

APPARATUS: Sonometer equipped with a steel and a brass wire of different diameters, approximately 0.50 mm diameter for brass and 0.32 mm diameter for steel, two tuning forks (say of frequencies 256 vibrations per second and 384 vibrations per second, about 12 kg of standard masses (6 two-kg masses, 2 one-kg masses), 2 one-kg hangers.

The sonometer (Fig. 102) consists of a hollow resonance box on which are mounted two wires (one shown here). The tension is determined by the known weights and the length of the string is controlled by a movable bridge.

[*Caution:* The twisted wire at the anchorages becomes weakened with use. Consequently one should keep the eyes as far from any direct line of the stretched wire as possible. Some sonometers will tip over easily with heavy loads.]

Note that the distance between two nodes (l), as used in equation (44) now becomes the distance between the fixed and movable bridges when the wire vibrates in its fundamental mode.

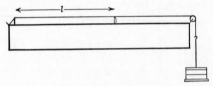

Fig. 102. Sonometer.

Place about 6 kg in the hanger to which the steel wire is attached. Adjust the movable bridge until the frequency of the wire of length l when plucked is the same as that of the one fork. Now readjust the bridge increasing the length so as to obtain a resonance with the fundamental of the fork for two segments and also for three segments where possible. The data may be recorded as in Table I.

Repeat the experiment on the steel wire with a 384-cycle fork, or any fork having another frequency characteristic. Use the same tension as before.

Then repeat the determination of the frequencies of both forks with resonant vibrations of the brass wire. Use the same tension as above.

Now repeat the above series of experiments for a lower tension by placing about 5 kg on the hanger. Make another table similar to Table I.

There are two convenient methods for telling when the frequencies of the fork and wire are the same. One method is to adjust the frequencies until no beats are heard. Beats are heard when the frequencies are close together and disappear either when the frequencies are the same or far apart. The other method is to place a tiny paper rider on the wire at the center between the fixed and movable bridge. Now start the fork into vibration and place the tip firmly on the top of the resonance board. When the frequencies are the same, the rider will jump off, due to resonance of the string with the fork.

Some tuning forks are so constructed that but little vibration is communicated to the stem of the fork. In this case, place the stem of the vibrating fork near or on the movable bridge.

TABLE I

Total mass, including hanger =

Wire	Frequency as Marked on Fork	Length of Wire (L)	Number of Segments k	Mean l l = L/k	f by Experiment $\left(\frac{1}{2l}\sqrt{\frac{\bar{3}}{\sigma}}\right)$	Mean Experimental Value for Frequency
Steel	256					
Steel	384					
Brass	256					
Brass	384					

[*Note.* The questions below are designed to illustrate how the terms in a formula may be checked. Thus, equation (44) shows that; (1), fl is a constant if the wire is not changed and the tension is held constant; (2) $l\sqrt{\sigma}$ is a constant if the same tuning fork is used and the tension remains constant; (3), $\sqrt{3}/l$ is a constant if the same wire and the same frequency are used.]

Questions

(a) There are four variables in equation (44). Rearrange your data, making clear what data are used, so that you may prove from your experimental results that

  (1) fl = constant
  (2) $l\sqrt{\sigma}$ = constant
  (3) $\sqrt{3}/l$ = constant

under certain specified conditions. State the conditions.

(b) What is the per cent of error of the frequency for all forks used, taking the frequency as given by the manufacturer as correct? Use the mean of all determinations for a given frequency as your average value for that frequency.

EXPERIMENT 22

THE RESONANCE TUBE

To find the frequency of a tuning fork by resonance and to determine the end correction for the resonance tube.

APPARATUS: Two heavy duty tuning forks (frequencies 512 and 768), glass or galvanized metal jar* with glass or metal resonance tube 22 to 24 inches in length, cork stopper or rubber mat.

* Galvanized metal cylinders about 36 inches in length and 4 inches in diameter may be easily made by a plumber. If provided with handles near the top, the cylinder may be fastened easily so as not to tip over during the experiment. A convenient resonance tube about 40 inches in length can be made of aluminum tubing about one inch in diameter. Tuning forks with frequencies of about 320 to 512 vibrations per second may be used with these tubes.

The apparatus consists of a tall jar filled with water. A glass tube

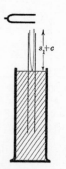

Fig. 103. Resonance tube.

about 1 to $1\frac{1}{2}$ inches in diameter is placed in the jar. The length is adjusted until resonance is obtained when the fork is struck against a cork stopper or other soft material and held over the tubing as shown in Figure 103. A rubber band around the glass tubing placed at the water line when resonance occurs aids materially in obtaining more exact measurements. Assume the length of the tubing is s_1, the corrected length is $(s_1 + c)$. Now find the second resonance point and call the length of the tube s_2. Independent readings are now obtained by your partner. By means of equation (46) calculate the wave length λ. Using the known velocity of sound find the frequency of the fork.

The end correction c is determined by equation (47),

$$c = \frac{s_2 - 3 s_1}{2}.$$

Repeat for the other fork.

DATA

Room temperature =
Radius of the tube =

$v = 331.5 + 0.6t \dfrac{\text{meters}}{\text{sec}} =$

Frequency of Fork (Manufacturer)	s_1	s_2	$f = \dfrac{v(\text{cm per sec})}{2(s_2 - s_1)\text{cm}}$	$c = \dfrac{s_2 - 3\,s_1}{2}$

Questions

(a) Calculate the per cent of error from the mean in each of your two resulting frequencies.

(b) Calculate the per cent of error in your result from that given by the manufacturer.

(c) Calculate the average deviation in the correction factor c. What is the per cent of error in c?

(d) Assuming that the correction factor is a linear function of the radius of the resonance tube, let $kr = c$, where r is the radius of the tube and k is the constant factor which is to be found. Calculate the value of k. How close does your result agree with the theory? (See page 175.)

PROBLEMS

Experiment 20

1 Show by graphical construction the production of standing waves. Choose a sine wave and take the time interval for wave construction as $T/8$ sec. (Use Figure 99 as a model and draw diagrams of the individual wave proceeding towards the wall and the wave receding from the wall at $T/8$ sec intervals for a distance of $9\lambda/8$.)

2 The equation for the frequency of the electric tuning fork is $f = \dfrac{k}{2L}\sqrt{\dfrac{\Im_k}{\sigma}}$ where L is the length of the string. Show that this equation is equivalent to equation (44), page 174

3   Show that the tension $\mathfrak{I}_k$ needed to produce any number of segments k in question 2 is related to that tension $\mathfrak{I}_{k+1}$ required to produce $(k+1)$ segments by the formula $\mathfrak{I}_k = [(k+1)/k]^2\mathfrak{I}_{k+1}$.

4   Does it require more or less tension to produce one segment than two segments? How much?

5   A cord of length 80 cm and a mass of 0.120 g is loaded as in Figure 103, so that it vibrates in one segment when actuated by tuning fork of 60 vibrations per sec. What is the string tension in dynes? in newtons?

6   What will be the tension in the above string for (a) two segments (b) three segments?

PROBLEMS

Experiment 21

1   Two wires, held at the same tension, have a mass per unit length ratio of $\frac{3}{4}$. What will be the ratio of lengths to give the same frequency?

2   Assume you had two wires, each supposedly of the same mass per unit cross section, but which were not homogeneous in reality, so that σ varies slightly from point to point in the following fashion: one wire a is a little thinner at the center of the string than the average, while the other wire b is a little thicker at the center than the average. These wires are tuned to unison and then the movable bridge (Fig. 102) is adjusted so that the wires are one-half the original length. The frequencies will be very approximately twice the original values but beats will be heard. Explain briefly why. Which wire will have the higher frequency?

3   Assume that 10 m of steel wire used in your experiment had a mass of 6.720 g. What will be the velocity of the transverse wave if the tension on the wire is 7 kg weight?

4   What will be the velocity of a transverse wave on a brass wire if 10 m of the wire weigh 17.805 g and the tension on the wire is 7 kg weight.

5   If the distance between supports for each of the above two wires in problems 4 and 5 is 30 cm, what will be the frequencies when vibrated?

6   What would be the diameters of the wires in problems 3 and 4 if the densities of brass and steel are 8.5 g per cm³ and 7.8 g per cm³, respectively.

PROBLEMS

Experiment 22

1   Referring to Figure 100 (c), which overtone (i.e., 1st, 2nd, etc.) is represented by the drawing of the nodes and loops as shown? What is the frequency relation between this overtone and the fundamental for this tube?

2 A closed organ pipe of 200 cm length is tuned correctly when the temperature is 20° C. What will be the change in frequency if the temperature rises to 30° C?

3 What would be the change in frequency for an organ pipe of 20 cm length under the conditions of problem 2 above?

4 The length of the part of a cylindrical tube out of water is 0.30 m. What will be the frequency of the fundamental, first overtone, and second overtone. Assume that the temperature is 20° C. Neglect the end correction.

5 The second resonant position (Fig. 100b) for a certain fork was found to be at 0.671 m. What is the approximate frequency of the fork? What is the fundamental frequency of the tube? Assume a temperature of 20° C, and neglect the end correction.

CHAPTER XV

VELOCITY OF SOUND

In experiment 22 with the resonance tube, it is clear that we could have found the velocity of sound by assuming the frequency of the fork. Since there are three terms in the expression $v = f\lambda$, we may find any one when the other two are known.

The Kundt's tube experiment is well adapted to the determination of the velocity of sound in a gas or in a metal; either is important. Certain physical characteristics of a piece of metal can be determined by noting the natural frequency characteristics of the metal.

Determination of the velocity of sound in a gas gives information about the molecular nature of the gas. The velocity of sound in a gas is determined from its bulk modulus k by use of the equation $v = (k/\rho)^{\frac{1}{2}}$. There are two bulk moduli for gases depending upon whether the expansions and contractions are adiabatic (i.e., no heat lost to the surroundings), or isothermal (i.e., heat interchanged with the outside so that the temperature remains constant). The compressions and rarefactions in a sound wave are found to take place adiabatically, so that $k = \gamma P$ where P is the pressure of the gas and γ is the ratio of specific heat (see Chapter XVII, also a general physics text) at constant pressure (s_p) to the specific heat at constant volume (s_v). The ratio of specific heats γ is important since it tells us something about the molecular complexity of the gas. Thus, γ equals 1.66, 1.40, and 1.30 for a monotonic, diatonic and triatomic gas, respectively. The general equation, then, for the velocity of sound in a gas is

$$v = \sqrt{\frac{\gamma P}{\rho}} \tag{48}$$

where $\gamma = 1.40$ for air.

The velocities of sound in certain gases are known to change at certain supersonic frequencies. By use of more extended mathematical analysis, considerable additional information may be obtained.

Direct velocity determinations are made with combinations of electronic and loudspeaker methods, and may be obtained by timing directly the propagation of sound over long distances.

EXPERIMENT 23

KUNDT'S TUBE

Part (a)   *To determine the speed of sound in a metal by the Kundt's tube method.*

Part (b)   *To determine the velocity of sound in a gas by the Kundt's tube method. Optional.*

APPARATUS: Usual Kundt's tube apparatus for part (a), lycopodium powder or cork dust, rosin, chamois, meter stick. Special tube fitted with side tubes and cocks to conduct gas to and from the sound chamber needed in part (b), also a source of gas, preferably carbon dioxide. Hydrogen or illuminating gas may be used with proper precautions.

Part (a)   The Kundt's tube apparatus (Fig. 104) consists of a hollow glass tubing closed at one end (right side) with a disk which

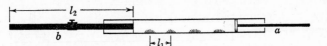

Fig. 104. Kundt's tube.

is fastened to a movable rod *a*. A steel or other metallic rod *b* is clamped to the other end (left) at its center. It also has a light metallic disk at the end located within the glass tube but not touching the tube. This metallic disk, if at all heavy, should be beveled at the face next to the rod. The tubing should contain some lycopodium powder or cork dust sprinkled the whole length.

The procedure is to stroke the portion of the metallic rod *b* to the left of the center with chamois which has powdered rosin sprinkled on it. A little practice will enable you to obtain the fundamental tone of the rod. Move the rod *a* back and forth until the powdered dust particles within the tubing form sharp heaps. Measure the distance between a number of these dust heaps and divide by the number of segments included within your measure. This will give the average distance l_1 between segments. These dust heaps represent nodes, the places of no motion. Hence l_1 is a half-wave length of frequency f, which is the tone being emitted by the metallic rod. If the velocity of sound in air is v_1, then

$$v_1 = f\lambda_1 = f(2\,l_1), \tag{49}$$

and if we call the velocity of sound in the metallic rod v_2, then

$$v_2 = f\lambda_2 = f(2\,l_2), \tag{50}$$

since the two ends of the rod are loops if the rod is secured at the center. Therefore

$$\frac{v_2}{v_1} = \frac{l_2}{l_1}$$

or

$$v_2 = v_1 \frac{l_2}{l_1}. \tag{51}$$

The value of v_1 (velocity of sound in air) for the temperature of the room is found from the theory as given earlier in Chapter 14.

Repeat for two other positions of the rod a.

Part (b) This apparatus (Fig. 105) differs from the form (Fig. 104) used in part (a) in that the end of the rod b now pushes against

Fig. 105. A Kundt's tube useful for many gases.

a rubber dam, and gas is allowed to flow in and out through small side tubes with cocks. The disk fastened to rod a should be provided with a hole or should fit loosely so that gas will go around freely to both sides of the disk. A cork or rubber stopper effectively stops the gas from leaking, which is important if illuminating gas is used. When illuminating gas is used, the outflow may be led by rubber tubing to a bunsen burner and burned. Once an initial good flow of the gas has been introduced, the rate of flow may be reduced or stopped entirely depending upon the condition of the apparatus. Consult the instructor on the regulation of flow of gas.

Procedure The procedure is the same as in part (a) if the velocity of sound in the metallic rod is wanted also. In any case, you now have the mean distances l_1 between nodes when air is in the tube. Now replace the air in the tube with carbon dioxide (CO_2) and find the average distance l_3 between the nodes. The velocity of sound in carbon dioxide will be $v_3 = f(2 l_3)$ and likewise

$$v_3 = v_1 \frac{l_3}{l_1}.$$

Determine the specific heat ratio γ for carbon dioxide from equation (48).

Repeat for two other positions of the rod a.

Questions

(a) Calculate the % AD for the velocity of sound in the metal for part (a).

(b) Calculate the % AD for the velocity of sound in the gas for part (b).

(c) Determine Young's modulus for your metallic rod from your experimentally determined speed of sound v_2 in the rod, by use of the equation $v_2 = (Y/\rho)^{\frac{1}{2}}$. Look up in tables the density of the rod you used.

(d) Stroking near the end of the rod, rather than near the center, is desirable. Why?

(e) The inner end of the stroked metallic rod is an antinode for the rod but a node for the air, or gas, column. Why?

(f) The specific heat ratio γ may be shown by kinetic theory to be related to the degrees of freedom n of the atom, or molecule, by the equation $\gamma = (n + 2)/n$. How many degrees of freedom has the gas with which you experimented in part (b)?

EXPERIMENT 24

SPEED OF SOUND BY DIRECT TIMING METHOD

To determine the speed of sound by a direct timing method.

APPARATUS: Two shotguns, ten black powder shells with shot removed, an accurately surveyed distance between two clear vision hill-tops preferably in excess of one mile, two pairs of binoculars, two or more stop watches, two thermometers, two white or handkerchief flags.

The students are divided into two equal groups. Each group is given a shotgun, five black powder shells* with shot removed, a

* We have obtained black powder shells in case lots from Remington Arms Co., Bridgeport, Conn.

pair of binoculars, one stop watch, one thermometer and a white flag. More stop watches are desirable if available. One person is designated to operate the gun; another operates the flag; a third person keeps the thermometer; and a fourth, or as many as have stop watches, time the intervals between gun smoke and arrival of the sound from the exploded powder; others record the data.

Before the two groups leave for their points of destination, directions as to which side is to fire first are given. Let the two groups be designated as A and B. The surveyed distances should be well marked, such as a large cut in a rock surrounded with white paint, cement block in the ground, portion of the trunk of a tree painted white, etc. The terminal designations will depend upon local conditions, including land ownership and permission. The standing positions should be noted so that the total distance between the measured points may be corrected if standing position is not directly over the measured course.

The group that has the farthest to go is usually directed to fire first. Assume then that group A has the farthest to go. Group B has spotted group A near its destination through the field binoculars. When group A arrives at its destination and is ready to start the experiment, the flagman waves his flag and the person with the binoculars waits for a response from group B. If group B is ready for timing, the flagman in group B will signal back. Then the man with the gun in group A fires the gun. Group B records the time interval required between the time the smoke is seen and the instant the blast is heard. The flag signaling in all cases is checked by means of the binoculars.

After group B has recorded the data and is ready, the flagman signals to group A. Group A signals when ready and then the man with the shotgun fires a shell. Group A records the time between the instant they see the smoke and the instant they hear the gun.

Thus the groups will fire and record data alternately until each has fired five times. The signal from the flagman is an important aspect of the experimental procedure. Otherwise considerable data will be lost and much other data will become quite uncertain.

Accurate timing is important since the total recorded time is going to be of an order of five seconds even if the distance is a mile. Distances up to two or three miles may be used if the binoculars are good and the flag is fairly large.

The data obtained in each group may be tabulated as in Table I. Combine the data from groups A and B. The experimental speed will be the distance divided by the average time interval. Certain corrections may have to be considered such as temperature differences and wind direction especially if the wind is fairly strong.

TABLE I

(Group A or B)

Shot	Temperature	Time (sec)	Deviations in Time
1			
2			
3			
4			
5			
Totals			
Averages			

Questions

(a) The theoretical speed of sound is given by the approximate equation $v = (331.5 + 0.6\,t)$ meters per sec. What is the per cent of error in your result if the speed as figured by this equation is considered correct? Can you account for any difference?

(b) What was the per cent of deviation of the mean of the time interval in (1) group A, (2) group B?

(c) How would you correct for the effect of the wind? Will wind correction improve your results? (*Note.* An anemometer and wind vane will be needed for any accurate check up on the effect of the wind.)

PROBLEMS

Experiment 23

1 Suppose that the distance l_1 between two adjacent nodes in the Kundt's tube apparatus, for a given metal rod, was 4.5 cm. If the metal rod clamped at its center was brass, determine its length. (*Note.* Velocity of sound in brass and in air may be taken as 3500 m per sec and 344 m per sec, respectively.)

2 Suppose that the tube above had been filled with hydrogen, what would have been the distance between adjacent nodes? (*Note*. The velocity of sound through hydrogen is 1270 m per sec.)

3 The density of air at 0 C and 76 cm of mercury pressure is 0.001293 g per cm³. What will be the velocity of sound at this temperature if calculated from equation (48)? The ratio of specific heats for air is 1.4.

4 If $\gamma = (n + 2)/n$ where n is the number of degrees of freedom in an atom, or molecule, what are the number of degrees of freedom in a gas atom (or molecule) if γ is equal to (a) 1.66, (b) 1.40, (c) 1.30?

Experiment 24

1 A man sees three short blasts of a steam whistle blown in succession at equal intervals. If two of the blasts are heard at the instant steam issues from the whistle and the third occurs without any steam appearing, what is the time interval between blasts if the man is known to be 4000 feet from the whistle? The temperature of the air is 20 C.

2 A flash of lightning is followed by the crash of thunder in the interval of one-half second as observed by a pendulum clock that beats in half seconds. What was the approximate distance of the lightning flash?

3 An echo is heard 3.4 sec after discharge of a gun bullet. From what distance was the echo sound reflected?

4 Pulses of sound are sent to the bottom of the ocean and reflected at intervals of 2.5 sec. What is the approximate ocean depth? Take the speed of sound in water as 4780 m per sec.

5 A blank pistol cartridge is fired within an empty stadium. The sound returned has a musical tone of 300 vibrations per sec. What is the depth of each seat between risers? Take the speed of sound to be 1140 fps.

PART 4   HEAT

CHAPTER XVI

EXPANSION OF SOLIDS

Most substances expand with increase of temperature; few, how-ever, contract, while others change but little. The amount of expansion with heat seems to be related very closely to the grouping of the molecules and the forces between them. Thus with gases the motions of the molecules are wholly random and the expansions are very uniform for many gases. Solids, on the other hand, vary widely in their rate of expansion with change of temperature. Some change in length but little with temperature while others expand considerably relative to other solids. In general, the expansions with increase of temperature, are less marked in the order: gases, liquids, and solids.

By expansion, we may refer to the change in length, surface, or volume, due to a change in temperature. Thus with the laying of pipe lines, the building of bridges, or the construction of steel buildings, it is the change in length that is important; while in the construction of thermometer bulbs or the filling of liquid containers, the volume expansion is important. Surface expansions will not be considered.

LINEAR EXPANSIONS

The linear expansion of a solid is measured in terms of the change of length per unit length per unit rise of temperature. We call this the linear coefficient of expansion of a solid, and it is designated by the letter α. Thus if Δl represents the total change produced in the length,

$$\alpha = \frac{1}{l}\frac{\Delta l}{\Delta t}. \tag{52}$$

Here α is the average linear coefficient of expansion for the temperature interval Δt, and l is the length at the initial temperature.

Linear expansions are very small although highly variable from solid to solid. Hence the same coefficient of expansion may be used for any initial length in the temperature ranges for which a mean linear coefficient of expansion is determined.

Most apparatus for the determination of α consists either of a solid rod housed within a cylindrical tube made to carry water or steam, or a hollow tube through which water or steam may flow. Many of these forms of apparatus may be packed with ice for determination of zero degrees centigrade as the initial temperature.

There are a number of convenient and ingenious devices for measurement of the expansion of the rod for any definite change in temperature of the rod. Some of the devices and instruments used for measurement of changes in length are* (1) the mechanical lever, (2) optical lever, (3) micrometer gage, (4) the spherometer with electrical contact, (5) wheel and axle bearing on which rests an axle with pointer, (6) micrometer microscope, and (7) interferometer. The last two methods are very accurate but difficult, especially the last method.

EXPERIMENT 25

LINEAR EXPANSION

To determine the linear coefficient of expansion of a rod.

APPARATUS: Linear coefficient of expansion apparatus, thermometer, steam generator, bunsen burner with rubber tubing, meter stick, micrometer screw.

The apparatus (Fig. 106) consists of a hollow tube of copper or brass, resting at one end, which is notched, on a pointed support; at the other, on a spindle which carries a pointer. The spindle, in turn, rests on a wheel and axle bearing. Since the notched end is fixed, it follows that when the length changes, the pointer turns in front of a dial graduated in degrees. In the process of setting up the apparatus, arrange the expansion rod so that the condensed steam will drain into the sink or into a small tin cup. This precaution will help preserve your books and insure acceptable care of the apparatus and all measuring devices. The apparatus should be set up ready to pass the steam through the tube before the initial dial reading is taken. Record the temperature of the room near

* See Chapter XXXIV for description of some of the measuring devices.

your apparatus, and assume it to be the initial temperature of your expansion rod. Take the initial reading of the dial. It is important not to disturb the apparatus after this initial dial reading is taken.

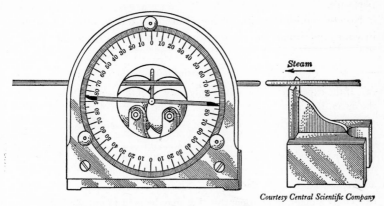

Courtesy Central Scientific Company

Fig. 106. Linear coefficient of expansion apparatus.

Then pass steam through the hollow tubing. After a short interval of time the dial will come to rest at a new position, the reading of which should be taken. The steam temperature is obtained from the table giving the boiling points of water for different atmospheric pressures.* Let the angular change in degrees between the initial and final dial reading be called θ. Then the change in length Δl of the rod is

$$\Delta l = 2\pi r \cdot \frac{\theta}{360} \tag{53}$$

where r is the radius of the spindle. This radius is measured with the micrometer screw by taking the average of several readings of the diameter and dividing by 2. The length l of the rod under consideration is, of course, the distance from the notch to the spindle.

The average linear coefficient of expansion of the rod for the temperature interval $\Delta t = (t_1 - t_0)$ is

$$\alpha = \frac{1}{l} \frac{\Delta l}{\Delta t}.$$

---

* The boiling point will be in error less than 0.1° C if 0.037° C is added (or subtracted) for each millimeter of mercury pressure difference from 760 mm when the actual pressure is between 700 and 800 mm mercury pressure. For regions of high altitude, tables must be consulted.

Repeat the experiment one or more times. Allow the rod to acquire room temperature before taking the initial reading. Blowing compressed air through the tube will hasten cooling to room temperature.

Note carefully the kind of metal used for temperature expansion in your experiment so that question (b) may be answered.

Questions

(a) If the experiment is repeated only once, find the per cent of error from the mean. If repeated more than once, find the per cent of error of the mean.

(b) Determine the per cent of error of your average result from the accepted value.

(c) Our method for obtaining the initial temperature of the rod is not very exact. Describe a more accurate method for obtaining the initial temperature.

(d) Draw a diagram of apparatus that may be used to test the linear relationship between change of length of a rod and the corresponding change of temperature.

PROBLEMS

Experiment 25

1   In order to test the linear relationship between the change in length of a rod and corresponding rise in temperature, water is run by means of an

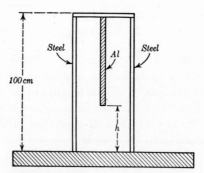

Fig. 107. Aluminum and steel rods joined at one end.

electrified circulating pump (of the type found in the cooling system of an automobile) through the apparatus. The rod was found to increase an average of 0.215 mm for every 15° C increase in temperature. What was the linear coefficient of expansion, if the rod was found to have an initial length of 81.5 cm?

2 With the pressure of the atmosphere as 73 cm of Hg instead of normal (76 cm), what would be the per cent of error in the calculated coefficient of expansion due to the temperature of steam being taken as 100° C? Assume the initial temperature to be 22° C, the length of the rod 75 cm, and the expansion 0.65 mm.

3 How much will a steel bridge one mile in length expand between extreme temperatures of −15° C and +40° C?

4 Two steel rods and an aluminum rod are joined as shown in Figure 107. How long must the aluminum rod be so that the difference h in lengths of the two rods will be constant for all temperatures? The coefficients of linear expansion for aluminum and steel are 0.000022 and 0.000011, respectively.

CHAPTER XVII

GAS LAWS

The average volume coefficient of expansion β for all fluids (liquids or gasses) is defined as the change in volume per unit volume per unit rise of temperature. If the initial volume is V and the change in temperature is Δt, then

$$\beta = \frac{1}{V} \frac{\Delta V}{\Delta t}. \tag{54}$$

If we write $\Delta V = (V_1 - V_0)$ and $\Delta t = (t_1 - t_0)$ where V_0 and t_0 are the initial volume and the initial temperature, respectively, then $V_1 = V_0 [1 + \beta (t_1 - t_0)]$. A more compact equation will be obtained if we substitute t for $(t_1 - t_0)$; then

$$V = V_0 (1 + \beta t) \tag{55}$$

where V replaces V_1 and is the final volume.

GASES

Gases expand so markedly that the volume (or linear) coefficient of expansion will have different values, measurable in the laboratory, if different initial temperatures from which the expansion is measured are chosen. The initial temperature usually referred to is 0 C.

The volume coefficient of expansion of a gas at constant pressure with an initial volume V_0 at $0°$ C is defined as

$$\beta_P = \frac{V - V_0}{V_0 t}, \text{ or } V = V_0 (1 + \beta_P t). \tag{56}$$

The pressure coefficient of expansion at constant volume is

$$\beta_V = \frac{P - P_0}{P_0 t_1} \text{ or } P = P_0 (1 + \beta_V t). \tag{57}$$

Theory shows that for a perfect gas

$$\beta_P = \beta_V = \frac{1}{T_0}$$

where $T_0 = 273$ (to a first approximation), the temperature on the absolute scale which corresponds to zero degrees on the centigrade scale.

If we wish to study the expansion of gases where the initial state of the gas is not given at zero degrees centigrade, it will be found more convenient, generally, to use the more general gas law,

$$PV = RT,$$

i.e.,

$$\frac{PV}{T} = \text{constant} = R. \tag{58}$$

In this equation, T is the temperature on the absolute scale and is related to temperatures t on the centigrade scale by the equation $T = 273 + t$.

BOYLE'S LAW TUBES

The differences in the designs of Boyle's law tubes are due largely to the attempts to obtain greater variations in the pressure and

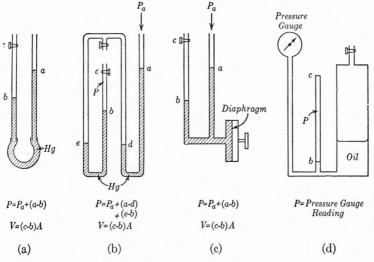

$P=P_a+(a-b)$

$V=(c-b)A$

$P=P_a+(a-d)$
$\quad +(e-b)$

$V=(c-b)A$

$P=P_a+(a-b)$

$V=(c-b)A$

$P=$ Pressure Gauge
Reading

(a)   (b)   (c)   (d)

Fig. 108. Four forms of Boyle's law apparatus.

volume, and to experiment with pressures both lower and higher than atmospheric. Compact, leakproof designs for experimenting safely with wide variations in pressure have given, and still do give, considerable difficulty in construction.

Most of the Boyle's law tubes work, in principle, in accordance with designs shown in the line drawings of Figure 108 (a), (b), (c), and (d). The volume V to be compressed or expanded is given in each case by $(c - b)A$, where A represents the inner cross-sectional area which is assumed to be constant. The total pressure P on this volume is indicated in each of the respective figures. The diagrams are not intended to illustrate any actual apparatus.

The volume of air V for the more accurate work, should be free from moisture, since water vapor does not obey Boyle's law. Dry air may be obtained by filling with air which has passed through some drying agent such as calcium chloride or sulfuric acid. Clean mercury should be used in the tubes. Any open end or ends of tubes may be stuffed with tufts of cotton to keep out the dust.

AIR THERMOMETER

An air thermometer may be of the constant volume or of the constant pressure type. In practice constant volume air thermometers are much more convenient to use, although any air thermometer is

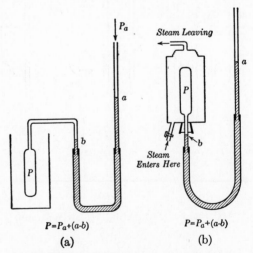

$$P = P_a + (a-b)$$

(a)

$$P = P_a + (a-b)$$

(b)

Fig. 109. Two forms of constant volume air thermometers.

much more cumbersome than a mercury-in-glass thermometer. Since the permanent gases behave so nearly like an ideal gas, gas thermometers are used for standardizing purposes. The constant volume type *dry*-air thermometers only will be described.

For experimental purposes, the air thermometer may be made by conversion of certain types of Boyle's law equipment, or may be made as an independent apparatus. When made by conversion, usually apparatus of the type shown in Figure 108 (a) or 108 (c) is used. The conversion consists of removal of the closed volume side or closing it off as in Figure 110 and replacing with a constant volume bulb.

The constant volume bulb may be operated with the open end of the bulb up, (Fig. 109 a) or with the open end down (Fig. 109 b).

If operated with open end up, it may be inserted in the usual steam generators. A special container with opening at both top and bottom is necessary if the bulb is used with open end down. The bottom is made water tight by use of a rubber stopper as shown in Figure 109 (b). The bulb in some apparatus is made of metal so that the bulb and container are a single unit (Fig. 110).

Courtesy Central Scientific Company

Fig. 110. Air thermometer with metal bulb.

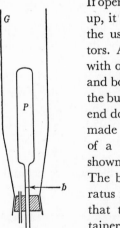

Fig. 111. An all-glass air thermometer — milk bottle type.

Figure 111 shows an all-glass air thermometer which operates in the same way as those shown in Figures 109 (b) and 110. The container is made from a milk bottle with the bottom removed and ground. A sheet metal is used as cover when steam is inserted from the top by means of a tube that reaches well down into the container. Since steam when used condenses on the sides of the glass vessel, it is usually necessary to allow the condensed water to rise so as to cover the initial point *b*, usually designated by some form of fixed straight edge. Of course, the initial point *b* could be below the stopper with but little error.

When the bulb is used with open end down, mercury may be removed easily if it should get into the bulb because of cooling the gas without proper adjustment of the other mercury column.

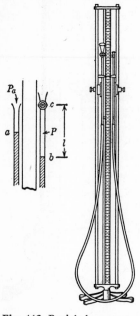

Fig. 112. Boyle's law apparatus.

EXPERIMENT 26

BOYLE'S LAW

To show that the product of the pressure and the volume of a gas (air) is a constant if the temperature is kept constant.

APPARATUS: Any standard Boyle's law apparatus (such as represented in Fig. 108 and Fig. 112).

In the apparatus to be described (Fig. 112), the closed side of which the volume is to be determined is on the right, while an open end is provided on the left. There are two pieces of glass tubing of uniform bore connected by a flexible rubber tubing. The apparatus is filled with mercury to levels *a* and *b*, as shown. The volume of the inclosed space is changed by altering the height of the mercury column on the left side.

Since the tube is of uniform bore, Boyle's law,

$$P_1V_1 = P_2V_2,$$

may be written in the form,

$$P_1l_1 = P_2l_2,$$

where A is the cross-sectional area of the tube, and $V_1 = Al_1$ and $V_2 = Al_2$. The pressure P inside the inclosed gas (air) will be

$$P = P_a + (a - b)$$

centimeters of mercury where P_a is the pressure of the atmosphere. If we do not alter the height of the tube on the right, then the top of the closed tube (c) will remain at some constant reading on the scale, and the whole experiment may be done by reading different positions of a and b on the scale when the left-hand column is altered in height. Always allow the air in the closed tube to stand for about three minutes after changing the level to allow the air to acquire the temperature of the room.

Take several (8 to 12) readings by changing the height on the left-hand side and plot a curve between the reciprocal of the length ($l = c - b$) of the inclosed volume, as abscissas, against the pressure in centimeters of mercury as ordinates.

$P_a =$ cm of mercury $c =$ cm.

READING OF MERCURY LEVELS		$a - b$ (cm)	$P = P_a + (a - b)$	$l = (c - b)$	$\dfrac{1}{l}$	pl
a (cm)	b (cm)					

Questions

(a) When P, the total pressure, is plotted against $1/l$ do you get a straight line, hyperbola, circle, ellipse, or what? Why is the form of "curve" obtained useful in the proof of Boyle's law?

(b) What is the ratio of maximum to minimum pressures obtained in the experiment? Is this ratio small, medium or large compared with the maximum possible experimental ratio for air that may be obtained with apparatus of special construction?

(c) Did your experimental work indicate that sufficient time was not allowed for equalization of temperature between readings?

(d) What kind of curve would a plot of P against l give in your experiment? Plot as a dashed curve on the same graph paper as used for the curve of question (a).

EXPERIMENT 27

THE AIR THERMOMETER

Part (a)   *To determine how the pressure of a gas changes with temperature.*

Part (b)   *To determine the pressure coefficient of expansion.*

APPARATUS: Air thermometer,* ice, large beaker, thermometer. A steam jacket will be needed if apparatus as illustrated in Figure 113 is used. A boiler with burner or an electric heater will be needed with apparatus as shown in Figure 109 (b).

The line drawing of Figure 113 is intended to illustrate the principle only of the air thermometer. It consists of a glass bulb with stem of capillary bore, connected to a flexible rubber tubing as shown.

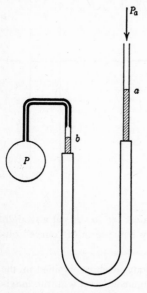

Fig. 113. Air thermometer.

A straight glass tubing of about $\frac{1}{4}$ inch in diameter is connected to the other side of the rubber tubing. Clean mercury fills the space between the levels a and b. The mercury level must always be returned to the position b before a reading is taken. The position b may be determined by some form of straight edge, or a predetermined convenient position on the scale near the capillary, or an etched line placed on by the manufacturer.

Part (a) The bulb is placed in a mixture of chopped ice and water to obtain the pressure P_o in the bulb for zero temperature. Care should be taken to make sure that pieces of ice are placed

---

* The bulb may be filled with dry air by thoroughly exhausting and then filling with air which has been dried by bubbling through concentrated sulfuric acid.

under the bulb without injury to the bulb. The pressure P_o in the bulb will be

$$P_o{}' = P_a + (a - b) \text{ centimeters of mercury,}$$

where P_a is the atmospheric pressure in centimeters of mercury and $(a - b)$ is the difference in height of the two sides of the mercury column, measured in centimeters. The height of a and b may be measured from the table top if the apparatus contains no scale of its own. It may turn out that a is lower than b. In such a case the pressure in the bulb is less than atmospheric pressure; hence the difference $(b - a)$ is subtracted from P_a. The atmospheric pressure P_a is obtained from any good barometer.

Now remove the bulb from the ice mixture if the bulb has the open end up* as in Figure 113 and surround the bulb with a water jacket and obtain the pressure corresponding to temperatures in the neighborhood of 20, 40, 60 and 80 degrees centigrade. *Watch the mercury level on the open side* and raise this side as the bulb is heated so that the mercury will not blow out the open side. Remember that the reading of the mercury column on the bulb side must be always from the same position b.

Next insert the bulb in a steam jacket** to obtain the pressure for steam temperature. The water should be at boiling state so that the transfer can be made without delay. *Before transferring to the steam bath* one person should be ready to lower the open side during transfer and raise this side after transfer, since the pressure is now going to be higher. The steam temperature may be obtained from your thermometer, if convenient, or from boiling point tables after reading the barometer (see Chapter XVI, page 195, or tables, Chapter XXXIV, page 415).

Plot a curve with pressures as ordinates and temperatures as abscissas. Your data may be entered in tabular form as shown in the table on the following page.

Part (b) Your curve between pressure and temperature should be a straight line. It terminates at 0° C on the low temperature side.

---

* If the bulb is used with open end down as in Figure 109(b) the ice may be more conveniently removed by melting out with steam or electric heater. The water is then raised in temperature as desired with the same source of heat.

** In apparatus as pictured in Figure 109(b), the water is drained out and steam inserted immediately from the top of the container.

Barometer Reading (P_a) =

| Temperature C | HEIGHT OF MERCURY | | $a - b$ | $P = P_a + (a - b)$ (cm of Hg) | $\dfrac{P}{T}$ |
	a (Open)	b (Closed)			
Ice					

For convenience, extend the curve to give the total pressure P_{100} corresponding to 100° C. Hence, from equation (57), we now obtain

$$\beta_V = \frac{P_{100} - P_0}{P_0\, 100},$$

from which β_V is calculated. Calculate the value of β_V from your curve.

Questions

(a) What is the value of $1/\beta_V$ from part (b)?

(b) What is the per cent difference between $1/\beta_V$ as found in question (a) and 273.16?

(c) What is the per cent of error in the values of P/T in the data of part (a)?

(d) Extend your curve obtained in part (a) until it crosses the abscissa axis and interpret the results. [The assumption is made that the origin chosen for the ordinates in part (a) is for $P_0 = 0°$ C.]

(e) The experiment apparently shows that $P/T = $ constant. How is this shown theoretically also, by use of the general gas equation?

PROBLEMS

Experiment 26

1   A one-cubic-foot tank of gas at 1050 lb per in.^{2} pressure is to be used to fill one-cubic-foot balloons at a normal pressure of 15 lb per in.^{2} How many balloons can be filled?

2   Would Boyle's law hold for carbon dioxide at ordinary (20 to 25° C) temperatures? Why?

3 A certain perfect barometer has a space of 8 cm above the mercury level when the atmospheric pressure is normal. A little air is allowed to enter the barometer so that the level of mercury falls 4 cm. If the diameter of the barometer tube is 4 mm, what was the volume of air before it entered?

4 Boyle's law in our experiment simplifies mathematically to the equation $P_1 l_1 = P_2 l_2$, where l_1 and l_2 are any two enclosed column lengths for pressures P_1 and P_2 respectively. Why?

5 An automobile tire has a pressure of 35 lb per in.^{2} as read by the tire gage. How many times more space would the air in the tire occupy outside the tire at the place where the pressure was read? Assume that the atmospheric pressure is 15 lb per in.^{2}

6 A tire of 0.9 ft^3 volume on a certain car shows a pressure reading of 30 lb per in.^{2} when the atmospheric pressure is 15 lb per in.^{2} The car is driven up a mountain where the new atmospheric pressure is 11 lb per in.^{2} What is the pressure in the tire as shown by the tire gage now? Assume that the volume of the tire does not change with increment of pressure.

7 What volume will the air in the tire of problem 6 have after it is allowed to escape from the tire at the place where the atmospheric pressure is (a) 15 lb per in.^{2}, (b) 11 lb per in.^{2}?

Experiment 27

1 Show that the volume coefficient of expansion is approximately three times the linear coefficient of expansion. [Hint: Cube the equation $l = l_0(1 + \alpha t)$].

2 If the temperature for any gas is given on the Fahrenheit scale, could we use the relationship in equation (58) that $T = 459.4 + t$ where t is in degrees Fahrenheit and 459.4 is the freezing temperature for ice on the corresponding absolute scale?

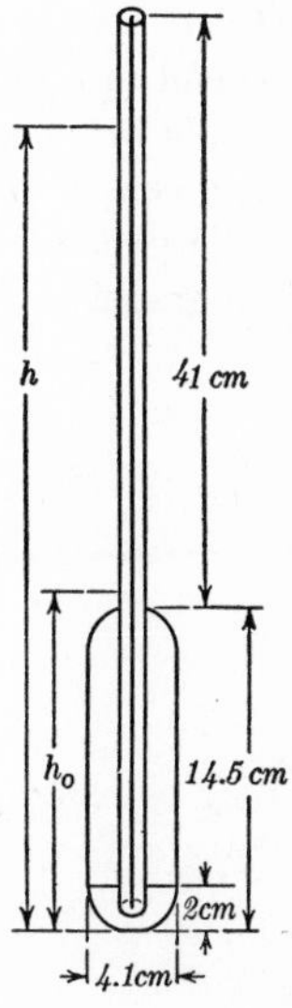

3 Prove mathematically that equation (57) follows from the general gas law as expressed in equation (58).

4 Why is the hydrogen gas thermometer called the "standard thermometer"?

5 Why is it necessary to specify some initial temperature from which to reckon the volume coefficient of expansion for gases, while with solids the exact position of the initial temperature is not so important?

6 An air thermometer is made by sealing a capillary tube to a bulb as shown in Figure 114. The cross-sectional area of the bulb is large compared

Fig. 114. An all-glass air thermometer, with capillary bore about 1 millimeter in diameter.

to the capillary tube cross-sectional area so that the surface level of the mercury in the bulb does not change appreciably with changes in level of the mercury in the capillary. What is the minimum height h for the capillary tube, if the change in pressure between steam and ice temperatures is to be measured? Assume that h_0, which is the height of the mercury column at $0°$ C from the bottom of the bulb to a point just above the top of the bulb, is 15 cm, and that the barometric pressure is 76.00 cm of mercury. (*Note.* This apparatus makes a good air thermometer. Approximate satisfactory dimensions are given in Figure 114.)

7   A moisture free capillary tube (Fig. 114a) with uniform bore, having a mercury sealed column (Cambosco Scientific Company) of length l as shown is useful in experiments on Charles's law. When the tube is placed horizontally in a deep freeze ($-25°$ C), a refrigerator ($5°$ C), a room ($25°$ C) and a constant temperature oven ($95°$ C), the readings of the length of the capillary bore were 29.2, 32.6, 35 and 43.0 cm respectively. Determine by a graphical method the absolute zero from the above measurements.

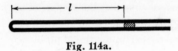

Fig. 114a.

CHAPTER XVIII

MEASUREMENT OF HEAT AND CHANGE OF STATE

The science of calorimetry deals with the measurement of quantities of heat. Since the absolute heat energy in any body is a rather vague quantity and of course would be very difficult to measure, we confine ourselves in calorimetry to measurements of heat changes and transfers from one body to another. In any case, in our practical life it is only exchanges of heat and their effects that are of interest to us.

Heat measurements have always formed a very interesting part of practical physics, yet they are a very difficult part when extreme accuracy is attempted. We find in this field scientists who have spent a whole lifetime in these researches and have won fame for the degree of skill and technique which they have developed. Such names as Joule, Rowland, and Regnault will never be forgotten, and the student would find the time well spent if he will read some of the records of the published works of these men.

UNITS INVOLVED IN HEAT MEASUREMENTS

The unit of heat is defined arbitrarily as the amount of heat required to raise the temperature of unit mass of water one degree in that system. The unit varies somewhat, depending upon the temperature, but the variation is so small that for ordinary work the difference is negligible. For our purposes, the variation is unimportant, being less than 0.1 per cent per degree change. We will assume that the unit is the same for all temperatures that will be used. The unit of heat in the cgs, the mks, and fps systems are called the *calorie* (*cal*), the *kilocalorie* (*k-cal*, also, *large calorie*) and the *British thermal unit* (*Btu*) respectively.

Heat (*or thermal*) *capacity* is defined as the quantity of heat energy required to produce a unit change of temperature in a body. Common units of heat capacity are cal per deg C and Btu per deg F. The heat capacity of course depends upon the mass of the body.

Thus a mass m of water has a heat capacity of m cal per deg C, if cgs units are used and m Btu per deg F, if English units are used. Heat capacity of m grams of water may be expressed also as 4.2 m joules per deg C in cgs units and 778 m ft-lb per deg F in English units.

Specific heat (s) of a body is in reality an abstract number and may be defined as the ratio of its heat capacity per unit mass to the heat capacity of water per unit mass. However, since the denominator, when expressed in the usual heat energy units, is always one, *the specific heat is equal numerically* to the number of heat units required to raise the temperature of a unit mass of the substance by unity. Thus, the heat capacity per unit mass of copper is 0.093 cal per g per deg C in the cgs system; the specific heat is likewise 0.093. Tables listing specific heats are given, usually, in cal per g per deg C.

Water equivalent (w) is the mass of water that has the same heat capacity as the given body. Since a mass m of water is numerically equal to its heat capacity, water equivalent is defined mathematically as the product of the mass of the body and the specific heat, i.e., $w = ms$, where m is the mass of the body.

The heat of fusion (L_f) is defined, in cgs units, as the increment of energy necessary to change 1 gram mass of the substance from the solid to the liquid state without change in temperature. The changes in normal atmospheric pressures have no appreciable effect on heats of fusion. [L_f for water is approximately 80 cal per g, 144 Btu per lb (i.e., numerically $80 \times \frac{9}{5}$), or 80 k-cal per kg].

The heat of vaporization (L_v) is defined, in cgs units, as the increment of energy necessary to change a mass of 1 gram of a body from the liquid to the gaseous state without change of temperature. Changes from normal atmospheric pressure will affect the heat of vaporization. The heat of vaporization of water at 100° C is approximately 540 cal per g, or 972 Btu per lb (i.e., numerically $540 \times \frac{9}{5}$). The variation of the heat of fusion with temperature t in degrees centigrade may be found very approximately from the equation $L_v = 598.8 - 0.599\, t$.

The following examples illustrate the use of these definitions.

1   The amount of heat necessary to change the temperature of $\frac{1}{2}$ kg of water from 15° C to 25° C is $ms(t_2 - t_1)$ calories = 500 $\times$ 1 $\times$ (25 − 15) = 5000 calories.

2 The amount of heat necessary to raise $\frac{1}{2}$ kg of iron through the same temperature interval would be

$$ms(t_2 - t_1) = 500 \times 0.115 \times (25 - 15) = 575 \text{ calories.}$$

3 The water equivalent of the iron block in example (2) is 57.5 grams because $m \times s = 500 \times 0.115 = 57.5$ grams.

4 The latent heat of fusion of lead is 5.4 calories per gram if the amount of heat necessary to change 500 grams of lead at 327° C (the melting point) to liquid lead at 327° C is 2700 calories.

5 The latent heat of vaporization of water is 540 calories per gram if 5400 calories are necessary to change 10 grams of water into steam at 100° C.

Thermometer calibrations Thermometers are calibrated for part immersion and for total immersion. The part immersion thermometers are usually calibrated for about a 3-inch immersion. They have a ring around the position above the mercury bulb indicating the upper limit of immersion and have less space between temperature intervals as compared to the total immersion type of the same length and temperature range. The difference in use becomes more important at the higher temperatures.

Thermometer sensitivity Boiling temperatures, to be described in the experiments on heat measurements, will be obtained from steam tables. The correct boiling point may be obtained between the pressures of 700 to 800 mm of mercury with an error less than 0.1° C by subtracting (or adding if the pressure is in excess of 760 mm of mercury) 0.037 deg C for each millimeter of mercury air pressure difference between 760 millimeters of mercury barometric pressure and the actual atmospheric pressure in millimeters of mercury. Tables are needed only if accuracy of the boiling point is desired to less than 0.1° C.

Temperatures for which thermometers are needed range between 0 and 50° C. Thermometers with $\frac{1}{10}$-degree intervals, in this range, can be obtained that are not much longer than the ordinary −10° C to 110° C interval thermometer, and have many advantages in terms of accuracy. *If 0 to 50° C $\frac{1}{10}$-degree-interval thermometers are used, one needs to remember only that they should not be used for boiling temperatures or any temperature in excess of their total temperature range.* Development of skill in laboratory techniques is indicated by long use of laboratory apparatus without mishap.

METHODS USED IN CALORIMETRIC DETERMINATIONS

Calorimetric measurement consists usually in the determination of some constant such as specific heat, heat of fusion or vaporization, melting point, or heat value of a fuel or of some food. Apparatus used for measurement of the above heat constants are called calorimeters, some of which are quite specialized, such as the oxygen bomb calorimeter used to measure the calorific value of a given solid or liquid fuel.

In our calorimetric measurements, *a double-walled calorimeter** of the type shown in Figure 115 will be used. The outer cup has a

capacity of about 1 liter. The inner cup has a capacity of about 300 cm³ and is insulated from the outer cup by a fiber ring. The cups are made usually of copper or of aluminum. If the metal is copper, it is usually plated with nickel and has a polished finish. A polished surface, whatever the metal, is desirable so as to reflect radiant heat. The inner cup is supplied with a stirrer of the same metal as the inner cup. Water is placed in the inner cup of the calorimeter only. Hence the inner cup only takes the temperature of the water, and its water equivalent must be known or determined. The outer cup is used only to prevent as far as possible heat interchanges from the inner cup to the outside. Even handling the inner cup with the hands may bring about appreciable errors.

Fig. 115. Calorimeter.

Method of mixtures   The principle used in our heat measurements is known as the method of mixtures. When two or more systems having different temperatures are placed in contact, they interchange heat until all acquire the same temperature, at which time the interchange stops. The principle underlying the method of mixtures, is that the total heat lost by all bodies whose temperatures are decreased is equal to the total heat gained by all bodies whose temperatures are increased. The heat gained or lost by each body is given by the product of its mass, specific heat, and increment in temperature. The principle of the method of mixtures is another statement of the principle of conservation of energy.

See Chapter XXXIV page 415 for other types of calorimeters.

Radiation correction In practice, some heat will be lost to the surroundings, even when Dewar type calorimeters are used. Many correction methods have been proposed. Newton introduced a method for calculating and measuring heat loss or gain due to surroundings. Use of this method is described in Chapter XXXIV. This method of correction is very instructive and gives good results, but requires a little skill and practice. We suggest that the more curious and skilled experimenter check his results by this method for obtaining the temperature change. No additional data need be taken as long as the time intervals corresponding to temperatures were recorded in accordance with directions of Chapter XXXIV, page 416.

In the experiments to be described here, we shall minimize this error as far as possible by arranging the experiment so that during half the period the calorimeter has a temperature above the surroundings, and gives off heat; whereas during the other half the calorimeter is below the temperature of the surroundings and absorbs heat from the surroundings. By arranging the experiment so that these two heats are approximately the same, this error is minimized, but not completely corrected, for a brief inspection will show that the total time interval below room temperature will be less than that above room temperature. A *slightly* greater difference in temperature below room temperature compared to that above will decrease the error due to radiation.

EXPERIMENT 28

SPECIFIC HEAT OF A SOLID

To determine the specific heat of some metal.

APPARATUS: A solid block (e.g., aluminum or copper) drilled with a number of parallel holes with attached thread for handling, double wall calorimeter (Fig. 115), a glass or metal vessel of about 1 liter capacity in which the solid can be raised to the boiling point, burner, tripod, balance, 0–50° C $\frac{1}{10}$-degree thermometer, and stirrer. A 0–110° C thermometer may be used if the $\frac{1}{10}$-degree thermometer is not available.

The method we shall use is the method of mixtures in which the solid, the specific heat of which we wish to determine, is first heated to boiling temperature. The hot solid is then quickly transferred to a calorimeter containing water at a known temperature. The temperature is observed continuously until the final temperature of the solid and water is reached. Then the heat given out by the solid in cooling to the final temperature is equated to the heat absorbed by the water, and thus the specific heat s is calculated.

The boiling temperature will be obtained from the steam tables or calculated as shown on page 195 or page 431.

The first operation consists in finding the mass M of the unknown solid by weighing. Next suspend the solid in a vessel in which water can be boiled, and leave it in the boiling water or steam for at least fifteen minutes so as to be sure the whole solid has this same temperature throughout. Read the barometric pressure so that the boiling temperature may be obtained. While the solid is heating get the calorimeter ready. This includes finding the mass of the inner cup of the calorimeter (m_1), first when empty, and then when half full of water. Let the mass of water in the calorimeter be m. When the object is immersed, the calorimeter should be about three-quarters full. The initial temperature t_0 of the water should be about as much *below room temperature* as the expected final temperature will be above room temperature. One trial experiment is needed to obtain the needed initial temperature.

When the solid has acquired uniform temperature of steam, transfer it quickly into the water, being careful to transfer as little condensed water along with the solid as possible, and also not to splash out any of the weighed water in the calorimeter. Note the temperature t_0 of the water, when the solid was introduced, and record the highest final temperature t_f attained by the water. The solid should be kept moving slowly, but no part of it should be allowed above water. Record all data with proper labeling on a data form.

If the instructor asks for a correction to be made for cooling in accordance with Chapter XXXIV, page 416, continue the temperature readings for 6 to 8 minutes after maximum temperature has been attained.

Write down the expression for the heat given out by the solid in cooling from boiling t_b to the final temperature t_f. This is according to our definition $Ms(t_b - t_f)$. Equate this to the heat taken in by the water and water equivalent of the calorimeter, which is $(m + w)$

$\times (t_f - t_0)$, where w is the water equivalent of the calorimeter. Ask your instructor what kind of metal is used in the inner cup of the calorimeter.

Solve for s, the specific heat of the unknown solid.

Repeat the experiment making use of the temperature range obtained in the first trial so that an initial temperature may be chosen that will take care of the heat radiation losses more completely.

Questions

(a) How much longer time was required for the water to reach the final temperature t_f after reaching room temperature than for the water to rise from the initial temperature t_0 to room temperature?

(b) If your temperature readings were continued long enough after t_f was reached as to obtain a reasonably constant slope, what was the rate of cooling in deg per min at the temperature calculated? How much was this temperature above room temperature?

(c) Is there a difference between the temperature of boiling water and the temperature of the steam immediately above the water?

(d) Compare your result with results as given for the metal in a book of tables.

(e) In what way might you expect the water which is transferred with the solid from the bath at boiling temperature to the calorimeter to effect the value of the specific heat as found in this experiment?

(f) Suggest a method by which the error referred to in question (e) may be overcome.

EXPERIMENT 29

CHANGE OF STATE. ABSORPTION OR EMISSION OF HEAT

Part (a) *To determine the heat of fusion of ice.*
Part (b) *To determine the heat of vaporization of water.*

APPARATUS: Double-walled calorimeter, 0–50° C $\frac{1}{10}$-degree interval thermometer, stirrer, blotting or filter paper, balance, ice, a liter beaker for heating water, tripod. If part (b) is performed, a steam generator and steam trap will also be needed.

Part (a) Preliminary. We shall again use the method of mixtures, by placing a piece of ice into a calorimeter containing water and noting the change in temperature produced when the ice has all melted. Equating then the total heats given out by the water and calorimeter and the heat absorbed by the ice, after equilibrium has been reached, enables us to find L_f.

The initial temperature should be above room temperature sufficiently so that the final temperature is below room temperature by about the number of degrees that the initial temperature was above room temperature at the start. An initial temperature of $5°\,C$ to $10°\,C$ above room temperature is usually sufficient for average conditions as employed in the experiment.

The **procedure** for part (a) is as follows: The mass m_1 of the inner cup of the calorimeter and stirrer must be found. The stirrer should be of special design so as to keep the ice below the surface (Fig. 116). Next, the calorimeter is half filled with water and weighed. The temperature of the water should be arranged to be about five to ten degrees above the room temperature. Let the mass of the water be m grams. A piece of ice should be chosen that will conveniently go into the calorimeter and that does not contain many corners or cracks that might have water clinging to them. The ice should be placed on a piece of blotting paper, dried, and *transferred as quickly as possible to the calorimeter. Handle the ice as little as possible,* so as to prevent melting after drying. Note the temperature of the water when the ice was introduced, and keeping the ice below the water surface and the water stirred, note the final lowest temperature (t_f) reached by the water. Finally weigh the inner cup of the calorimeter with its contents again and determine the mass M of the ice which must have been added.

Fig. 116. Stirrer.

Calculation to find L_f   The heat given out by the water and calorimeter in cooling from t_0 to t_f is given by $(m + w)(t_0 - t_f)$ calories, where w is the water equivalent of the calorimeter and stirrer.

The heat taken in consists of two parts: (1) heat taken in melting M grams of ice $= ML_f$ calories (see definition of L_f), and (2) heat necessary to change M grams of water from $0°\,C$ to $t_f°\,C = M(t_f - 0)$ calories. Hence the total heat taken in is $ML_f + Mt_f$.

Now since the heat given out is equal to the heat taken in, we have:

$$ML_f + Mt_f = (m + w)(t_0 - t_f), \qquad (59)$$

from which L_f can be found.

(*Note*. The student should not try to remember formulas such as (59) above; but should rather form the habit of following the reasoning in order to be able to reason through similar and allied cases of heat transfer.)

If both parts (a) and (b) of this experiment are to be performed during the same laboratory period, before repeating the experiment for better adjustment of initial and final temperatures with respect to room temperature, proceed to part (b).

Part (b) Preliminary. In this part of the experiment, steam is passed from a steam generator (Fig. 117) through a water trap into

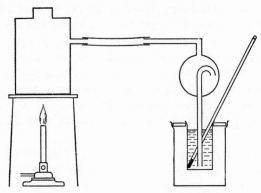

Fig. 117. Heat of vaporization apparatus.

a known mass of water until the temperature rises so that the excess temperature above room temperature is equal approximately to the number of degrees the temperature was depressed below room temperature at the start. The inner cup of the calorimeter and the stirrer have been weighed already, and presumably the calorimeter is about two-thirds full of water and has been sufficiently, or nearly sufficiently, cooled by the ice that has just been melted. The temperature should be about 10 deg. below room temperature. If further cooling is needed, add more ice until the temperature desired is obtained. Reweigh the calorimeter and contents.

The steam generator should have a good stream of steam coming out before the steam is passed into the calorimeter. The steam should be passed through a so-called "steam-trap" (Fig. 117) which really catches any water condensed on the way over, and prevents it from getting into the calorimeter. *It is most important that no condensed steam be allowed to get into the water in the calorimeter* if accuracy is to be obtained. In order to help prevent this condensation before reaching the calorimeter, the tubing coming out of the steam-trap and going into the calorimeter should preferably be heat-insulated by lagging with cotton wool. *Any drops that might otherwise adhere to the glass nozzle should be shaken off before introducing the nozzle into the calorimeter.*

The procedure for part (b) is as follows: Insert the nozzle into the water, recording the temperature of the water at the moment of introduction. Stir the water continuously while passing in steam. The nozzle of the steam generator should not be inserted very far. Any steam that escapes from the surface does not introduce an error because it does not condense. Keep on passing in steam until the temperature is approximately as much above room temperature as the water was below when the steam was introduced initially. Then remove the steam nozzle from the calorimeter but keep on stirring, and record the maximum temperature reached. (The temperature will drop after a while on account of cooling toward room temperature.)

Find the mass of the steam which has condensed by weighing the inner cup of the calorimeter and contents after the steam has condensed and subtracting the previous mass before introducing the steam. Let the mass of steam so found be M.

[*Note* 1. It is a good policy in recording the temperature of the water to read this every minute before and after introducing the steam and about every half-minute while the steam is being introduced. Then plot time against temperature and determine t_0 and t_f from your curve.]

[*Note* 2. Before calculation of the heat of vaporization, the experiment on the heat of fusion may now be repeated with the heated water, but first remove some of the water so as to leave room for the ice. Reweigh the calorimeter and water contents. Proceed as in part (a), and then repeat part (b).]

Calculation. The water and calorimeter and stirrer start with a temperature t_0 and end with a temperature t_f. The total mass of water before introduction of the steam is the mass m of water plus the water equivalent of the calorimeter, viz., $m + w$. [*Note.* $w = m_1 s$, where s = the specific heat of the copper vessel = 0.093

cal per gram.] Hence the heat taken in by the water and calorimeter is

$$(m + w)(t_f - t_0).$$

Now the steam had to supply this heat. The heat given off by the steam consisted of two parts. One part was given off when the M grams of steam condensed. For every gram this amount is L_v, and hence for M grams this part will be ML_v calories. The other part consists of heat given out by the M grams of steam, which have now already condensed but are still at a temperature $t_b°$ C (i.e., the steam temperature as determined from tables listing the temperature of boiling water for various air pressures). This condensed steam now cools until it reaches the same temperature as the surrounding water, viz t_f. The heat necessary for this part is, of course, $M(t_b - t_f)$.

Hence the total heat given out by the steam is:

$$ML_v + M(t_b - t_f)$$

Equating the heat given out to the heat taken in we have:

$$ML_v + M(t_b - t_f) = (m + w)(t_f - t_0) \qquad (60)$$

Solve this equation for L_v.

Questions

(a) What would be the per cent of error in part (a) if the mass of the inner cup of the calorimeter were neglected?

(b) If the ice you used in part (a) had been taken from a refrigerator freezing unit at $-10°$ C and placed immediately in the calorimeter, what would have been the error caused by this factor alone?

(c) What is the per cent of error in your value [part (a)] of L_f from the accepted value, assumed here to be 79.8 cal per g?

(d) If you had taken the boiling temperature to be 100° C, what would the per cent of error in your value of L_v in part (b) be from this factor alone.

(e) What is the per cent of error in your value of L_v in part (b) from the accepted value, assumed here to be 538.7 cal per g?

(f) Assume that 0.1 g of condensed water escaped into the calorimeter while doing part (b) of the experiment. Would this cause the value of L_v to be too large or too small? What would be the per cent of error due to this cause alone?

EXPERIMENT 30

THE FREEZING POINT OF A SOLID

To determine the freezing points of a crystalline and of an amorphous solid.

APPARATUS: Two* pyrex test tubes about ¾ inch in diameter; stand provided with appropriate clamps; an amorphous solid such as
paraffin or beeswax; a crystalline solid such as acetamide,
sodium acetate, sodium thiosulphate, or salol (phenol salicy-
late); two thermometers (0–100° C); hot-water bath; tripod;
burner; watch.

Introductory remarks   Crystalline solids have definite and fixed
melting points. When melted and allowed to cool, the temperature
decreases in accordance with Newton's cooling law until the freezing
point is reached. The liberation of heat in the freezing process
becomes equal to the loss of heat to the surroundings so that there
is no change in temperature in the time interval required for freezing. The temperature drops after the substance is frozen, in accordance with the law of cooling. Sometimes a liquid will supercool
10 degrees or more below its normal freezing point before starting
to freeze. But once the liquid does start to freeze, the temperature
rises rapidly to its normal freezing temperature and remains constant until the substance is frozen. The supercooling appears to be
due to lack of a nucleus about which crystals may grow. A minute
crystal of the substance dropped into the supercooled liquid will
start the freezing process. If a substance of relatively high freezing
point like acetamide is used, a temperature indicating device that
changes quickly with the temperature is preferable. A sluggish
thermometer will indicate considerable rounding of the temperature-time curve that actually is not present. Substances of complex
molecular structure may change form upon repeated melting, especially if subjected to intense heat, and thereby lose in part their
former crystalline forms. The freezing point of the substance, in
this case, will not be the same as the original. The melting (or fusion)
point of a crystalline solid is the same as the freezing point.

An amorphous substance does not have a definite and fixed melting point but the temperature-time curve will flatten at the solidifi-

---

* The freezing point for a crystalline and for an amorphous substance will
be found unless otherwise specified by the instructor.

cation process in a manner dependent upon the range of temperature required in the freezing process. The freezing portion of the curve is essentially flat for many substances.

Procedure You are provided with two test tubes with a crystalline solid in the one and an amorphous solid in the other. Heat the two test tubes in a water bath or a liter vessel, until melted.* The test tubes are now clamped to a rod (Fig. 118) and a thermometer is inserted and rotated in a manner to make the degree readings easily read. More reliable results are obtained when the thermometer bulb does not come in contact with the bottom or sides of the test tube. Provision may be made for clamping the thermometer with an appropriate cork or rubber bearing, or for hanging the thermometer by means of a string. Or the thermometer may be suspended by use of a one hole rubber stopper. The experiment should be performed in a location where there are no air currents to cause uneven cooling.

Fig. 118. Melting point apparatus.

Record the time and temperature every minute. One person may take the readings while the other records the data and at the same time plots these data on temperature (ordinate)-time (abscissa) curves. The period of observation will be usually thirty minutes or more before the melting points have been well passed. This time, of course depends upon the substance and on conditions. Hence the advisability of plotting the curve (or curves) as the experiment progresses. Pick out from your curves the horizontal portion and thus find the melting point.

Check your result by looking up the fusion temperature in a book of physical tables. [*Note.* Before leaving, heat the substances again so that they are just molten, and remove the thermometer. Use hot water baths for this purpose if so directed. Do not try to remove the thermometers in any other way, for fear of breaking them.]

[*Note.* An alternative and better way to measure the temperature for one, or both of the substances is by use of a thermocouple, which

* The instructor may decide to melt the substances in baths he has prepared for this experiment.

has a very small heat capacity. If the thermocouple is used in this experiment, it is necessary to first calibrate it at two fixed temperatures, 0° C and 100° C, and adjust the resistances so that the change in temperature from 0° C to 100° C will not cause too much deflection in the galvanometer. After calibration of any thermocouple, a thermometer in the above experiment can be replaced by the one junction of the thermocouple. In this case, plot galvanometer deflections (ordinates) against time (abscissa). Then convert the galvanometer deflection for the melting point into temperature from the calibration.]

Questions

(a) At two different temperatures, definitely above the change in slope of the temperature-time curve as affected by freezing, determine the rate of cooling per second for each substance. Repeat for two different temperatures sufficiently below the freezing point where the curve follows the usual cooling curve fashion. Are the rates of cooling the same for any substance at the same temperature before and after freezing?

(b) From the above data estimate the approximate rate of cooling at the freezing point of each substance.

(c) Why do we not find the melting point by performing a similar experiment when heating up the solid?

(d) Why does the temperature remain fairly constant during solidification?

(e) What difference, if any, is noted between the temperature-time curve for the crystalline solid and for the amorphous solid?

(f) Note the length of time required for each substance to freeze. Calculate the heat of fusion of each substance by calculation of the product of the specific heat of the substance in the liquid state, the rate of cooling (i.e., the change of temperature per minute of time in the liquid state at the temperature of freezing), and the length of time in minutes. Obtain the specific heats from some handbook.

(g) What do you think of the probable accuracy of the resulting heat of fusion (really heat of solidification) as obtained in question (f)?

PROBLEMS

Experiment 28

1 Define the following terms: (a) calorie, (b) British thermal unit (Btu), (c) heat capacity, (d) specific heat, (e) kilocalorie.

2 Why is specific heat very commonly defined with dimension of cal per gram per deg C?

3   How many calories are there in one Btu? in one k-cal?

4   If there are 11,000 calories in 1 g of gasoline, how many Btu are there in 1 lb of gasoline?

5   A copper calorimeter weighs 110 g and has a specific heat of 0.093. How many calories of heat are necessary to change its temperature from room temperature at 21° C to 26° C? What is the water equivalent of this vessel?

6   A piece of iron of mass 150 g and temperature 100° C is put into a calorimeter having 500 g of water at 14° C. If the final temperature acquired is 16.5° C, find the specific heat of iron. (The water equivalent of the calorimeter = 50 g.)

7   Two hundred g of lead shot (specific heat, 0.031) at a temperature of 100° C are poured into a container (water equivalent, 30 g) which contains a liquid of 100 g at an initial temperature of 20° C. Find the specific heat of the liquid if the final temperature is 25° C.

Experiment 29

1   How much heat is necessary to change 70 g of ice at 0° C into water at 10° C?

2   What will be the fall in temperature if 75 g of ice are put into a copper calorimeter of mass 50 g and containing 200 g of water at 35° C? (Specific heat of copper = 0.093 cal per g, and L_f = 80 cal per g.)

3   Find the latent heat of fusion of ice, given that in a certain experiment a piece of dry ice of mass 60 g was put into a calorimeter, having a water equivalent of 6 g and containing 200 g of water at 36.2° C. The final temperature was found to be 10° C.

4   If an electric refrigerator cube of ice weighs 60 g, what power in watts must be used to freeze 10 of these cubes in 6 hours if the water was originally at 20° C? Assume an efficiency of 100 per cent, and that 4.2 joules are required to extract each calorie of heat from the water. (Watt = joule per sec.)

5   An airplane flies through a cloud at −5° C, and receives an ice deposit on impact with the water droplets. What percentage of each drop will have to freeze in order to bring the ice and water to the equilibrium temperature of 0° C? (*Note.* Water and ice may be in temperature equilibrium at 0° C only.)

6   An airplane flies through a cloud at −10° C, and receives an ice deposit on impact. What percentage of each drop will freeze in bringing the water and ice to equilibrium at 0° C? How much of the remaining water at 0° C must evaporate in order to freeze the rest of the water?

7 Find the final temperature if 5 g of steam at 100° C are introduced into a copper calorimeter of mass 60 g containing 200 g of water at 10° C. Specific heat of copper is 0.093.

8 Find the amount of heat necessary to raise 20 g of ice from −30° C to steam at 130° C. The specific heat of ice is 0.54 and the specific heat of steam is 0.42.

Experiment 30

A sample of acetamide was melted in a water bath and allowed to cool. The following data, which gives the time intervals in minutes and corresponding

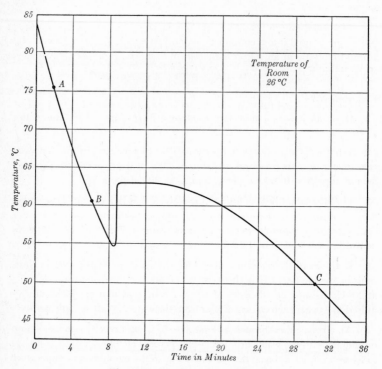

Fig. 119. Cooling curve-acetamide.

temperature readings in degrees centigrade, were obtained: 0, 84; 1, 80; 2, 75.5; 3, 71.5; 4, 67.5; 5, 63.8; 6, 60.5; 7, 57.9; 8, 55.0; 8.5, 54.5; 9, 62.2; 10, 63.0; 11, 63.0; 12, 63.0; 13, 62.9; 14, 62.5; 15, 62.1; 16, 62.0; 17, 61.5; 18, 61.0; 19, 60.6; 20, 60.0; 22, 58.6; 24, 57.0; 26, 54.9; 28, 52.5; 30, 50.5;

32, 48.0; 34, 45.5. The temperature-time curve for these data is shown in Figure 119. *Questions 1 to 8 inclusive are based on the above data and graph.*

1 What phenomenon is illustrated by the dip in the curve (Fig. 119) which is lowest near the 8-min interval in the cooling process?

2 What phenomenon is illustrated by the horizontal position of the curve beginning at the 10-min interval?

3 What does the length of the horizontal interval indicate in terms of magnitude of the heat of fusion?

4 Show that the average rate of cooling at A (75.5° C), is about 4.1 deg per min.

5 Show that the average rate of cooling at B (60.5° C) is about 3.1 deg per min.

6 Construct a graph with rate of cooling as ordinates and temperature as abscissas. Locate the two points in questions 4 and 5 on this graph and draw a straight line between them. The temperature corresponding to each of these two rate-of-cooling figures will be the average temperature in the time interval concerned. From the straight line drawn between the two points, determine the rate of cooling of the liquid at 63° C, the freezing temperature. (*Note.* If the liquid does not supercool, then point B must be well above the freezing temperature. A zero rate of cooling at room temperature (26° C here) may be taken as the other point besides point A. However, the linear relationship between rate of cooling and temperature does not hold accurately over such a wide temperature interval.)

7 Show that the average rate of cooling at C (50.0° C), is about 1.2 deg per min.

8 Locate the point given in problem 7 on the graph of problem 6. Assume also a zero rate of cooling at 26° C. Draw a straight line between the two points and extend so as to cross a perpendicular line drawn from abscissa axis at the freezing temperature of 63° C. What is the approximate rate of cooling of the acetamide in the solid state at 63° C? Compare with problem 6.

CHAPTER XIX

RELATIVE HUMIDITY

The determination of the quantity of water vapor in the atmosphere per unit volume is an important adjunct to the study of atmospheric conditions. The number of grams of water vapor per cubic meter is a common measure used. We will follow the cgs system exclusively in this discussion.

The air is said to be saturated when it contains the maximum number of grams of water vapor per cubic meter without condensing. The maximum quantity of water vapor per unit volume increases with temperature, but not linearly.

The number of grams of water vapor actually present in the atmosphere per cubic meter is called the *absolute humidity* (ρ), while the temperature to which the air must be reduced to reach saturation is called the *dew point*. Below this point, the excess water above the amount necessary for saturation will precipitate on some solid or even in the air as mist, clouds, fogs, etc.

A term which is more frequently used to express the moisture content of the air at any temperature t is called the *relative humidity*. This is defined as the ratio of the mass of water vapor actually present per unit volume (absolute humidity) at temperature t to the maximum mass of water vapor per unit volume that the atmosphere can hold at this temperature (saturated vapor). To express the relative humidity as per cent, multiply the above ratio by 100.

Our experiments on relative humidity will be confined to (1) dew point methods and (2) wet- and dry-bulb methods.

DEW POINT METHODS

In the dew point method, one lowers the temperature of a mass of liquid until dew forms on the outside of a polished metal cylinder. Let this temperature be t_d. We may find now the relative humidity by consulting such tables as (a) mass of water vapor in saturated air, (b) pressure of saturated water vapor, or (c) depression of dew point $(t - t_d)$ versus dew point temperature (t_d).

Consider method (a) first. Let ρ_s be the mass of saturated water vapor per cubic meter (see table 7, page 431) at the temperature t for which the relative humidity r is desired, and let ρ_t be the mass of water vapor per cubic meter actually present. Then, the relative humidity r is, $r = \rho_t/\rho_s$. Actually ρ_t is determined by experimentally finding the dew point temperature t_d. At this temperature, our tables show that the mass of saturated water vapor per cubic meter is ρ_d. Since the temperature of the air at the dew point is less than that for which the relative humidity is desired, a volume correction based on the relative change in absolute temperature is needed. This correction, based upon Charles' law, relates ρ_t to ρ_d by the equation, $\rho_t = \rho_d(t_d + 273)/(t + 273)$. Hence, the relative humidity becomes

$$ r = \frac{\rho_d\left(\dfrac{t_d + 273}{t + 273}\right)}{\rho_s} = \frac{\rho_d}{\rho_s}\left(\frac{t_d + 273}{t + 273}\right). \tag{61} $$

Since the temperature correction is relatively small, the temperature effect is often neglected, in which case the term in brackets (equation 61) will have a value of 1.

Method (b) is based on the fact that the pressure of a gas (see Table 7, page 431) is proportional to its density, and the pressure of saturated water vapor depends upon temperature only. If the pressure of saturated water vapor at temperature t is p_s and the pressure of saturated water vapor at the dew point temperature is p_d, then the relative humidity r is,

$$ r = \frac{p_d}{p_s} \tag{62} $$

We assume that *no temperature correction* is needed in equation (62), since the whole surrounding region is subjected to the same pressure. In addition, we do not expect any fractional change in pressure between water vapor pressure and the air pressure. The density of the water vapor near the cup will increase as noted in the discussion leading to equation (61), but the pressure may still remain constant by a change in velocity of the gas.

Equations (61) and (62) lead to the same value for relative

humidity when one neglects the small secondary effects, but a definition for relative humidity based upon equation (61) has certain fundamental advantages.

Method (c) makes use of a table of relative humidity values based upon the difference between observation or room temperature t and dew point temperature (i.e., $t - t_d$) and the dew point temperature t_d.

WET- AND DRY-BULB METHODS

These methods are based upon a difference in temperature found between a dry bulb and a wet bulb when air is blown past the pair of thermometers in excess of three meters per second. Actually the air may be blown past the thermometers or the thermometers may be whirled (sling psychrometer) in a circular motion in a stationary air field.

The resulting value for the relative humidity may be calculated by use of (a) a table, (b) an equation giving the actual water vapor pressure p_t in terms of the water vapor tension p_w at the wet-bulb temperature, the atmospheric pressure P_a and dry-bulb temperature t.

Method (a) makes use of a table giving the difference between the dry and wet bulb temperatures $(t - t_w)$ versus the temperature t of the dry bulb. Convert to the proper temperature scale when necessary.

Method (b) makes use of the equation,*

$$p_t = p_w - 0.00066 \, P_a(t - t_w)[1 + 0.00115(t - t_w)],$$

for reduction of psychrometric observations in deg C to give the water vapor pressure at the temperature of the dry bulb. By looking up in a table the saturated vapor pressure p_s for a temperature t, the relative humidity may be determined from equation (62), where $p_d = p_t$.

EXPERIMENT 31

RELATIVE HUMIDITY

To find the relative humidity of the atmosphere by (a) the dew-point method; (b) the wet- and dry-bulb thermometer.

---

* Handbooks provide tables for a quick calculation of the term $0.00066 \, P_o$ $(t - t_w) [1 + 0.00115(t - t_w)]$ versus $(t - t_w)$. Temperatures in deg. C.

APPARATUS: Part (a) Small nickel vessel, a medium-sized vessel, salt, and ice; or a nickel tube fitted with bulb and ether or equivalent, thermometer.

Part (b) Wet- and dry-bulb thermometer or a sling psychrometer.

Part (a) *The dew-point method.* To determine the dew point with ice and salt, chop the ice into small portions and add slowly to water, which is to about one inch depth in the polished nickel can. Stir with a thermometer and take the reading of the thermometer when the dew first appears. Now add lukewarm water until the dew disappears and take the temperature reading again. The average of these two temperatures gives a fair estimate of the dew point and becomes more accurately located the smaller the difference between the two readings for the appearance and disappearance of the dew. Make several trials, recording all readings, and find the average. Water should be removed from time to time to keep the height about one inch. Do not handle the polished side of the can with the fingers or breathe on the can while the experiment is in progress.

Courtesy Central Scientific Company

Fig. 120. Dew point apparatus — ether cooling method.

When ether is used, partially fill the small nickel tube, fitted with a compression bulb (Fig. 120), with ether. The quantity of ether used depends upon the apparatus. The increased evaporation brought about by forcing air through the ether with the compression bulb cools the apparatus quickly. The dew point is noted as in the previous salt and ice method. The ether evaporation method is very useful for obtaining low temperatures. It is desirable not to inhale the ether more than necessary. Repeat two or more times.

The relative humidity may be calculated by use of any one of the three methods outlined beginning on page 226.

Part (b) *The wet- and dry-bulb thermometer method.* If a wet- and dry-bulb thermometer is used (Fig. 121), see that the container holding the lower side of the wick is filled with distilled water and then start the fan, which should be at a distance of about two feet from the wet- and dry-bulb thermometers. The air velocity past the two thermometers should be at least 3 meters per sec. When the temperatures of the thermometer cease to change further, take readings of both the wet and dry thermometers. Repeat two or more times, relocating the apparatus each time.

If a sling psychrometer is used (Fig. 122), the instrument, consisting of a wet and a dry thermometer fastened to a metal frame, is whirled until both thermometers cease to change any in temperature. Record the wet-bulb thermometer reading first, and then the dry-bulb thermometer reading. In this instrument, the wet-bulb thermometer is kept moist by means of a wet cheese cloth which is wrapped around the bulb. (Use distilled water for this purpose.)

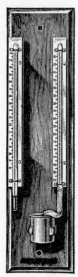

Courtesy Central Scientific Company

Fig. 121. Wet and dry bulb thermometers.

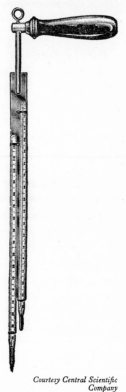

Courtesy Central Scientific Company

Fig. 122. Sling psychrometer.

Repeat two or more times, relocating the apparatus each time. Calculate the relative humidity by use of method (a) as outlined on page 227.

Questions

(a) What is the relative humidity as calculated by each of the three methods outlined beginning on page 226.

(b) What is the per cent of error from the mean between the value of the relative humidity as found in part (a) compared to that found in part (b)?

(c) What is the vapor pressure p_t in the experimental location as determined from the equation given in method (b), outlined on page 227.

(d) Knowing the relative humidity from part (b) of our experiment and p_t from question (c) above, calculate the saturated vapor pressure and compare with that found in part (a) from the determination of the dew point.

(**e**) What causes the appearance of dew on the side of the vessel?

(**f**) What would be the relative humidity out of doors today according to your experiment? (Assume the dew point out of doors the same as in the room where the experiment was performed.)

PROBLEMS

Experiment 31

1 Specific humidity, which is defined as the number of grams of water per kilogram mass of air, is often more useful than absolute humidity. Thus a parcel of rising air will have a constant specific humidity until it rises to the condensation height. Its absolute humidity, on the other hand, will be decreasing. The maximum masses of water vapor per kilogram of air the air can hold at temperatures of -20, -10, 0, 10, 20, 30, and 40 deg C are 0.77, 1.76, 3.77, 7.58, 14.40, 26.10, and 45.65 grams, respectively. Plot the saturation specific humidity curve from this data.

Assume that we have a parcel of air at $20°$ C containing 8 g of water vapor per kg of air. With this data and with the saturation specific humidity curve of problem 1, answer questions 2 to 8 inclusive.

2 What is the specific humidity?

3 What will be the specific humidity if the parcel of air is heated to $25°$ C?

4 What will be the specific humidity if the pressure increases 2 per cent?

5 What is the relative humidity of the parcel?

6 What is the relative humidity if the parcel of air is heated to $25°$ C?

7 What is the dew point for the parcel?

8 What happens if the temperature of the parcel is reduced to $5°$ C?

9 Why does warm, moist air cause more discomfort than warm, dry air?

10 If air has a dew point of $50°$ F, what will be the relative humidity if the air is at a temperature of $95°$ F, $77°$ F, $68°$ F, and $50°$ F?

11 If air has a temperature of $20°$ C and the relative humidity is 52 per cent, approximately how much water will condense if the temperature is reduced to $0°$ C?

12 Which has the lower reading, the wet- or dry-bulb thermometer?

13 Under what conditions will the wet- and dry-bulb thermometer show large differences? Why?

14 Why must the air be circulated about the wet- and dry-bulb thermometer by a fan or by other methods?

15 The following readings were obtained with a sling psychrometer: dry-bulb reading 76° F, wet-bulb reading 63° F. What is the relative humidity? (Look up in tables.)

16 What would have been the relative humidity in the above problem if the wet-bulb had read 71° F?

17 What is the vapor pressure of the water at 76° F in problem 15?

18 What is the vapor pressure of the water at 76° F in problem 16?

PART 5   ELECTRICITY

CHAPTER XX

ELECTRIC AND MAGNETIC FIELDS

All materials are composed of many billions of atoms or combinations of atoms (molecules). According to present theories an atom consists of a *nucleus* surrounded by one or more *electrons*. The electrons of all atoms are similar in mass and charge. Relatively speaking, in terms of atomic mass, they are very light. They have associated with them the same amount of negative charge ($e = -4.80 \times 10^{-10}$ esu.).

The nucleus on the other hand is found to contain nearly all the mass of the atom and consists usually of two kinds of particles called *protons* and *neutrons*. These have practically the same mass, but the proton, which is identical with a hydrogen nucleus, carries a positive charge ($+e$, esu.) whereas the neutron has no resultant charge as far as one can tell from the experiments made with neutrons.

The electron is very mobile. Certain of the electrons are easily removed from some substances. On the other hand, positive charges, being associated with the mass of the nucleus, which is heavy compared to the electron, appear to be fairly immobile so far as experiments have shown.

ELECTRIC PROPERTIES OF MATERIALS

Consider a hard rubber rod which is rubbed with fur, or a glass rod which is rubbed with silk. The hard rubber takes on a negative charge because the fur loses electrons more easily than hard rubber does in the process of rubbing. The glass takes on a positive charge because it loses more electrons than it accumulates. The above substances are known as dielectrics (nonconductors) because a charge will not flow from one point to another through the material.

All substances may be charged as above. If conductors (i.e., metals) are to be charged, however, they must be insulated so that the charge will not leak off as fast as it is generated. Ebonite, hard rubber, sulfur, and dry air are examples of good insulators. Moist air, however, is a much better conductor than dry air and slowly conducts charges off metallic surfaces. Many experiments in electrostatics are partial or complete failures in damp weather. Moreover, the air becomes more conducting in the presence of sparks, radioactive compounds, lighted matches, etc., which serve to ionize the air.

The fundamental law governing the force between charges is *Coulomb's law.* * This law states that for like charges in empty space its force is one of repulsion and of amount

$$F = k\, \frac{q_1 q_2}{d^2} \tag{63}$$

where q_1 and q_2 represent electric charges (statcoulombs in the cgs system and coulombs in the mks system) and d their distance apart.

Since k is unity in empty space for the cgs system, a *unit charge* is defined as that positive charge which when placed 1 cm distance from another equal and like charge will repel it with a force of 1 dyne. In the mks system, the forces and distances are measured in newtons and meters respectively with $k = c^2 10^{-7}$ (page 297).

The region around an electric charge or system of charges is called an *electric field*. When charges or uncharged bodies are placed in this electric field, forces due to this field act on them. If the object or body which is placed in the electric field *is charged*, then there will be a reaction or force on this charge. If on the other hand the body which is placed in the electric field is an *uncharged* conductor then a redistribution of the free electrons will occur throughout the conductor so that opposite charges occur at the ends, resulting again in forces acting on these charges. If the conductor had been placed near a highly charged rod, the two forces which act in opposite directions will be unequal in magnitude and the conductor will be attracted toward the rod. Such charges in a conductor are called *induced charges*. Lastly if the body which is placed in a strong electric field is a nonconductor or dielectric such as for example glass, paper, mica, etc., it will also exhibit opposite charges at its ends. These

---

* In the rationalized mks system, k is written often as $k = 1/4\pi\epsilon_0 = c^2 10^{-7}$ ($= 9 \times 10^9$ approximately) where ϵ_0 is the rationalized empty space constant, the permittivity. For the normal mks system, $k = 1/\epsilon_0'$ where $\epsilon_0 = 1/4\pi k = \epsilon_0'/4\pi$.

charges are not due to the motion of free electrons throughout, but are produced by the slight distortion or separation of the charges in the neutral atoms constituting the dielectric. Such charges produced by *polarization* of the dielectric are noticeable only at the ends of the dielectric.

It is necessary to define and measure what is usually termed the *field intensity* or *strength of the electric field*. There are two ways in which an electric field E can be defined and measured. In the final analysis the two methods can be shown to be the same.

First, the field intensity at a point P (Fig. 123) is defined as the force which would act on a unit charge placed at the point in ques-

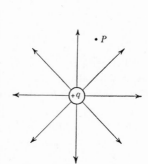

Fig. 123. Electric field.

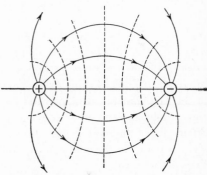

Fig. 124. Lines of force (solid) and equipotential lines (dotted) between two point charges.

tion. In order to find the strength of the electric field at all points in a certain region it would be necessary to put the unit charge at all these points and measure the force acting on it.

Secondly, the field intensity at any point P can also be defined in terms of the space rate at which a quantity, called the potential V, varies $\left(E_x = -\dfrac{\Delta V}{\Delta x} \right)$. From this definition it can be seen that a knowledge of the potential at all points in the field enables us to find the field intensity. This method is similar to the method used in geographical maps of representing the country by lines having equal elevations. These topographical maps show right away whether the country is fairly level or mountainous, and enable us to calculate the grade or steepness (corresponding to field intensity in the electrical case).

Lines of force are often drawn in the electric field. These are lines which show at all points through which they pass the direction of the electric field. They also represent the direction in which a positive unit charge will travel if allowed to do so, on account of the repulsion. The method of locating *equipotential lines or surfaces* is usually used for experimental determination of an electric field. Although the idea of locating the paths taken by unit charges in the field sounds very simple, it is experimentally very difficult to work with isolated point charges. An *equipotential line* or surface in an electric field is one of which every point has the same potential. Such lines or surfaces can be determined experimentally by making use of the fact that when two points in the electric field do not have the same potential, a potential difference exists between them, and under suitable conditions this will cause an electric current to flow. Having found a number of such equipotential lines, the direction of the electric field in this region can be determined by making use of the fact that the equipotential line and the electric field are at right angles to each other at every point in the field (see Fig. 124). Some idea of the relative magnitudes of the electric intensities at the various points in the field can be estimated from the closeness of the lines of force.

We will next analyze the effects produced by some electric charges. Consider, for instance, the electrophorus (Fig. 125), the

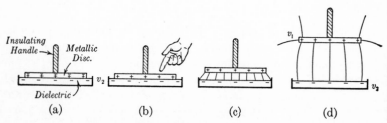

Fig. 125. Metallic disk charged by induction.

dielectric plate of which has been charged negatively by whipping with catskin or flannel. The metallic disk will have a positive charge induced on the under side when in "contact" (Fig. 125a) with the dielectric. A negative charge is induced on the upper side. The effect of the contact points of the disk along the dielectric is negligible, for these points are relatively few, and besides, charges in a dielectric are not conducted from point to point. The induced negative charge is allowed to flow to ground by touching the top of the metallic disk with the hand (Fig. 125b). Remove the hand and the metallic disk has left a positive charge (Fig. 125c). This is called *charging by induction.* Referring again to Figure 125b, we will call the potential v_2 of the metallic disk a "ground" potential. If the disk is raised slightly, as in Figure 125c the "lines" are stretched and

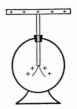

Fig. 126. Charged electroscope.

work is required to raise the disk. Moreover, it may be shown that these "lines" tend to separate from each other. That is, there is a "pressure," or force, at right angles to the lines tending to split the lines off from their present terminals. The higher the plate is raised, the more work it takes and the greater the number of lines split off, so that a large number of lines (Fig. 125d) will now terminate

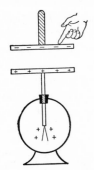

Fig. 127. Grounded metallic disk near a charged electroscope.

on other surrounding objects and the charge on the disk itself becomes less bound to the dielectric. This means that the potential of the disk is now raised to a value v_1. The difference in potential $(v_1 - v_2)$ is measured by the work done in raising the disk with a charge q from a potential v_2 to a potential v_1, i.e.,

$$W = q(v_1 - v_2), \qquad (64)$$

where W is expressed in joules when q and $(v_1 - v_2)$ are measured in the mks system.

By similar reasoning it may be shown that a body will hold a greater charge (i.e., its capacitance increased) for a given potential if another conducting body, usually well grounded, is brought near to it. This can be shown with the electroscope which has a metallic disk attached to it and charged as shown in Figure 126. The leaves diverge by an amount depending upon the charge given to the system. Now bring a grounded conductor such as a metallic disk (Fig. 127) into the vicinity of the electroscope. The leaves of the instrument come closer together, indicating that the potential is lowered. This means that the charge which the electroscope arrangement could hold, for a given potential, is increased.

MAGNETIC PROPERTIES OF MATERIALS

The magnetic properties of lodestone have been known for centuries. The Greeks called it *magnetite* (Fe_3O_4). It has the property of picking up iron filings and small pieces of iron. Later compasses were discovered and the magnetic nature of the earth was observed. Magnets have a north-seeking (N) and a south-seeking (S) pole. Like poles repel, while unlike poles attract.

The unit which is used in the experiment on magnetic poles described in this chapter is the so-called unit magnetic pole which forms the basis of the absolute electromagnetic system of units. Since the introduction of the practical system of units (mks) there has been a tendency to minimize the idea of magnetic poles as a starting point and rather derive and define magnetic effects in terms of the electric currents which are usually used in practical work to produce very strong magnetic fields. The emphasis in such cases is placed on the medium (such as air or iron) and the polarization produced in it by the magnetic field of the electric current. In this chapter we will think of the magnetic effect inside and outside the magnet as being a static phenomenon (magnetostatics), and think of the poles as regions where the lines of magnetic force originate or end. The early development of the subject of magnetism followed along these lines (see Coulomb's law) and the idea and definition of a unit pole is an essential part of the development of the absolute electromagnetic units.

The space surrounding a magnet is called the *magnetic field*. We can

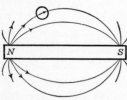

draw in this field *lines of force* which, in reality, are directions along which a positive (N) pole would travel if placed in the field. These lines of force may be located readily by means of iron filings or a small compass. The magnetic field near a magnet is shown in Figure 128. This field will change its characteristic pattern, at larger distances from the

Fig. 128. Magnetic field surrounding a bar magnet.

magnet, because of the effect of the earth's magnetic field. In fact, the earth's field itself may be distorted at any given position in a building because of the nearness of steel girders, steam pipes, and other iron or steel structures.

When a magnet is placed in a magnetic field (Fig. 129), there will be two points, P_1 and P_2, for which there will be no resultant field in any direction. Since a compass needle has no tendency to turn in any particular direction at such points, they are referred to as *neutral points*. Their positions will depend upon the direction of the magnet relative to the earth's field. The phenomenon is useful in determining the pole strength (m) of the magnet, knowing the strength of the earth's field.

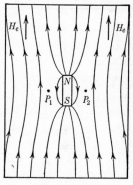

Fig. 129. Effect of the earth's field (cgs units).

The magnitude of the pole strength is based upon Coulomb's experimental law which states that if m_1 and m_2 represent the strength of two "isolated" poles of like sign, the force (F) of repulsion will be

$$F = \frac{k'}{\mu_r} \frac{m_1 m_2}{d^2}, \tag{65}$$

where d is the distance between them and μ_r is the relative permeability. The latter, for empty space, is unity in either the cgs or mks system.

In the cgs system, where k' is unity, a field intensity (H) is defined as the force in dynes which would act on a unit pole placed at same point P due to an isolated pole of strength m. That is, $H = m/d^2$ for empty space where d and H are measured in cm and in oersteds (dyne/pole) respectively.

The magnetic flux density (B), commonly used to measure field strengths in the mks system, will have a magnitude $B = k'm/d^2$, due to an isolated pole of strength m, where d is measured in meters and B has the dimensions of webers/m^2. The constant k' is equal to $1/10^7$. Its relationship to the often used permeabilities in empty space for the rationalized system (μ_0) and for the normal system (μ_0'), as an equation, is $k' = 1/10^7 = \mu_0/4\pi = \mu_0'$.

EXPERIMENT 32

ELECTROSTATICS

Methods of obtaining and detecting electric charges.

APPARATUS: Ebonite, sealing wax, glass rod, fur, flannel, silk, pith ball, two aluminum-covered pith balls, capacitor, electroscope with metallic disk attachment, electrophorus, electrostatic voltmeter (one is sufficient), stand with horizontal rod for suspending pith balls.

The *electroscope* (Fig. 130) is an instrument to detect (and measure) electric charges. It consists essentially of an insulated metal rod with very thin gold, or aluminum, leaves attached to the lower end. The rod is suspended in a metal container with glass windows by

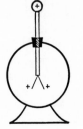

Fig. 130. Electroscope.

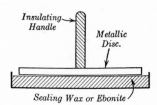

Fig. 131. Electrophorus.

means of the insulating plug, which may be made of ebonite (or better, of amber or sulfur).

The *electrostatic voltmeter* is a form of calibrated electroscope.

The *electrophorus* (Fig. 131) an instrument designed to obtain large charges, consists of a dielectric, usually inclosed in a metal dish, and a metallic disk with an insulating handle. The procedure in obtaining a charge on the metallic disk is as follows: The ebonite is charged negatively by whipping or rubbing with flannel or catskin. Bring the metallic disk down on the charged ebonite. The disk touches the ebonite in relatively few places, so that the metallic disk becomes charged by induction, positively on the lower side and negatively on the upper side. Touch the upper side with the hand for an instant. The negative charge becomes grounded. Remove the metallic disk. It is now charged positively. We say that the plate was charged positively by induction. All charging by induction is carried out in the above manner. If the metallic plate had been in contact at all points with the charged dielectric, the former would have become charged negatively by conduction.

Procedure For the most part, the data are to be recorded by transferring the diagrams to your data sheet, filled in with the correct sign of charge (i.e., + for positive and − for negative) and any other additional drawings to make the data sheet more complete. The experiment is to be done in parts as provided below.

Part (a) Charge the ebonite rod with fur. Bring the ebonite rod near bits of paper. If the paper is very dry it will probably be charged

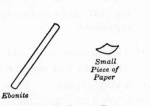

Ebonite

Small Piece of Paper

Fig. 132. Refer to Part (a) of the experiment.

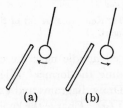

(a)　(b)

Fig. 133. Refer to Part (b) of the experiment.

by becoming polarized. In such a case it will be attracted and will stick to the rod. If, however, the paper is damp it will be attracted because of the induced charges, but the behaviour is very different once it touches the rod. Explain the behaviour in your experiment and indicate the nature of the charges on the bits of paper and rod (Fig. 132).

Part (b) A charged ebonite rod is brought near a suspended aluminum pith ball (Fig. 133a) and attracts it. After hitting the ebonite, it flies away (Fig. 133b). Fill in the proper signs of electric charges for Figure 133 (a) and 133 (b).

Part (c) Charge the electroscope negatively by conduction. Record nature of the electrification on figures as in Figure 134 (a), (b), and (c). Note that the position of the leaves of the electroscope as well as the nature of the charges in Figure 134 (a), (b), are left to the student to supply. Write in the kind of rod used and indicate its charge.

Part (d) Charge the electroscope positively by induction. Referring to Figure 135, record the results as above in part (c). Repeat part (d) in such a way as to charge the electroscope negatively by induction — record your results as before.

Part (e)   Charge the electroscope and place a lighted match near it. What happens?

Part (f)   Place the metallic disk attachment on the electroscope and charge the system negatively. Bring the metallic disk with

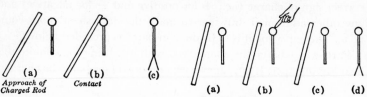

| Fig. 134. Refer to Part (c) of the experiment. | Fig. 135. Refer to Part (d) of the experiment. |

insulated handle near the charged electroscope with and without grounding the former* (Fig. 127). What do you observe in each case? Draw diagrams and explain, in your report.

Part (g)   Charge the knob of the Leyden jar (capacitor) by means of the charged metallic disk of the electrophorus, repeating until the capacitor has acquired a considerable charge. Bring the finger near the knob.

Part (h)   Discharge the charged metallic disk of the electrophorus once on the electrostatic voltmeter. Record the voltage obtained.

Questions

(a) How could you tell whether an unknown charge was positive or negative by means of an electroscope?

(b) Explain what happened in part (e) of the experiment.

(c) What is the cause of the result observed in part (f)?

(d) Why is the magnitude of voltage (see part (h)), which you have produced by means of the electrophorus, usually dangerous but not so in this experiment?

(e) Did you observe any other unusual results in part (a)? Explain.

* In order to keep the distance between the plates constant, while making the grounding test, it is desirable to place a *glass* plate on top of the plate on the electroscope. Then the second ungrounded metal plate is placed on this glass plate. After noting the deflection of the leaves of the electroscope the effect of grounding the plate will become evident.

EXPERIMENT 33

MAGNETIC FIELDS AND POLES

Part (a) *To determine the field about a magnet for a given direction of the poles.*

Part (b), (c) *To find the strength of the poles from the position of the neutral points.*

APPARATUS: Two bar magnets, two small magnetic compasses, two drawing boards, thumb tacks, large sheet of paper (about 12 x 15 inches), meter rule. It is desirable that each person should perform this experiment by himself if the apparatus is available.

Part (a) Determine, by means of a small compass needle, which is the north-south magnetic direction of the earth, at the particular location of your experiment. Place the long edge of the data sheet parallel to this direction and then tack the paper down upon a drawing board or table top. Determine, next, which is the north pole of your bar magnet and place the axis of the magnet parallel to the previously determined direction of the compass needle (consequently also parallel to the edge of the paper), so that the north pole of the bar magnet is in the same direction as the north pole of the compass needle (Fig. 136). When determining the north-south

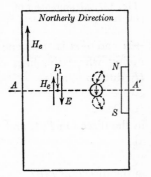

Fig. 136. Plotting lines of force (cgs units).

magnetic field of the earth by means of the compass needle, keep the bar magnet as far away as possible. Draw an outline of the magnet on the paper and also construct a line AA' bisecting the magnet at right angles. In order to plot some lines of force, place the small compass on AA' about one inch away from the magnet. Make dots with a sharp pencil at both ends of the compass needle. Now move the small compass so that the last dot falls at the one end of the needle and make another dot at the other end. Continue in this way, following up from the previous dot, until the magnet or the edge of the paper is reached. Having drawn a line of force through these points, plot other lines by starting at points two, three, four, five, and six inches away from the magnet. A non-magnetic (e.g., wooden) pencil should be used for this work. Plot the magnetic field for all the remaining unexplored regions by starting at the edges of the paper.

Part (b) It can be shown that the neutral point P_1 will lie on the line AA'. It must satisfy the condition that the earth's field H_e must

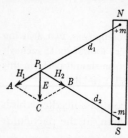

Fig. 137. Measurement of pole strength (cgs units).

be just equal in magnitude to the field E of the magnet. Consequently the resultant field at P_1 is zero. This point P_1 can be quite accurately located by moving the small compass needle back and forth along AA'. The needle will turn around after passing through the neutral point.

To find the pole strength, consider the neutral point P_1 to have been found (Fig. 137). If there are no secondary poles, the distance from P_1 to the poles $+m$ and $-m$ is the same. The position of each pole is found by noting where the lines of force converge.* The field intensity H_1 due to $+m$ is

$$H_1 = \frac{m}{d_1{}^2}$$

in the direction P_1A, and the field intensity due to $-m$ is

$$H_2 = \frac{m}{d_2{}^2}$$

in the direction P_1B.

Now the magnitude of H_1 is equal to the magnitude of H_2. The distance d_1 (or d_2) can be measured, so that the magnitude of m may be calculated if H_1 can be found. The resultant field due to H_1 and H_2 we will call E. For the neutral point P_1 it is E which is equal and opposite to the earth's magnetic field H_e.

To find H_1, construct a parallelogram as in Figure 137, where P_1C is drawn parallel to the magnet so that 1 cm represents† 0.1 dyne

---

* If mks units are to be used, replace $H_1 = m/d_1{}^2$ with $B_1 = m/10^7 d_1{}^2$, $H_2 = m/d_2{}^2$ with $B_2 = m/10^7 d_2{}^2$, and E with B. The resultant magnetic flux density (B) will be equal and opposite to B_e due to the earth. If $H_e = 0.2$ dynes/pole, then $B_e = 0.2 \times 10^{-4}$ weber/m^2.

† The scale chosen should be such as to make the parallelogram as large as possible and still be able to draw it on the sheet.

of force. Look up in a handbook the horizontal intensity for the earth's magnetic field for your locality. If it is 0.2 dyne per unit pole, then make P_1C two centimeters in length. From P_1 continue the line drawn from $+m$ to P_1, and from C draw a line parallel to the one from $-m$ to P_1. These two lines intersect at A. The line AP_1 represents the magnitude of H_1, each centimeter of length representing 0.1 dyne. Calculate the pole strength from the relation,

$$m = H_1 d_1^2.$$

Part (c) Another way in which the magnetic pole strength of the magnet can be determined is by finding the neutral points along the longitudinal axis of the magnet. In this case the magnet must be arranged so that the $N - S$ axis points in the direction of the earth's horizontal intensity with the S pole of the magnet pointing north (see Fig. 138). For this case the field E of the magnet at the neutral point which balances the earth's horizontal

field is $\dfrac{m}{d^2} - \dfrac{m}{(d + l)^2}$.

Hence $\qquad E = H_e$

or $\quad H_e = \dfrac{m}{d^2} - \dfrac{m}{(d + l)^2}$

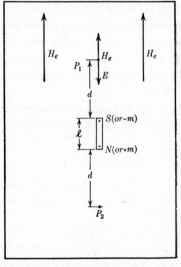

Fig. 138. Position of neutral points when magnet is reversed (cgs).

Assuming that H_e is known in this region it is possible to calculate m since d and l can be measured. Compare this value with that found for the same quantity in part (b).

Questions

(a) In what way would secondary poles affect your result for the pole strength? Draw a magnet with secondary poles.

(b) Does P_1C (Fig. 137) represent the resultant field due to the magnet or the field due to the earth?

(c) What is the resultant field intensity at point P_1 in part (b)?

(d) Will there be any neutral points if a magnet is placed at right angles to the earth's field?

PROBLEMS

Experiment 32

1   State two definitions for field intensity at a point.

2   What kind of charges are actually transferred, as far as we know, when two dissimilar substances are rubbed together?

3   What is meant by the terms charging a body by (1) conduction, (2) induction? What is meant by polarization of a dielectric?

4   What is meant by an electric field?

5   State Coulomb's law in words and by formula.

6   What is meant by (1) difference in potential, (2) field intensity?

7   What is the field intensity at a distance of 10 cm from a charge of 400 esu?

8   Two pith balls, each with the same charge q, and each weighing 0.1 g, are suspended from the same point by strings of 100 cm in length. Find the magnitude of the charge on each if they are separated by a distance of 5 cm.

Experiment 33

1   If magnetism is a molecular property of iron, how would you expect heat or hammering (in general) to affect the piece of steel which has been magnetized?

2   Can magnetic poles be isolated?

3   What would be the magnetic field intensity at a point on the longitudinal axis of a bar magnet at a distance of 20 cm from one end? The poles are at the very end of the bar which has a length of 4 cm. Consider the strength of each pole to be 40 electromagnetic units.

4   Suppose the poles of the last problem were at the very ends of a magnet of length 50 cm. What would be the error introduced if the far pole were neglected in the calculation of the field intensity?

5   The neutral point is found to be on the perpendicular bisector of a magnet at a distance from each end of the magnet just equal to its length. Assume that the magnetic poles are at the ends, that the length of the magnet is 10 cm, and the earth's horizontal magnetic flux density is 0.2×10^{-4} weber/m^2. Calculate the pole strength of the magnet.

CHAPTER XXI

THE MEASUREMENT OF RESISTANCE AND SIMPLE CIRCUITS

Whenever a charge flows through a conductor we speak of an *electric current* and define it as the rate of flow of charge past any cross section of the conductor. Hence,

$$I = \frac{\Delta q}{\Delta t}$$

where Δq is the charge and Δt the time taken for this charge to flow past. If the current is constant, we can simply write $I = q/t$.

The analogy between electric current and rate of flow of water in a pipe (for example in cubic feet per second) is seen to be a very close one. In the case of water some driving force is necessary before the water flows. This is usually supplied by a pump or by having a difference in level (potential energy) between the two ends of the pipe. The same is true in the flow of electric current. A potential difference e is necessary before the current flows.

Now it is found that the potential difference existing between the two ends of a conductor is directly proportional to the current flowing through this conductor, all other conditions remaining the same. Hence we can state that

$$V \alpha I$$

The proportionality sign can be replaced by a sign of equality if we put in a constant and write:

$$V = RI$$

where R is now a constant for the conductor and called its resistance. This equation was first stated by G. S. Ohm and is known as *Ohm's law*.

In the practical system of units we measure the potential difference in *volts*, the current in *amperes*, and the resistance in *ohms*. The relation between these and the fundamental units (emu) will be found in college physics texts and need not be given here.

Ohm's law was extended by Kirchhoff to take into account the continuity of the currents and the potential difference relations in any arrangement of conductors that may arise in practice. These relations are put in the form of two laws, known as Kirchhoff's laws of electric circuits. *

Kirchhoff's first law: The algebraic sum of all currents meeting at a point is zero. This means that at any point in an electric circuit there is as much current flowing away from the point as towards it.

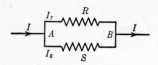

Fig. 139. Currents flowing through resistances in parallel.

Kirchhoff's second law: In any closed circuit the algebraic sum of the products of the current and resistance of each part of the circuit is equal to the applied electromotive force in that circuit.

As an example of the use of these two laws, consider a case which often occurs in practical work. Let us find the current through one branch when two resistors are connected in parallel. This case is shown in Figure 139. Call the currents flowing into a point +, and the currents flowing out −. Then for the point A the first law gives:

$$+I - I_s - I_r = 0$$

or

$$I = I_s + I_r. \tag{66}$$

Next we shall consider the closed circuit $ASBR$ and apply the second law of Kirchhoff. There is no applied electromotive force in this circuit. Let us go around in a counterclockwise direction, starting at B. Then the second law gives

$$+RI_r - SI_s = 0,$$

and hence

$$I_r = \frac{SI_s}{R}.$$

Substituting this value of I_r in (66), we get

$$I = I_s\left(1 + \frac{S}{R}\right) = I_s\left(\frac{R+S}{R}\right),$$

or finally,

$$I_s = I\left(\frac{R}{R+S}\right). \tag{67}$$

There is a Kirchhoff's law of heat radiation.

This result is used so often that it is well to remember it as follows: *When a current enters two branches connected in parallel, the current through one branch (say S) equals the main current (I) multiplied by the resistance of the other branch (R) and divided by the total resistance of both branches* (R + S).

These two laws of Kirchhoff are very general, and enable us to solve practically any case that may arise. A very frequent application consists in finding the current in a branch of a complicated network of wires when a certain electromotive force is applied to the network. Suppose we have a simple circuit with several resistors, having resistances R_1, R_2, R_3, etc., in series. Then by use of these laws we can show that as far as the current is concerned these resistors behave as if we had a resistor in the circuit with resistance R, where R equals $R_1 + R_2 + R_3$, etc. When these resistors are connected in parallel, then it can be shown that the equivalent resistance R has a value such that

$$\frac{1}{R} = \frac{1}{R_1} + \frac{1}{R_2} + \frac{1}{R_3} + \cdots$$

METHODS USED IN THE MEASUREMENT OF RESISTANCE

In practical work, currents and potential differences are usually measured directly with instruments made for the purpose. These instruments, we have seen, are called ammeters and voltmeters and their indications give us the result directly. For most commercial work these readings have the necessary accuracy. Other more complicated methods must be resorted to if the accuracy so obtained is not sufficient.

The measurement of resistance, however, is not quite so simple and direct. We shall discuss here only measurement of resistances of such magnitude as are commonly found in practice.

These values might range from 0.01 ohm to 100,000 ohms. For values beyond these two limits, that is, larger than 100,000 ohms and less than 0.01 ohm, the accurate methods are considerably more complicated, require an exceptional amount of skill, and, in the case of extremely high resistances, require a technique all their own.

The simplest way of measuring a resistance is the *volt-ammeter method*. The principle of the method consists simply in measuring the current through the resistor, and the potential difference existing at the terminals. Then applying Ohm's law in the form: $R = \dfrac{V}{I}$, we find the resistance. The difficulty comes when we measure V and I. Using a voltmeter, as in Figure 140 (a), we note that the

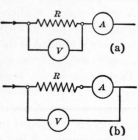

Fig. 140. Volt-ammeter method of measuring resistance.

voltmeter reads the potential difference across R, but the ammeter reads the current through both R and V. We want the current only through R. However, the current through V in Figure 140 (a) becomes relatively less important the larger the resistance of V relative to R. Hence, assuming we are given a voltmeter V having a fixed resistance (say 100 ohms per volt), the smaller the resistance of R the more accurate our result will be.

If we connect the voltmeter and ammeter as shown in Figure 140 (b), we find that the ammeter reads the correct current through R, but the voltmeter now measures the potential difference, not only across R, but across A also. In this case, therefore, the smaller the potential drop across the ammeter A relative to the potential difference across R, the more accurate our result. Hence R should have a relatively high resistance value compared to the resistance of the ammeter. Usually of course the ammeter has a fixed resistance of fairly low value (say 0.01 ohm or less), and hence the method is quite accurate for resistances from 10 ohms up.

It can be shown* that the dividing line between methods (a) or (b) occurs at a value $R = \sqrt{R_v R_a}$, where R_v is the resistance of the voltmeter and R_a is the resistance of the ammeter. Hence for resistors having a resistance less than this value of R, use the method shown in Figure 140 (a), and for resistors with resistances larger than this use the method of Figure 140 (b). With caution, therefore, the volt-ammeter method can be made to give fairly accurate results. Its main advantage of course is its simplicity.

The Wheatstone bridge   The method used for all accurate measurement of the resistance, in the range under discussion, is

* A. W. Smith, *Electrical Measurements in Theory and Application*, p. 23, Fourth Edition, McGraw Hill Book Company Inc., 1948.

the *Wheatstone bridge method*. The method finds its application in various forms of apparatus having entirely different appearances. The principle of the balanced Wheatstone bridge network, however, can be traced in each one. Consider the arrangement of resistors as shown in Figure 141. The current entering at *a* splits into two parts, one part going along *ad* and the other along *ab*. The branch *db* is connected to the circuit at *d* and *b*. If a current is to flow through *db*, then there must exist a potential difference between *d* and *b*. If, then, we say that there is no current flowing between *d* and *b* (a fact which we can easily determine by noting whether the

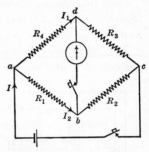

Fig. 141. Wheatstone bridge network.

galvanometer in this circuit shows no deflection), we can reason conversely and say that no potential difference exists between the points *d* and *b*. This does not mean that the potentials of the points *d* and *b* are zero — they will not be — it simply means that they are the same.

Consider then the two paths for the main battery current, viz., *adc* and *abc*. The potential of *a* is common to both, and we have seen that *b* and *d* have the same potential; hence the potential drop from *a* to *d* must equal the potential drop from *a* to *b*. Hence,

$$R_4 I_1 = R_1 I_2. \tag{68}$$

and similarly,

$$R_3 I_1 = R_2 I_2. \tag{69}$$

This, of course, is only true if no current flows from *d* to *b* or, in other words, if the bridge is balanced. Eliminating I_2 and I_1 from equations (68) and (69), we get,

$$\frac{R_1}{R_2} = \frac{R_4}{R_3}. \tag{70}$$

Now if we had one resistor whose resistance was unknown (say $R_4 = X$), and knew the other three values, then we could find the unknown X by the relation $R_4 = X = R_3 \left(\dfrac{R_1}{R_2}\right)$.

Usually the battery and galvanometer are interchangeable in their relative positions, but if the values of the resistances are very different, say R_1 and R_4 very large, and R_2 and R_3 very small, then the galvanometer should be connected between the points joining the two higher and the two lower resistors.

Only two common forms of apparatus will be described, although from this description one should be able to use any other form, the similarity in their use being extremely close.

The slide wire bridge (meter bridge)   Essentially this form consists of a uniform wire exactly one meter in length stretched along or above a meter rule. The

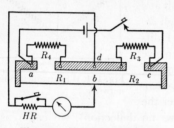

Fig. 142. Slide wire bridge.

ends of this wire are soldered to heavy copper or brass pieces shown shaded in the diagram of Figure 142.

A slider which can make contact on the wire is so arranged that its position can be read on the scale. The two parts of the wire form two arms of the

bridge. The other two resistors are inserted by means of binding posts at R_3 and R_4. By tracing through the remaining connections, one will see the exact analogy between this and the Wheatstone bridge. The student should do this so as to be able to write down the conditions for the balance. In using such a bridge, the unknown is inserted at, say R_4, a variable standard resistance box being connected in at R_3. Balance is then obtained by moving the slider until the galvanometer reads zero. Then assuming that the wire has constant resistance per unit length,

$$R_4 = X = R_3 \left(\frac{R_1}{R_2}\right) = R_3 \frac{l_1}{l_2},$$

where l_1 and l_2 are the distances between slider and the two ends of the wire.

Although this form of apparatus is very simple to understand and use, there are several possibilities of a considerable error being introduced when accuracy is required. First, we have neglected the effects of the end pieces to which the wire has been soldered. These should be included in the balance condition. The bar resistance from d to R_3 and R_4 has also been neglected. Further, the wires may not be soldered exactly at the 0 and 100 division marks on the scale. (This is very difficult to accomplish in practice.)

Other errors which need consideration when accurate resistance measurements are to be made with slide wire resistance bridges concern the nonuniformity of the wire. Even if the wire was originally uniform it will lose its uniformity with use, because contact must be made on the wire. In a well-designed bridge, contacts are made so as to deform the wire as little as possible.

Thermal effects due to the heating of the several parts of the wire and bridge components cause changes in resistance, and thermal electromotive forces at the connections in the bridge are difficult to find and overcome. As a precaution against thermoelectric effects the battery terminals are often reversed so as to send the current through the bridge in the opposite direction and the measurements of R repeated. The average R is taken as the true resistance. In other arrangements of slide wire bridges provision is made to interchange the standard and unknown resistors in the bridge arms without making any other changes. Such improvements add several complications to the slide-wire bridge method and are beyond the scope of this text.

STANDARD RESISTORS

In the case of standard resistors, where permanence and accuracy are paramount, great precaution must be exercised to see that the principles to be mentioned are carefully considered and taken into account.

It is important that the resistors used have a small temperature effect, i.e., the temperature coefficient of resistance be very small. The resistance wire used should also have a high resistivity or specific resistance so as to economize in bulk and cost.

It is found that various alloys of copper-nickel, etc., can be made to have high resistivity. It has been a difficult matter, however, to find alloys which have at the same time a low temperature coefficient. For example, German silver, which is an alloy of copper, zinc, and nickel, has high resistivity but an objectionable high temperature coefficient. The most satisfactory material at present for use in the construction of standard resistors is *manganin*, an alloy of copper, nickel, and manganese. This material has a very low temperature coefficient and high resistivity. It has, however, another very important property which has not been mentioned before — its thermoelectric electromotive force between it and copper or brass is very small. When we connect a resistance box with binding posts into a circuit, we do not wish to introduce bothersome thermal electromotive forces which would have to be allowed for. On account of this, such materials as German silver and constantan are not desirable for use in electrical measuring circuits.

Finally, great care and ingenuity must be exercised in the mounting of resistances. The calibration should be permanent. Temperature must not distort the forms on which the wires are wound so as to strain the material. Humidity and dust should not affect the insulation between coils, and, in the case of highest precision, provision must be made to keep the coils at a constant known temperature.

The student is referred to other more advanced texts on electrical measurements* for a detailed description of the methods used in mounting resistance coils. The methods used in varying the resistances are of two types: plug or dial. In the use of such standard resistors the student should not employ brute force on the plugs or dials. Insert or remove plugs with a slight twisting motion, pressing down gently while so doing.

EXPERIMENT 34

MEASUREMENT OF THE RESISTANCE OF RESISTORS IN SERIES AND PARALLEL

(AMMETER—VOLTMETER METHOD)

Part (a)   *To calculate the resistance of single resistors by the ammeter-voltmeter method.*

Part (b)   *To measure the resistance of three resistors connected in series.*

Part (c)   *To measure the resistance of three resistors connected in parallel.*

Part (d)   *To determine how the resistance of a tungsten lamp changes with increment of filament current. Optional.*

APPARATUS: Parts (a), (b), and (c)   Block with 3 unequal resistors (10–20 ohms) and 6 terminal posts, storage battery (6 v), d-c ammeter (0–1.5 amp), d-c voltmeter (0–10 v).

---

* See F. A. Laws, *Electrical Measurements*.   McGraw Hill Book Company Inc., N. Y., 1917.

Part (d) Fifty-watt tungsten bulb in screw socket with terminals, rheostat (0–2000 ohms, 1 amp), switch, ammeter (0–1.5 amp), voltmeter (0–150 v). (Note that this part of the experiment can also be performed satisfactorily with a 6–8 v flashlight bulb and suitable instruments.)

Part (a) The block with the three resistors is shown in Figure 143 (a). To obtain the resistance of any one of the resistors R_n (where n = 1, 2, or 3), connect the battery B, ammeter A and one resistor (n = 1) as shown in Figure 143 (b). *Leave one of the wires leading to the battery unconnected until the circuit has been inspected by the instructor.* Since the voltmeter is not connected permanently into the circuit, its position relative to the resistor is shown dotted. If you are given test prods with leads, connect the lead terminals to the voltmeter and test for potential drops as needed by use of the prod tips. Notice the positive and negative designations on the meters and the

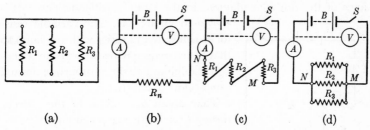

(a) (b) (c) (d)

Fig. 143. Resistances which can be connected in series or parallel.

battery terminals, and connect the positive battery terminal to the positive terminals of the meters. *After the circuit has been inspected*, close the switch and read both meters as accurately as you can, estimating to tenths of the smallest division. Then open the switch to save the battery. Express the current in amperes, and the potential difference in volts, and solve for the resistance (in ohms) by means of the equation $R_n = V/I$. Repeat and check your values.

Without disturbing the rest of the circuit, replace the resistor by each of the other two in turn and find the magnitude of each in the same way.

Part (b) Disconnect the circuit of part (a) by *removing the battery connections first*, so that all the wires shall be dead while changes are being made, and set up the circuit shown in Figure 143 (c), again leaving one side of the battery unconnected until the circuit is inspected. In this case the three resistors are connected in series. Read both meters and then use Ohm's law again to find the resistance of the part of the circuit included between M and N. Compute the per cent error from the mean between this value and the sum of the resistances already obtained for the three coils.

Part (c) Disconnect the circuit, beginning at the batteries, and set up as shown in Figure 143 (d), again leaving one battery terminal unconnected until the circuit is inspected. Read the two meters, and by the equation $R = V/I$, find the resistance of the part of the circuit between M and N. Note that the three coils are in parallel. Check this value by computing the resistance of the three in parallel by the equation, $\frac{1}{R} = \frac{1}{R_1} + \frac{1}{R_2} + \frac{1}{R_3}$, and find the per cent error from the mean between the results.

Part (d)   The electric circuit for the determination of the resistance of the tungsten filament in the lamp at different currents is

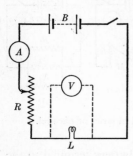

Fig. 144. Resistance of a tungsten lamp. Ammeter-voltmeter method.

shown in Figure 144. The variable resistor R is inserted in series with the lamp so that the current may be varied from a negligible minimum to the appropriate normal rate of flow of electricity.

Take about 6 readings of the current through, as well as the potential difference across the lamp, and calculate its resistance for each current. Since the temperature of the filament is different the values of the resistance will also change. Plot a curve with current as ordinates and resistance as abscissas. Estimate the resistance of the lamp for no current from your graph. Check this value with a resistance measurement on this lamp by means of a Wheatstone bridge using very small currents.

Questions

(a) A 110-volt flatiron of 11 ohms resistance and a 110-v electric lamp of 100 ohms are connected in series to a 110-v line. A shock is received if the hand is placed across the terminals of the electric lamp, but not if placed across the terminals of the flatiron. Why?

(b) What is the approximate per cent change in resistance of the bulb above its value for zero current when the current has reached (1) $\frac{1}{8}$ normal current, (2) $\frac{1}{6}$ normal current, (3) $\frac{1}{4}$ normal current, (4) $\frac{1}{2}$ normal current, (5) $\frac{3}{4}$ normal current, (6) normal current?

(*Note.* Assume that the current through the lamp when placed directly across the line is the normal current. Consult the instructor if in doubt. The resistance increases rapidly above $\frac{1}{6}$ to $\frac{1}{4}$ normal current. If your meters are insensitive to small currents, your instructor may wish to give you the resistance of the bulb when negligible current is passing through the bulb.)

(c) A carbon lamp decreases in resistance with rise of temperature. Compare its prospects of failure with a tungsten filament when both are placed in an overvoltage home circuit.

EXPERIMENT 35

KIRCHHOFF'S LAWS

Part (a)   *To check the first law involving currents.*
Part (b)   *To check the second law concerning potential drops.*
Part (c)   *To calculate resistance using Ohm's law.*

APPARATUS: A board containing a network of resistors similar to that shown in the diagram (Fig. 145). A source of electric power — for example a 6-volt storage battery or 110-volt d-c power line, etc., ammeter, voltmeter.

The resistors forming the network are shown in the diagram (Fig. 145). The seven resistors L_1, $L_2 \cdots L_7$, are connected to-

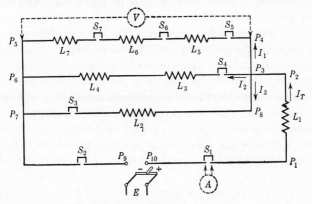

Fig. 145. A Kirchhoff's law board.

gether when the short-circuiting bars or switches (S) are inserted. E represents a source of electric power.

Precaution: In this experiment a voltmeter and an ammeter will be used. Great care must be exercised in the proper and safe use of these instruments (see Chapter XXXIV, p. 423). Remember that the voltmeter measures the potential difference *between* the two points to which it is connected. It has, therefore a high resistance so that when it is connected to any two points of the circuit the current flowing will not change appreciably. On the other hand, the ammeter is used to measure the current flowing *in* the circuit. The circuit must therefore be opened at the point where one wishes to measure the current, and the ammeter inserted so that the same current will now flow through the ammeter. This requires that a good ammeter have negligible resistance so that the current will not be changed appreciably. By removing any of the short-circuiting links S_1, $S_2 \cdots S_7$ the circuit can be opened at this point and an ammeter inserted instead of the link. Be sure that the range on the ammeter is the correct one. (Check with the instructor about this). Never make any changes in the circuit without first opening the switch at E.

For example, in order to measure the current I_T which is flowing into the board, the ammeter is connected at the insert S_1 as shown in the figure. The bar is removed from the insert and replaced by the ammeter so that any current which flows in this part of the circuit must flow through the ammeter. The instructor may wish to provide the ammeter with specially prepared leads and contacts for use across the switches.

As a further example, to measure the voltage difference which exists between the points P_4 and P_5 it is necessary to connect the voltmeter terminals to those points as shown. Or if the voltage drop across a single resistor is desired, connect the voltmeter across the resistor terminals. Cords with long-handled tips will be provided for making voltmeter connections. The cords are connected permanently to the voltmeter. Contact of the tips with the circuit is made wherever the difference of potential is desired. First touch the terminals lightly and reverse the prods if the meter reads backwards.

In most cases the side of higher potential ($+$) in the circuit to be measured is known by referring to the $+$ and $-$ terminals of the source of power. The + terminal of the voltmeter must be connected to the higher potential (+) in the circuit whose voltage is to be measured.

Part (a) **1** To show that the current flowing *from* the board is equal to the current flowing *to* the board, one first measures the current at insert S_1, and then at insert S_2

$$\text{Current input } (S_1) \quad = \quad \quad \text{amp}$$
$$\text{Current output } (S_2) = \quad \quad \text{amp}$$

Part (a) **2** To show that the current everywhere in a single series circuit is the same, place the ammeter successively in inserts S_5, S_6 and S_7

$$I_5 = \quad \quad \text{amp}$$
$$I_6 = \quad \quad \text{amp}$$
$$. \; I_7 = \quad \quad \text{amp}$$

Part (a) **3** Measure I_T by placing the ammeter at insert S_1 as before. Then measure I_3, I_2, and I_1 by placing the ammeter successively in inserts S_3, S_4, and S_5

$$I_1 = \quad \text{amp}$$
$$I_2 = \quad \text{amp} \qquad I_T = \quad \quad \text{amp}$$
$$I_3 = \quad \text{amp}$$
$$\overline{\text{Sum} = \quad \text{amp}}$$

Why do parts (a) 2 and (a) 3 check the validity of Kirchhoff's first law?

Part (b) **1** To check the voltage relationships: The total voltage drop from P_4 to P_5 should be equal to the sum of the individual voltage drops along the path from P_4 to P_5. Measure the individual voltage drops across the resistances by placing the voltmeter terminals successively across the terminals of each resistor. Designate the voltage drop across the resistor L_5 by V_{L_5} and use a similar notation for the others. Thus:

$$V_{L_5} = \quad \text{volts}$$
$$V_{L_6} = \quad \text{volts} \qquad V_{P_4P_5} = \quad \quad \text{volts}$$
$$V_{L_7} = \quad \text{volts}$$
$$\overline{\text{Sum} = \quad \text{volts}}$$

Part (b) **2** Show also that if the voltmeter terminals are connected at two points between which the resistance is very low there is practically no voltage difference although the current flowing from one of these points to the other may be large. Thus the voltage drop:

$$V_{P_3P_4} = \qquad \text{volts}$$

even though the current I_1 as measured in part (a) 3 was shown to be $I_1 = \qquad$ amp.

Part (b) 3 Thus it makes no difference in our electric circuit whether the parallel circuit is supplied by a wire from P_2 to P_3 or from P_2 to P_8 or from P_2 to P_4. The student should prove this to his own satisfaction by inserting the ammeter at several different places and then noting any difference in its reading as the supply wire is changed from P_3 to P_8 or to P_4.

Part (b) 4 As in part (b) 1, measure:

$V_{L_4} =$	volts	$V_{P_6P_3} =$	volts
$V_{L_3} =$	volts	$V_{P_8P_7} =$	volts
$V_{L_2} =$	volts	$V_{L_1} =$	volts

Then compare $V_{P_4P_5}$ with $V_{P_3P_6}$ and $V_{P_8P_7}$

Part (b) 5 We will next check Kirchhoff's second law, starting at any point such as P_2, around the closed circuit $P_2P_3P_4P_5P_6P_7$-$P_9P_{10}P_1P_2$. Measure the voltage drops as you go around the circuit being sure to keep straight the "direction" of the voltage drops in each case. The algebraic sum should be zero. Thus:

$V_{P_2P_3} =$	volts	$V_{P_5P_6} =$	volts
$V_{P_3P_4} =$	volts	$V_{P_6P_9} =$	volts
$V_{L_5} =$	volts	$V_{P_9P_{10}} = E =$	volts (watch sign)
$V_{L_6} =$	volts	$V_{P_{10}P_1} =$	volts
$V_{L_7} =$	volts	$V_{P_1P_2} =$	volts
		Algebraic sum $=$	volts

Part (c) 1 Ohm's law may be used to find the values of the resistances. This law states that $V = IR$, where R (in ohms) represents the resistance of that part of the circuit across which the potential difference is V volts, and in which a current I amperes is flowing. Designate the resistance of L_5 by R_{L_5} etc., and from the values of V and I determine

$R_{L_5} =$	ohms		
$R_{L_6} =$	ohms	$R_{P_4P_5} =$	ohms
$R_{L_7} =$	ohms		
Sum $=$			

In the same way determine R_{L_2}, R_{L_3}, R_{L_4}, R_{L_1}

Questions

(a) Show that Kirchhoff's first law applies to the currents flowing at the following points: P_6, P_7, P_3. Use the current values determined in part (a).

(b) Relate Ohm's law and Kirchhoff's law for the circuit $V_{P_3P_6}R_{L_2}$.

(c) Show that Kirchhoff's second law can be verified for the following circuits: $P_3P_4P_5P_6P_3$ and $P_1P_2P_3P_8P_7P_9P_{10}P_1$.

(d) Using the values found for the resistances in part (c) 1, determine the total effective resistance of the circuit.

(e) From the measured value of E as determined in part (b) 5 and the effective resistance of the whole circuit as determined in question (d), calculate the value of I_T. Compare this with the measured value in part (a) 1.

(f) What effect does the resistance of the ammeter have on $V_{P_1P_2}$ and $V_{P_3P_6}$ when it is inserted at S_4?

(g) Do your experimental results check Kirchhoff's two laws within what you estimate to be the experimental error? If not, what explanation have you?

EXPERIMENT 36

MEASUREMENT OF RESISTANCE WITH A SLIDE WIRE WHEATSTONE BRIDGE

Part (a) *To measure the resistance of several resistors with a slide wire bridge.*

Part (b) *To check as accurately as the apparatus will allow the laws of combination of resistances.*

APPARATUS: A slide wire bridge, a standard plug or dial type variable resistance box, galvanometer of medium sensitivity, a battery or other source of electromotive force, single-contact key, protective resistor for the galvanometer circuit (10,000 ohms), short-circuiting switch.

Part (a) Connect up the slide wire bridge as shown in figure 142. If there are to be any variations from this circuit consult the instructor. One of the unknowns should be connected at R_4. The resistance value of the standard resistor R_3 should be so chosen as to bring the balance point on the slide wire somewhere near the middle (or anywhere in the middle third) of its length. When making the first attempts at finding the balance point proceed as follows: Make a guess at the resistance value. If you have had no experience with resistance wires have the instructor help you in making this guess. Set the value of the standard resistance R_3 somewhere near the value of your guess. Be sure that the current through the galvanometer also flows through the protective resistor. This of course means that the short-circuiting switch across HR must *not* be closed. Now close the battery key and then the galvanometer circuit key. This latter should be closed very lightly and only long enough to see in which direction the galvanometer starts to deflect. For this test, the slider should have been set somewhere near the middle of the slide wire scale. Next increase or decrease R_3 until the galvanometer starts to deflect in the opposite direction. By this means the value R_3 can be determined so that when the key is held down and the slider is moved along the middle third of the wire there will be a point for which there will be no deflection of the galvanometer. After this approximate setting the final adjustment of the slide is made when HR is short-circuited, and the galvanometer circuit then has the greatest sensitivity to an unbalance in the arms of the bridge.

Measure the resistance (X) of each unknown resistor three times by using three different values for R_3 and then repeat the measurement by interchanging the position of R_3 and X in the arms of the bridge. Average all six readings to find the unknown X and calculate the per cent error. Read positions on the slide wire as accurately as you can. In the same manner determine the resistance of the other unknown resistors. As an added precaution, close the battery circuit only long enough to make the measurements, so that the currents do not heat the resistors more than necessary. Put your data in neat tabular form. Label all data carefully so as not to get the ratio upside down when interchanging R_3 and X.

Part (b)   Connect either two or three resistors in series or in parallel (depending upon the wishes of the instructor) and measure the total resistance of the combination using exactly the method outlined in part (a). This means finding an average of several readings.

Next calculate from the values as determined in part (a) what the resistance of the series or parallel combination should be. Compare this calculated value with the value determined experimentally in part (b) and determine the per cent error from the mean.

Questions

(a) Why is it desirable to have the balance point in the middle third of the wire?

(b) Why does the value of $H\,R$ not affect the balance point?

(c) Discuss some factors which concern the magnitude of the error found in performing part (b) of the experiment.

(d) Would there by any advantage in increasing the length of the wire by a factor of two?

PROBLEMS

Experiment 34

1 Three resistors, each of 15 ohms, are connected so as to give a resultant resistance of 5, 22.5, and 45 ohms. How are they connected? Draw diagrams to represent the connections.

2 How much current will flow through three 30-ohm resistors connected in (a) series, (b) parallel? Assume a 120-v d-c line.

3 How many 10-ohm flatirons can be used as the same time in a house furnished with power at 100 v and fused with a 25-amp fuse?

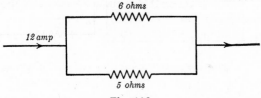

Fig. 146.

4 Thyrite is a trade name for a nonlinear resistance material made of compressed silicon carbide with a suitable binder. Its resistance varies as a power of the applied voltage. The instantaneous current I passed by the thyrite may be expressed as $I = KV^n$, where V is the potential difference and K is a constant expressing the amperes at one volt. If $I = 4 \times 10^{-6}$ amperes at one volt for a certain thyrite resistor, plot the current versus potential difference for voltages of 1, 5, 10, 15, and 20. Assume that n has a value of 5. (In practice, $3.5 < n < 7$.) What is the resistance for each of these voltages? What are some of the uses for nonlinear resistors?

Experiment 35

1 A battery has an internal resistance of 0.04 ohm and an electromotive force (i.e., the potential difference between the terminals when no current is drawn from the battery) of 1.50 v. A radio tube operating on 1.1 v and requiring a current of 0.25 amp is to be operated with this battery. How much resistance must be put in the circuit (usually done with a so-called rheostat) so that the tube will just be operating under the required condition? What is the resistance of the radio tube?

2   Given two parallel circuits as shown in Figure 146. Calculate the current through each branch, using first Kirchhoff's laws and secondly the rule as given in this chapter for two parallel circuits. Calculate also the total resistance.

3   In the network shown in Figure 147, calculate the total resistance and also the current that the battery has to furnish.

4   Apply Kirchhoff's laws to Figure 148 and find the current flowing through each 7-ohm resistor.

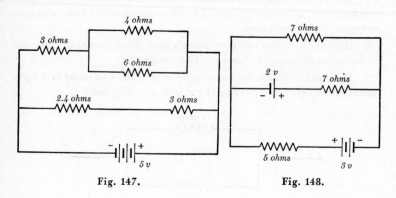

Fig. 147.   Fig. 148.

Experiment 36

1   Write down the similarities between the slide wire bridge and the Wheatstone bridge. State all the errors that come into a slide wire bridge measurement and give methods of overcoming some of these.

2   How much resistance would have to be placed in parallel with two parallel resistances of 70 ohms and 50 ohms, so that the total resistance be 20 ohms?

3   A standard resistor of 450 ohms (R_4 in Fig. 142) is being used to measure an unknown resistance R_3 by means of the slide wire bridge with a slide wire 2 meters long. Where will the balance point be if the value of R_3 happens to be 200 ohms? Where will it be if the battery is reversed? (Refer to Fig. 142.)

CHAPTER XXII

THE MEASUREMENT OF CURRENT — GALVANOMETERS

Our present knowledge of the structure of matter, and particularly that of metals, brings us to the conclusion that what is usually termed an electric current is really a drift of free electrons. The electrons are of course invisible and known to be travelling with very great speeds even though the general drift velocity through the metal is not large. By definition the *electric current* is the charge flowing per second through any cross-section of the conductor. The presence of the electron flow in conductors can be detected by the magnetic, heating or chemical effect. Quantitative measurements on the laws governing these effects will be made in Chapter XXIV.

All three effects can be used to measure current since we know the laws governing the relationships between current and any one of these effects. The only question, then, is which we shall use under the particular conditions of convenience, accuracy, speed, portability, etc. Considered from this standpoint the magnetic effect lends itself much more readily to practical use.

THE MOVING MAGNET GALVANOMETER

Almost all current-measuring instruments make use of the magnetic effect in one form or another. The tangent galvanometer (or moving-magnet type) is an instrument which can be used to measure a current in terms of absolute units if the earth's magnetic field (H_e) has been first determined in absolute measure. Accurate measurements of this kind, involving determination of H_e, are very difficult and tedious. If the apparatus is not to be used as an absolute instrument, it is possible to redesign it in such a way as to obtain great sensitivity to current flow. It is then known as the moving-magnetic-needle type of galvanometer. Unfortunately under these conditions the instrument is also very sensitive to any changes in the magnetic field in the vicinity. This and other difficulties limit its usefulness.

The moving coil or D'Arsonval galvanometer The conductor carrying the current to be measured is put in the form of a coil and either suspended by means of a thin wire or strip (Fig. 266, p. 422), or else mounted between delicately constructed jeweled bearings so as to enable the coil to rotate (Fig. 267, p. 423). The magnetic field is supplied by a permanent magnet. The interaction of the two fields produces the rotation. With a carefully designed galvanometer of this type, the current can be made to give deflections proportional to this current. These instruments can be made very sensitive and are not subject to as many of the difficulties in their use as is the moving-magnet type.

The following table gives some idea of the sensitiveness of the various types:

TYPE	APPROXIMATE RESISTANCE	CURRENT SENSITIVITY	VOLTAGE SENSITIVITY	PERIOD
Moving magnet (tangent galvanometer)	$1 \longrightarrow 4000$ ohms	1×10^{-9} amp to 3×10^{-11} amp	1×10^{-9} v to 1×10^{-7} v	about 6 sec
Moving coil (D'Arsonval)	$10 \longrightarrow 2500$ ohms	1×10^{-7} amp 1×10^{-11} amp	0.2×10^{-6} v to 0.5×10^{-7} v	2 to 22 sec

In this table the sensitivities are all stated in terms of a standard deflection, and the following definitions are used:

1 A **standard deflection** is chosen as the deflection of 1 mm on a scale 50 cm from the galvanometer when viewed through a telescope, the latter being also placed 50 cm from the galvanometer.

2 The **current sensitivity** (figure of merit) is the current necessary (usually given in amperes) to give a standard deflection.

3 The **megohm sensitivity** is the number of millions of ohms (megohms) that must be placed in series with a galvanometer, when one volt is applied, to give a standard deflection.

4 The **voltage sensitivity** is the potential difference (usually given in volts) which must be applied to the instrument directly to give a standard deflection.

5 The **period** is defined as the time for a complete vibration.

Example: Suppose that the current sensitivity, or figure of merit, is 10^{-9} amperes per standard deflection, then the megohm sensitivity would be very approximately

$$\left(\frac{1}{10^{-9}}\right)\frac{1}{10^6} = 1000 \text{ megohms},$$

if the galvanometer resistance is neglected. Suppose that the same galvanometer has a resistance of 100 ohms, then its voltage sensitivity would be $10^{-9} \times 100 = 10^{-7}$ volts per standard deflection.

EXPERIMENT 3

SENSITIVITY OF A D'ARSONVAL GALVANOMETER

A determination of the current sensitivity, megohm sensitivity, and voltage sensitivity of a moving coil galvanometer.

APPARATUS: D'Arsonval galvanometer, two high-range resistance boxes, one low-range resistance box, one key, dry cell, voltmeter (0–3 v range).

Theory   There are many circuits that may be designed to measure the sensitivity of a galvanometer. They are all so arranged that the current passed through the galvanometer is of the proper magnitude so as not to burn out the galvanometer by being excessive in amount, but rather to give a reasonable deflection.

Referring to Figure 149 it will be seen that the current through the galvanometer can be made small by arranging P to be very small and R and Q very large in resistance. In this experiment S will not be used. The value of Q should if possible be always kept at least 100 times as large as the value of P. Let I_g = current through the galvanometer and I = main current through the battery. Then

$$I_g = I\left(\frac{P}{P + R + G}\right)$$

(see Chapter XXI, p. 250) where G is the galvanometer resistance. Since $I = \dfrac{E}{Q}$ approximately, where E is the voltmeter reading, we get

$$I_g = \frac{EP}{Q(R + G)},$$

approximately.

To adjust a galvanometer telescope and focus on the scale   Before passing a current through the galvanometer, it is necessary to get the cross hairs and scale in focus. Look through the telescope and you will observe a *cross hair*. This will be seen distinctly and sharply if the eyepiece end (the end you look through) is moved slightly in or out. Next, without looking through the telescope, you will find, if the scale is at all illuminated, that you can see an image in the galvanometer mirror of this scale when you get your eye at the proper level. Move your eye up or down, next to the telescope, until you see this image when looking into the mirror. Having spotted this image, see that the telescope is at the same height as

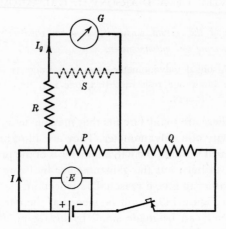

Fig. 149. Sensitivity of a galvanometer.

your eye. (Use the raising or lowering screw on the telescope arm for this purpose.) Now if you look through the telescope and it is pointing in the proper direction and is at the correct height, you will probably see the image of the scale faintly or blurred. Bring this image finally into sharp focus by the adjustment on the telescope tube (not the eyepiece). When final adjustment is obtained, both cross hairs and scale should be in clear or sharp focus and no parallax should exist between them. Having made these adjustments, try not to jar the instrument any more. If you experience difficulty, do not hesitate to ask the instructor for help in making these adjustments.

To obtain data for calculating the sensitivity Having connected the apparatus as shown in Figure 149 be sure that the resistance in boxes R and Q is as high as possible and the resistance in P is very low before closing the key. The first time you close the key, this should be done with extreme care. Just press the key down for an instant. If there are any wrong connections, this fact will show up in such a brief deflection, and furthermore, such a procedure might save some valuable apparatus. It is always a safe policy to call the instructor over to your desk and have him check your connections. Having closed the key after everything is connected up correctly, you will probably find that the deflection produced, on looking through the telescope, is very small. To obtain a larger deflection reduce the value of R. In this experiment we would like to get a deflection right up to the end of the scale, namely, 24 or 24.5 cm. If reducing R does not produce the required deflection, then reduce Q in steps, being careful, however, not to make Q less than 50 ohms. If this manipulation still does not give the required result, then use a larger value of P.

Knowing that the deflection of 25 cm can be obtained, adjust R and Q until the steady deflections to the right or to the left are obtained at *approximately* 4, 8, 12, 16, 20, 24 cm. Read the voltmeter and deflection when the key is depressed and the deflection is steady, stating on which side your deflection was taken.

Record your data as follows:

Galvanometer resistance =   ohms

Scale distance =   cm

P (ohms)	R (ohms)	Q (ohms)	Deflection (mm)	E (v)	Sensitivity (current) (amp per mm)	Sensitivity (megohm) (megohms per mm)	Sensitivity (voltage) (v per mm)

(*Note.* The calculation of sensitivity should be for a standard deflection.)

Plot a curve with current sensitivity as ordinate and deflection as abscissa. Draw a smooth curve and do not join the plotted points.

Questions

(a) Why should the value of P be small for a sensitive galvanometer?

(b) In an accurate calculation for I_g should the resistance of the voltmeter E be considered? Explain.

(c) Why may the sensitivity depend upon the amount of deflection?

(d) If a galvanometer is not very sensitive (for example 10^{-3} amp per mm deflection) devise a simple method for measuring the sensitivity, knowing the galvanometer resistance.

EXPERIMENT 37–0

MEASUREMENT OF THE RESISTANCE OF A GALVANOMETER

APPARATUS: The same apparatus as used in Experiment 37 with the addition of one more variable standard resistance box (total resistance 1000 ohms — see Fig. 149).

Theory One of the necessary known constants in finding the galvanometer sensitivity as outlined in Experiment 37 is the galvanometer resistance. In order to measure this quantity the choice of method to be used is determined largely by the sensitivity of the galvanometer. If the galvanometer is relatively insensitive perhaps the simplest way is to clamp the coil (this should be done only by the instructor) and measure the resistance using a Wheatstone bridge method (Chapter XXI). This method is not to be recommended if the galvanometer is of a very sensitive type since the amount of current required for such a measurement may be sufficient to damage the galvanometer coil. The method outlined here can be used for any galvanometer even if it is a very sensitive one.

The setup is exactly the same as for Experiment 37 except that an additional variable standard resistance box (S) is placed as a shunt right across the galvanometer. This resistance box should have a total resistance of about 1000 ohms and be variable in 1-ohm steps. First make $S = \infty$. This can be done by leaving off one of the two wires connecting S to G. The procedure, as before, is to begin by making R large and P reasonably small and adjusting the value of Q until a fairly large deflection is obtained.

Next set S to about 100 ohms and adjust its value until the original deflection is halved. In doing this, however, increase R by an amount $S/2$ so as to keep the resistance of the galvanometer circuit unchanged and make the final adjustment on S. When the correct setting has been made this last galvanometer reading should be exactly half of the original reading. Under these conditions the galvanometer circuit (G and S in parallel with R in series) will have the same total resistance as before and the resistance S will be equal to the galvanometer resistance G.

If time allows, use another value of P and repeat the experiment.

Questions

(a) Explain why it is necessary to change the value of R. Why not just adjust S until G shows half of the original deflection?

(b) Why does a very sensitive galvanometer usually have more resistance than a less sensitive one?

(c) In deriving the value of the galvanometer resistance G, why is it unnecessary to know the emf of the battery and the values of P and R?

(d) Explain fully why $S = G$ under the conditions of this experiment.

PROBLEMS

Experiment 37

1 A galvanometer of 300 ohms resistance has current sensitivity of 1.2×10^{-9} amp per mm. What is the megohm sensitivity? What is the voltage sensitivity?

2 A battery of emf of 2.5 volts furnishes current to two resistances of 12 ohms and 26,000 ohms in series. Across the 12-ohm resistance is connected a galvanometer of resistance 300 ohms. The deflection produced is 20 cm. Calculate the current through the galvanometer and the current sensitivity.

3 A galvanometer has a resistance of 30 ohms, and requires a current of 40 ma (0.04 amp) to give full-scale deflection. What is the potential difference across the galvanometer when giving full-scale deflection?

Experiment 37-0

1 A galvanometer has a resistance of 80 ohms. How much resistance must be placed in parallel with this galvanometer so as to reduce the deflection to one-third of the original value if the current entering this combination remains the same?

2 If the current in problem 1 (Exp. 37) is obtained from a source of emf and a resistor in series, how much must the resistance of the series resistor be changed (increased or decreased) to keep the main current at the same value when inserting the shunt in problem 1.

3 Two equal resistors each of the value S are connected in parallel and the combination is then connected in parallel with a galvanometer G. If the deflection originally was 20 cm and now is 10 cm, what is the value of the galvanometer resistance if the main current was kept the same? How much must R be changed to keep the main current constant (Fig. 149).

CHAPTER XXIII

MEASUREMENT OF ELECTROMOTIVE FORCE

We have seen in Chapter XXI that a voltmeter will measure the potential difference across the terminals of a resistor. As a matter of fact this formed a very quick and convenient way of performing the measurement. There are, however, two drawbacks which in many types of measurement preclude this method of measuring potential difference. These are: first, very limited accuracy, and second, the fact that the insertion of the voltmeter changes the conditions in the original circuit to some extent (as to current and potential difference), so that it is not possible by this method to measure the original potential difference.

In such cases, where a voltmeter cannot be used, and in cases when great accuracy is needed, especially in the case of thermocouple electromotive forces, the potentiometer will give excellent results.

The potentiometer uses essentially a null method in its measurement of potential differences, meaning by this that when a balance obtains, the instrument gives its reading, and *no current is drawn from the source of potential difference to be measured*. Hence the instrument measures the original potential difference.

In practical work, for example in power stations, the temperature is measured by having a thermocouple in the furnace connected by leads to the switchboard in front of the operator. The electromotive forces produced are measured either with a millivoltmeter, or else with a potentiometer when greater accuracy is needed. In many cases a continuous record of the temperature is kept on an instrument which balances the potentiometer and records the electromotive force or temperature automatically.

The theory underlying the operation of a potentiometer can be studied by reference to Figure 150. This figure represents, schematically, the wiring of a simple potentiometer. A main battery E is the source of electromotive force for the current I which flows through a resistor with variable resistance R and a uniform slide wire AB, one meter long. The current I can be varied by changing R.

Now when a current flows through the slide wire from A to B a potential drop will exist from A to B (let us say about 2 volts). From A to the middle of AB, i.e., at about C_2, the potential difference (drop) will be just one-half the value from AB (hence about 1 volt). Let us next connect in at B another cell e so that the negative pole of the battery e is connected to B. In series with this cell we place a galvanometer G and connect this in turn to the contact maker or the slider. Suppose the contact, however, is not yet made, i.e., C_1 is not yet connected to a point C_2 on the slide wire. Now if the cell e

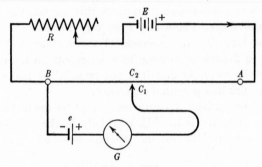

Fig. 150. Simplified potentiometer circuit.

has an electromotive force of 1 volt, then of course the potential drop from C_1 to B even before making the contact between C_1 and C_2, must be 1 volt. But we have seen that when the current I flows in the main circuit, the potential drop from C_2 to B is 1 volt, hence if the drop from C_1 to B, and from C_2 to B is in each case 1 volt — and the potential B is common to both circuits, then C_1 and C_2 must have the same potential even before the contact is made. Now since no current flowed in the circuit from C_1 to B (i.e., through the galvanometer circuit) before making the C_1C_2 contact, no current will flow after making the contact, because C_1 and C_2 have the same potential. If we had made contact at some other point on the wire, then the potentials at the point of contact would not have been the same and a current would have passed through the galvanometer, in one direction when C_1 is at the left of C_2, and in the other direction when C_1 is at the right of C_2.

In practice, the potentiometer wire can be made to have an effective length greater than one meter. This is accomplished by connecting extension coils in series with the slide wire. The resistance of each must be equal to that of the slide wire. The apparatus shown in Figure 151 uses three extension coils AB, BC and CD. Note that when no current flows through the galvanometer circuit the same current flows through the extension coils and the slide wire. Let us assume that the slide wire is one meter long and has such a current flowing through it that the potential drop across it is 1 volt. Then the potential drop across each extension coil will also be 1 volt. If now an unknown cell of electromotive force E_u is placed in the

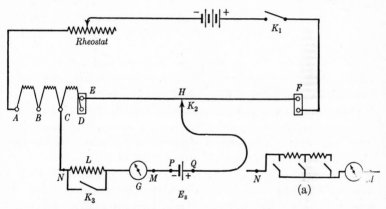

Fig. 151. A potentiometer with extension coils.

galvanometer circuit at PQ, instead the standard cell (E_s), Figure 151, a balance point can be found so that no current flows through the galvanometer. Let this point be at H, where the distance EH equals 47.6 cm. Note that the other end of the cell E_u is connected to the point C. The electromotive force of the unknown cell is therefore 1.476 volts, since the potential drop across CD is 1 volt. In this way, the instrument can be made direct-reading — the division along the scale instead of reading centimeters can be interpreted as volts — 100 cm being the equivalent of 1 volt. The equal extension coils can be placed on either end of the stretched wire, but care must be used in evaluating the proper distances.

The next question that naturally suggests itself is: How did we know what was the fall of potential across the slide wire originally? This leads us to the question of the use of standard cells.

A standard cell, as the name suggests, is a source specially designed to give a very steady and constant electromotive force. The development of such a cell has required years of experimental research with only the purest of chemicals. As a result, however, of this intensive study, using certain prescribed chemicals and standard methods of preparation, it is now possible to write down what the electromotive force will be, for a given temperature, to approximately 1 part in 100,000.

For a *Weston normal cell* the electromotive force at a temperature t C is given by:

$$E_t = 1.01830 - 0.0000406(t - 20° C) - 0.00000095(t - 20° C) + 0.00000001(t - 20° C).$$

Such a cell has for its electrodes mercury and cadmium, the solution being mercurous sulfate. The student should refer to his textbook for a detailed description of standard cells.

Other standard cells have been constructed, two of which are known as the *Eppley cell* and the *Weston unsaturated cell*. They differ from the normal cell described above in that they have an electromotive force which is not quite as reproducible, when constructed over and over again, but they have the advantage that their electromotive force does not vary considerably with change in temperature, as is the case with the normal cell. They are usually calibrated, after being constructed, by comparison with a Weston normal cell and then used with this calibration.

As with all chemical sources of eletromotive force, standard cells have the disadvantage that they *polarize*. However, if small currents are drawn from the cells, the polarization is negligible, and even if it should occur, the cell will, when allowed to stand, rectify itself again. Remember any appreciable current drawn from the standard cell will ruin its use as a standard source of electromotive force. Never use a standard cell to furnish current. *Even connecting a voltmeter across a standard cell will spoil it*, the current used by the voltmeter being too large. No current larger than 0.0001 ampere should ever be drawn from the cell, and even then only for an instant.

The important requirement of having only very small currents go through the standard cell is fulfilled in a potentiometer, by using a high resistance coil which can be placed in series with the standard cell in the galvanometer circuit. When one has no idea as to where the balance point occurs on the wire, this very high resistance coil L is put into the standard cell circuit so that if the two potential drops are not the same, and the standard cell tends to furnish current, then this current will be cut down to a very small value by this high resistance. As the balance point is approached, the resistance can be cut out, but not before.

EXPERIMENT 38

THE POTENTIOMETER

Part (a)   *Calibration by use of a standard cell.*

Part (b)   *Measurement of the electromotive force of three cells singly, of two cells in parallel and in series.*

Part (c)   *Measurement of the electromotive force of the same cells with a voltmeter.*

Part (d)   *Measurement of the electromotive force at various points on the potentiometer.*

APPARATUS: Potentiometer, 20- or 40-ohm rheostat, 6-volt storage battery, two single-pole single-throw knife switches, fixed high resistance (1000 to 10,000 ohms) if the galvanometer is not supplied with its own protective resistors, portable galvanometer, standard cell (good quality dry cell calibrated and housed preferably in a box with high series resistor), three dry cells (new and old), voltmeter (0–10 v, d-c).

The apparatus is set up as shown in Figure 151 with the standard cell E_s properly located. The wire EF is of uniform cross section and has a high resistance. Its length is exactly one meter. The three coils, terminated at the pairs of binding posts AB, BC, and DC, each have exactly the same resistance as EF and are employed so as to extend the maximum possible value of electromotive force measurable. A convenient method of calibration is to make the fall in potential across EF equal to 1 volt; then each centimeter along EF will be 0.01 volt. Since the standard cell has a voltage of about 1.5 volts (exact value is obtained from the instructor), balance will be obtained when the positive side of the standard cell makes contact with the wire at H about midway between EF and the negative side connected to C. *Have your circuit approved before connecting any battery.* The storage battery will have a voltage of about 6 volts. In any case its voltage must not change during the experiment. Note that the battery is connected through a variable rheostat and a single-pole single-throw switch to A and F.

The portable galvanometer, with series protecting resistor, is placed between the points M and N. When near balance is reached, the resistor is shunted out with key K_3. If a three-button galvanometer is used, its terminals are connected at M and N. The three-button galvanometer has two resistors of medium and high resistance. It is therefore more convenient but is more easily damaged (Fig. 151 a).

Part (a)   In order to calibrate the potentiometer, assume as a specific case that the electromotive force of the standard cell E_s is 1.524 volts. Slide the key K_2 along the slide wire until it reads 52.4 cm. Now adjust the rheostat R until the galvanometer G shows no deflection when key K_2 is closed. Then close key K_3 for a finer adjustment. The key K_3 *should not be closed* until balance is obtained as closely as possible with the key open. This procedure is for protection of the standard cell and the galvanometer. Follow this procedure in reference to key K_3 in all measurements whether using the standard cell or not. If a three-button galvanometer is used, close the button with highest series resistance first. Then depress successively the other two buttons in turn as balance is approached. When a balance has been obtained, the potential drop across each of the extension coils and across the total slide wire is 1 volt.

Part (b)   Remove the standard cell E_s and replace with a cell whose electromotive force E_u is unknown. Obtain balance by sliding key K_2 back and forth along the slide wire until a balance is obtained. (*Note*. Do not change the magnitude of the resistance of the rheostat R again, except for purposes of recalibrating with the standard cell.) Having obtained the balance point for the unknown cell it is an easy matter to convert the distance reading into volts since the current has been so adjusted in part (a) to give 1 volt for 100 cm of wire. Convert the reading into volts and so obtain E_u.

In order to check on the main current replace E_u by E_s and readjust the current if necessary. Remeasure E_u. This should be repeated three times — record each reading and find the average value of E_u. Do likewise for any other cells which you are asked to measure. Recheck your potentiometer current between readings.

Select any two of the cells you have measured and find their electromotive force when connected (1) in series, and (2) in parallel.

Part (c) Measure the potential difference across each of the unknown cells with a voltmeter and compare with the electromotive force obtained by means of the potentiometer. Explain any differences. Also, measure with the voltmeter the potential difference of the two cells above that were connected in series and in parallel. Explain any discrepancy.

Part (d) Disconnect the standard cell and the unknown cell from the potentiometer. Measure the potential difference across the following points of the potentiometer with the voltmeter: *AB*, *BC*, *CD*, *DE*, *EF*, and *AF*. Are your results in keeping with what you expected?

Questions

(a) In precision measurements with a potentiometer, both the cell whose emf is desired and the standard cell are connected to the potentiometer so that either may be placed in the potentiometer circuit by proper closing of a double-pole double-throw switch only. Make the proper switch and cell connections between points *P* and *Q*, after removing the cell E_s from its present location, so that either of two cells may be placed in the potentiometer circuit.

(b) If the current passing through the wire *FE* is 0.2 amp, what is the resistance of the length of wire *EF*? What will be the resistance of the length of wire *BC*?

(c) Assume that a balance for the branch circuit containing two unknown cells in series is obtained when the positive side shows a reading on the slide wire of 27.2 cm and when the negative side is connected to point *A*. What is the emf of the cell combination?

(d) Explain any advantages of the potentiometer over the voltmeter for measuring emf.

(e) Why was the difference in reading between the voltmeter and the potentiometer larger for old cells than for new cells?

(f) Obtain the internal resistance of the voltmeter used from the instructor. Then calculate the internal resistance of any one of the cells from the data taken.

PROBLEMS

Experiment 38

1 Assume that the standard cell E_s of Figure 151 has an emf of 1.54 volts. The slider is placed at the 54 cm position when N is connected to C and the galvanometer deflection is reduced to zero by adjustment of resistor R. Then, without changing R, E_s is removed and a cell E_u is inserted. The galvanometer now shows no deflection when the slider is placed on the 48.3 cm division. What is the electromotive force of the cell?

2   Two cells of unknown emf are connected in series to the above potentiometer and inserted in place of E_s. The connecting wire at C is placed at A and the slider at 5.0 cm for no deflection of the galvanometer. What is the electromotive force of this series combination?

3   Assume that the potentiometer reading for a certain cell is 1.48 v while a voltmeter gives a reading of 1.42 v for the same cell. If the voltmeter has a resistance of 200 ohms, what is the internal resistance of the cell?

CHAPTER XXIV

THREE EFFECTS PRODUCED BY ELECTRIC CURRENTS

The presence and even the amount of an electric current can be recognized by the *effects* which accompany such currents. These are the *heating, chemical,* and *magnetic* effects. An electric current, which is by definition the time rate of flow of electric charges across any imaginary area placed normal to the flow, cannot be seen directly since the charges are invisible. One can therefore depend only upon effects which accompany a current flow to give us information in regard to the amount and nature of the current. For convenience in engineering practice a current is nearly always measured in terms of the magnetic effect (see Chapter XXII on galvanometers). In this chapter we shall not concern ourselves primarily with measurement of current, but rather perform some quantitative experiments to show how the physical laws and definitions applying to these three effects can be used to make certain types of measurements. Such measurements require very tedious and difficult experimentation if the quantities involved are to be measured by the more direct and logical methods used in the historical development of these matters. The quantities which will be evaluated in the experiments to be described in this chapter are: (a) Joule's mechanical equivalent, (b) the electrochemical equivalent of the bivalent copper ion, (c) the horizontal component of the earth's magnetic field strength.

The heating effect Every conductor of electricity has some resistance and therefore, when a current passes through it, will have work done on it which produces a rise in temperature. Since the definitions of the volt and the ampere depend on the mechanical units of work and force, the amount of work done by a current is measured by the *product* of the potential difference V across the conductor, the current I through it, and the time t for which the current flows.

$$\text{i.e., Work } (W) = V \text{ (volts)} \cdot I \text{ (amp)} \cdot t \text{ (sec)}$$
$$= I^2Rt \text{ joules}$$

Joule's equivalent of heat is the amount of mechanical or electrical work (joules) which must be done on a system in order to produce the same rise in temperature in it as will be produced by addition of an amount of heat of one calorie. The system in this experiment consists of a coil of resistance wire immersed in a calorimeter containing water. When a known current is passed through this coil for a given time the temperature of the water will rise. The amount of electrical work (joules) done on the resistance coil by the current can be calculated by measuring the current through it, the potential difference across it, and the time of flow. The required number of heat units (H, in calories) which is equivalent to this work can also be calculated from a knowledge of the water equivalent of the system and the rise in temperature produced in the water.

i.e., $$\text{Heat } (H) = Ms(t_2 - t_1) \quad \text{calories}$$

where M = total water equivalent of the system
s = specific heat of water
$(t_2 - t_1)$ = temperature rise (deg C)

The ratio of $\dfrac{\text{Work } (W)}{\text{Heat } (H)}$ gives the mechanical equivalent of heat (Joule's equivalent) = J.

The chemical effect — electrolysis   When an electric current is sent through a chemical compound in solution or a fused chemical, certain chemical changes take place. We call this breaking down of the compound by the electric current *electrolysis*.

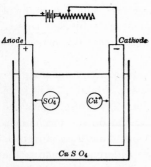

Fig. 152. Electrolytic cell.

The current is generally led into the solution by means of metal plates called *electrodes*. If a metal is deposited at one of the electrodes, the process is called *electroplating*. We shall confine our discussion to the simple case of electrodeposition of copper from an acid copper sulfate solution, because this example will be sufficient to illustrate the application of the laws of electrolysis.

Consider a solution of copper sulfate, through which a current is passed, as pictured in Figure 152. The electrode at which the current enters the solution is known as the anode, while the other electrode is called the cathode. The copper sulfate, which is ionized because of its solution in water, begins to travel towards the electrodes as soon as the current is turned on. The negative SO_4^{--} ions move towards the positive electrode pole, while the copper ions are attracted to the negative electrode. The solution of copper sulfate will continue to dissociate as long as energy is supplied to keep the ions in motion so that the electrodes will be kept in a charged condition. The ions which reach the respective electrodes lose their charge, the copper atoms are deposited at the cathode, and the SO_4^{--} ion reacts with the anode to produce more copper sulfate.

The reactions at the electrodes are not always as simple as described. We have chosen copper sulfate because the chemical changes are fairly well understood and the laws of electrolysis, first stated by Faraday (1853), may be readily demonstrated. Faraday's laws may be summarized briefly as follows:

1 *The mass* (M) *of material deposited is proportional to the quantity* (Q) *of electricity which flows through the solution.*

2 *The mass* (M) *of material deposited for different substances is proportional to the chemical equivalent* (m/v), *where m and v stand for the atomic weight and valence respectively.*

Hence the mass deposited is proportional to the product of the two quantities as stated in Faraday's laws.

$$M \propto \frac{m}{v} Q.$$

That is,
$$M = \frac{1}{F}\frac{m}{v} Q = \frac{1}{F}\frac{m}{v} It,$$

where I is the current (in amperes) flowing for a time t seconds. The constant of proportionality (F) is known as the faraday, and $Z = m/Fv$ is called the *electrochemical equivalent*, i.e.,

$$M = ZIt \text{ grams,} \tag{71}$$

where Z can be defined as the *number of grams of substance* liberated by one coulomb of electricity.

Note that the faraday (F) is the number of coulombs required to liberate one chemical equivalent (m/v) of the element.

Furthermore if we let M_a be the mass of one atom, e the charge of one electron and A be Avogadro's number (i.e., the number of atoms in a gram atom), then

$$M_a = \frac{\text{chemical equivalent}}{\text{number of atoms in a chemical equivalent}}$$

$$= \frac{m/v}{F/ev} = \frac{m}{Fv} \cdot ev = Zev$$

Some atomic constants for reference:

A = Avogadro's number = 6.03×10^{23} atoms per gram atom

e = charge on the electron = 1.592×10^{-19} coulomb

F = Faraday's constant = 96,500 coulombs per chemical equivalent

m/v = chemical equivalent = 31.78 for copper of valence 2.

There are some practical difficulties in testing these laws because of secondary reactions which may occur at or near the electrodes. Thus, if a neutral solution of copper sulfate is used to test the laws by weighing the copper deposited, one will find that the deposit may be brown due to formation of a copper compound at the cathode. This is caused by the alkaline condition at the cathode due to the reducing action of copper when being precipitated out. This difficulty at the cathode is remedied by making the solution acid.

A satisfactory solution for plating copper on copper, as done in our experiment, is the following:

$CuSO_4 \cdot 5\ H_2O$ . . . 200–250 grams per liter
H_2SO_4 (conc.) . . . 50–80 grams per liter

Every object to be plated must first be cleaned. For our purposes, polishing the copper strip with clean emery paper will be sufficient. After cleaning, the fingers should not touch the portion to be plated. If there is any question about the cleanliness of the strip then it is well to use a cleaning solution (see page 424, Chapter XXXIV).

The magnetic effect   The fact that a magnetic field exists near a wire carrying a steady current can be readily shown with the aid of a small compass. A careful study will show that the magnetic field near a long straight wire will be normal to the wire and will reverse its direction when the current is reversed. The magnetic lines of force are circular around the wire in keeping with Oersteds right hand rule as indicated in Figure 153. When the hand grips the wire with thumb pointing in the direction of the current, the finger tips point in the direction of the circular field. The circular field will be modified in some specified manner in experimental measurements due to the superimposed effect of the earth's field.

Neglecting the earth's magnetic field, the magnetic field intensity H in cgs electromagnetic units* at a point P (Fig. 153) near a long straight wire and at a distance d cm from the wire, will be

$$H = \frac{2\,I_m}{d} = \frac{2\,I}{10\,d} \text{ oersted} \tag{72}$$

where I_m represents the current in electromagnetic units, and I represents the current in amperes (*Note.* $I_m = I/10$).

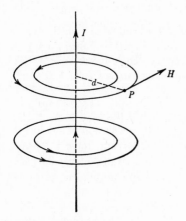

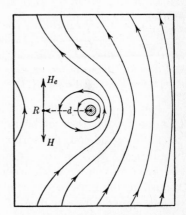

Fig. 153. Magnetic field around a long straight wire carrying a current I (cgs units).

Fig. 154. Resultant field produced by the earth's horizontal magnetic field and the field around a vertical wire carrying current (cgs units).

Considering next the presence of the earth's magnetic field, let us arrange the wire to be vertical. Then the horizontal magnetic field

* In mks units, the magnetic flux density (B) at point P will be

$$B = k' \frac{2I}{d} = \frac{1}{10^7} \frac{2I}{d} \frac{\text{webers}}{\text{meter}^2} \tag{72a}$$

where I and d are in amperes and meters, respectively. The vector B is measured also in ampere-turns/meter (rationalized units).

of the vertical straight wire (H, circular around the wire) will be able to neutralize the horizontal component of the earth's field (H_e) on one side of the wire (see Fig. 154) at some point such as R. If this point has been found at a distance d from the wire we can equate the two magnetic fields, viz.:

$$H_e = H = \frac{2\,I}{10\,d} \text{ oersted}$$

EXPERIMENT 39

JOULE'S EQUIVALENT OF HEAT

An electrical method for determining the relation between the units of heat and work.

APPARATUS: Electrocalorimeter consisting of a heating coil which can be immersed in a calorimeter, voltmeter (15-v range), ammeter (0–5 amp), rheostat, double-pole single-throw knife switch, thermometer, balance with standard masses, some ice, watch, a-c or d-c supply.*

The electrocalorimeter consists of a heating coil and stirrer mounted so that they can be immersed in the inner cup of a calorimeter. Since the coil, the stirrer and the inner cup have a "water equivalent," the "equivalent mass" of water of these materials will be given to you by the instructor. This water equivalent must be added to the mass of water m placed in the calorimeter. Let the water equivalent be w, then $M = m + w$, and

$$\mathcal{J} = \frac{VIt}{MS(t_2 - t_1)} \text{ joules per calorie} \tag{73}$$

The electrocalorimeter is connected in series with the source, rheostat, and ammeter as shown in Figure 155. The voltmeter is

---

* The voltage required depends considerably upon the resistance of the heating coil in the electrocalorimeter. If only one piece of equipment is being used, a storage battery is probably most convenient. A motor generator with a capacity of 200 to 300 watts and an output of 10 to 20 volts will do well for several sets connected across the line. Another convenient arrangement is to use a variable step-down autotransformer.

connected with its proper range and polarity across the terminals of the resistance in the calorimeter. The rheostat is adjusted initially to offer maximum additional resistance to the line. *Connection to the source, however, should not be made until after inspection and after the calorimeter is filled with water.*

Weigh the electrocalorimeter, and then fill nearly full of water after placing in the calorimeter cup sufficient ice to reduce the temperature of the water to about 10 degrees below that of the room. *After* the ice is melted stir thoroughly and turn on the switch momentarily to see whether the apparatus is in working order. *Do not close the switch if the coil is not completely immersed in the water.* More water should be added if the coil is not covered. Turn on the switch and adjust the rheostat to obtain the current indicated by the instructor. Now turn off the switch, stir thoroughly, and take the temperature. Then close the switch, record the time, and allow the

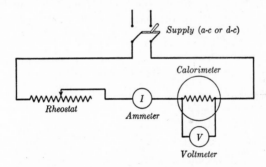

Fig. 155. An electrocalorimeter being used to determine Joule's equivalent of heat.

temperature to rise. If the current fluctuations are not too great, record the current and voltage as accurately as you can at definite equal time intervals so that you will have about 10 readings of each at the finish. If the current varies consistently by too great an amount it may be necessary to readjust the current. Even if this needs to be done, record all readings. Allow the temperature to rise to a value as much above room temperature as the starting temperature was below. Record the time when the current was stopped and the highest temperature reached. Repeat the experiment, using a different temperature interval if time permits.

DATA

Mass of electrocalorimeter empty =
Mass of electrocalorimeter with water =
Mass of water =
Water equivalent of calorimeter, stirrer and coils =
Room temperature =

V (volts)	I (amperes)	Total time (seconds)	$W = VIt$ (joules)	$H = MS(t_2 - t_1)$ (calories)	J (joules per calorie)

Calculate the value of J at the end of each total time interval and fill in the last column of the table above. Plot a curve with values of the electric energy W as ordinates, and values of heat energy (H, in calories) as abscissas.

Questions

(a) Is your curve of W versus H a straight line? Explain any departures from a straight line if you find any!

(b) Obtain a value of J from the average slope of your curve. What is the per cent difference between this average value and the value given in the last row of the table of data above?

(c) What is the per cent difference of your best value from the accepted value of 4.185 joules per cal?

(d) Why is the temperature range so chosen as to begin with an initial temperature as much below room temperature as the final temperature is above?

(e) What is the relationship between the calorie and the joule when the work is done by a force of friction instead of electrically, and the observed rise in temperature is the same? Explain.

(f) According to the makers, the voltmeter and ammeter may be incorrect by as much as 2 per cent of full scale reading, and the thermometer interval incorrect by 1 per cent. What is the largest possible per cent error in J that could be produced by such inaccuracies acting together? How much will this be in the actual value of J?

(g) The ammeter measures the current through both the heater and the voltmeter and therefore does not represent the true current through the calorimeter. From the fact that the voltmeter has a resistance of about 1500 ohms, estimate the size of this error.

EXPERIMENT 40

THE COULOMETER

Part (a)   *To determine the electrochemical equivalent of copper.*
Part (b)   *To calculate the value of the faraday constant.*
Part (c)   *To calculate the mass of the copper atom.*
Part (d)   *To determine Avogadro's number.*

APPARATUS: Copper coulometer, ammeter, resistance unit of about 15 ohms and 1.5 amperes capacity, knife switch, fine balance, 4-6 v (d-c).

The apparatus is assembled as shown in Figure 156. A low voltage supply of about 4 to 6 volts is connected to an adjustable resistance which, in turn, is connected in series with the copper sulfate solution, ammeter, and knife switch. The copper sulfate solution is made up as described in the theory.

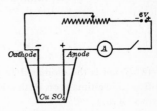

Fig. 156. Copper coulometer.

Before starting your weighing in this experiment, the connections should be inspected and current turned on to see if the ammeter is connected so that the current will flow in the proper direction. It is also necessary to adjust the rheostat to see that an excessive current does not pass through the solution to "burn" the deposit. Adjust the rheostat so as not to deposit copper at a rate in excess of 5 amp per dm². A current density of 3 to 4 amp per dm² will give a rapid deposit and yet be well within the safe limit.

Now throw the switch off and remove the cathode (strip of copper to be plated). Rinse, dry, clean by polishing with emery paper, and then weigh accurately on the fine balance. Do not touch the portion to be plated with the hands after cleaning. Replace the weighed cathode and deposit copper on it for one-half to three-fourths hour. Take readings on the ammeter every two minutes if the fluctuations are small, or else keep the rheostat adjusted so as to keep the current constant. Record the total time during which the copper is being deposited. After the copper has been deposited, clean with several rinsings of water, and dry. The drying process is hastened considerably by pressing filter paper against the surfaces of the deposit, but avoid any rubbing. Handle the deposit as little as possible with the hands before weighing. Weigh the plate. The increase in weight will be the mass of copper deposited. Your data now consist of the *mass* of copper deposited, the *time* of current flow, and several current readings from which an *average current* I may be obtained. From these three quantities calculate:

Part (a): the electrochemical equivalent (Z) of copper
Part (b): the faraday constant F from Z obtained in part (a)
Part (c): the mass of a copper atom M_a from Z obtained in part (a)
Part (d): Avogadro's number from the gram atom and the value of M_a obtained in part (c)

Questions

(a) What is the estimated or probable error in your determination of Z? Base this estimate on evaluation of the precision of the several quantities measured.

(b) Look up the value of the electrochemical equivalent for bivalent copper in a handbook. Does the table value fall within the limits estimated in (a)?

(c) Assuming that the experimental procedure can be refined and made fairly accurate, suggest a possible method of procedure to calibrate an ammeter by using the chemical effect.

(d) If all the copper deposited did not adhere to the cathode because of a dirty portion of the surface, how would this affect the calculated value of Z?

(e) Determine the number of atoms deposited on the cathode during the time of your experiment.

(f) How many electrons passed through any cross section of the circuit during this time?

EXPERIMENT 41

ELECTROMAGNETISM

Part (a) *To plot the lines of force around a straight wire carrying a current.*

Part (b) *Determination of the neutral points and the calculation of the earth's horizontal magnetic intensity (H_e).*

APPARATUS: Vertical wire carrying about 5 amp, ammeter (0–10 amp) rheostat, source of d-c supply, small compass, Scotch drafting tape.

Part (a)   When the student enters the laboratory he will find the experiment set up as indicated in Figure 157 (a). A straight copper

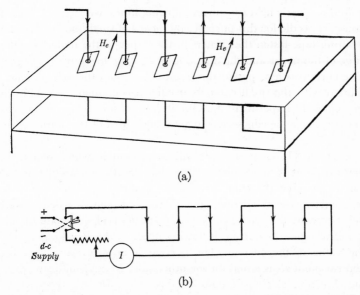

(a)

(b)

Fig. 157. Resultant horizontal magnetic field of long vertical wires carrying currents and the magnetic field of the earth (cgs units).

(a) arrangement.
(b) electric circuit.

conductor will be found coming up vertically through a small hole in the table top. The current will be made to flow through this wire and then continue to flow through a similar wire for the next student. The wires are therefore all connected in series, and the amount of the current can be adjusted by a rheostat and measured with an ammeter at one end of the series circuit. Furthermore, a reversing switch makes it possible for the instructor to reverse the current through the wires. For this reason the instructor will ask the students to complete the several parts of this experiment in unison. The current will be adjusted by the instructor to be about 5 amperes.

Begin by ruling two pencil lines at right angles to each other down the middle of a sheet of paper. Cut a slit to the centre along one of the longer lines and slip the paper around the wire so that the vertical wire passes normally at the centre through the plane of the paper.

Next line up the longer edge of the paper with the earth's horizontal magnetic field (no current flowing in the wire) — use a small compass needle for this purpose. By means of small pieces of Scotch drafting tape fasten the corners of the paper to the table, after the edge of the paper and the direction of H_e have been made to agree. The current is now passed through the wire and the magnetic field plotted with the small compass needle in a manner similar to the procedure in Experiment 33. Obtain lines of force close to the wire and also near the edges so as to get a good idea of the nature of the magnetic field.

Part (b) From part (a) it will be evident in which region the neutral point is to be found. Locate this point as carefully as you can by moving the compass toward or away from the wire in a magnetic east-west direction. At the neutral point it will probably point toward the wire. Mark this point R_1 and designate on the paper whether the current is flowing up or down. Read and record the value of the current. The current is now reversed, and the neutral point R_2 is found on the other side. Near R_2 indicate again the direction of current flow for this point. Record the current, which should be the same as before. Measure the distances d_1 and d_2 from the centre of the wire to the points R_1 and R_2 and thus determine an average value for d.

Using Equation 72 (or 72a) for the field due to a straight wire, evaluate the value of the earth's field H_e (or flux density B_e).

Questions

(a) When the straight wire is arranged as in this experiment and has current flowing vertically up, why is there a neutral point only on one side of the wire?

(b) If the earth's horizontal intensity should decrease would the neutral point be found nearer or further from the wire for the same current flowing?

(c) Choose about four points on some of the lines of force drawn in part (a) and account roughly by vector addition of the two component magnetic fields involved the direction of the resultant magnetic field found.

PROBLEMS

Experiment 39

1 A calorimeter contains water and has a resistance coil immersed in it. A current of 3 amp is passed through the coil for 15 min. If the potential difference across the coil is 20 v and the total water equivalent of the calorimeter and its contents is 450 g, what will be the rise in temperature? Assume no losses to the surroundings.

2 A current of 5 amp is flowing through a coil having a resistance of 20 ohms. How much heat will this produce in (a) 10 sec (b) 2 hr?

3 A calorimeter made of copper has a mass of 60 g. It contains 100 g of water all at a temperature of 20° C. How much heat must be supplied to raise the temperature to 100° C? (Specific heat of copper is 0.094 cal per g per deg C.)

4 An electric light bulb operates with a potential difference of 100 v across its terminals. If the lamp has 1 amp flowing through it how much work is being done on the lamp every second? How much heat (in cal) would this work be equivalent to?

Experiment 40

1 What are meant by (1) chemical equivalent, (2) electrochemical equivalent, (3) Avogadro's number, (4) the faraday?

2 If a copper sulfate solution and a nickel sulfate solution are connected in series with a source of current and it is found that 4 g of copper have been deposited from the copper sulfate solution, how much nickel would be deposited from the nickel solution? (Consult handbooks for electrochemical equivalents.)

3 If nickel is to be deposited on a rectangular block of copper of dimensions 10 by 20 by 30 cm^3 at the rate of 1.5 amp per square decimeter, how long will it take to deposit 200 g?

4   How many electrons are needed to have a total charge equivalent to one coulomb?

5   How many coulombs of electricity are required to deposit 5 g of bivalent copper? How many atoms will this be? (Electrochemical equivalent of bivalent copper = 0.000329 g per coulomb.)

Experiment 41

1   A long straight wire carries a current of 10 amp. What is the strength of the magnetic field at the following distances from the wire: (a) 1 cm, (b) 2 cm, (c) 3 cm, (d) 4 cm, (e) 5 cm? Make a graph of the field strength (ordinate) and distance from the wire (abscissa). What are the units of magnetic field strength?

2   If the wire in the previous problem is mounted vertically (in the earth's field of strength 0.18 oersted) and the current is 10 amp, flowing upwards, where will the neutral point be? Illustrate your answer by means of a diagram showing the magnetic field.

Note: The horizontal component of the earth's magnetic flux density B_e will be $B_e = 0.18 \times 10^{-4}$ webers/meter^2 in the mks system, if the magnetic field intensity H_e in the cgs system is $H_e = 0.18$ oersted.

3   Two straight wires, spaced 10 cm apart, are arranged vertically in the earth's magnetic field having a horizontal intensity of 0.18 oersted. If the wires are in a plane normal to the magnetic meridian plane and the currents are the same, but in opposite directions, what value of current will neutralize the earth's horizontal intensity at a point midway between the wires? Illustrate your answer by means of a diagram.

CHAPTER XXV

THE MEASUREMENT OF CHARGE

The fundamental or absolute unit of charge is defined from Coulomb's law. This law states that when we are given two electric charges q_1 and q_2, the force exerted by one on the other is directly proportional to the magnitude of either charge and inversely proportional to the square of the distance separating them. Expressed in symbols we can therefore write:

$$F \propto \frac{q_1 q_2}{d^2}. \tag{74}$$

Upon inserting a proportionality constant for empty space, Equation 63 on page 236 is found giving the magnitude of the force between any two isolated charges.

If any medium, other than empty space is to be taken into account, an additional term must be included, giving the more general equation

$$F = \frac{k}{\epsilon_r} \frac{q_1 q_2}{d^2} \tag{75}$$

where ϵ_r is the relative permittivity, or dielectric constant, of the medium. Referring to the footnote on page 236, Equation 75 may be written also as

$$F = \frac{1}{4\pi\epsilon_r\epsilon_0} \frac{q_1 q_2}{d^2} = \frac{1}{4\pi\epsilon} \frac{q_1 q_2}{d^2} \tag{75a}$$

where $\epsilon = \epsilon_r\epsilon_0$, in the rationalized mks system. The above equation determines the magnitude of k in the mks system.

Now in measuring a charge, the first question to consider is: Is the charge at rest, or in uniform motion (constant velocity), or does its velocity change? The method to be adopted in each case is different.

In the first case, in which the charge to be measured is at rest (such as in electrostatics) we use some form of electroscope or electrometer. The method used by Coulomb, which consists in finding the amount of twist in a wire when charges are placed at the ends of an insulated crosspiece attached to the end of the wire and the unknown charge placed near one of these, is theoretically the most direct, but practically offers many experimental difficulties and objections. At the present time the method used for qualitative work, where great accuracy is not necessary, involves use of the leaf electroscope, in which the deflection depends upon the amount of charge. The instrument of course must be calibrated. For accurate work, a modified form of torsion balance, known as a quadrant electrometer, in which the unknown charge is made to attract an oppositely charged suspended system, is used.

Now in the second case in which the charges are in uniform motion we have a steady electric current. The methods used in finding the strength of electric currents have already been discussed in the chapter dealing with the measurement of electric currents (see Chapter XXII). If the currents are very small, such as ionization currents in the air, then we must use electrometer methods, by finding the rate at which charge accumulates on, or leaks off, an insulated system.

In the last case, in which the currents are variable, the measurement of charge resolves itself mostly into measuring the total charge which has passed in a certain small interval of time. Some important cases of common occurrence come in for consideration here; usually when a capacitor* charges up to a certain potential through the application of a potential difference a definite amount of charge flows into this capacitor. This charge flows in rapidly in the beginning and more slowly towards the end, the whole process being

---

* The term "condenser" has been largely used in the past. Instead of this the term "capacitor" is finding much wider use due to the fact that "resistor" and "inductor" are also being used more generally. The term "condenser" is misleading because nothing is being condensed. The constant C in Equation (76) is called the "capacitance" to correspond to the terms "resistance", and "inductance."

over in a fraction of a second. A somewhat similar process occurs when the discharge takes place.

When the capacitor is fully charged, we have:

$$Q = CV, \tag{76}$$

where Q = total charge, C = capacitance, V = potential difference. In practical units these are measured in coulombs, farads, and volts, respectively. Of course at any instant the current flowing is defined as the rate of flow of charge, viz.,

$$i = \frac{\Delta q}{\Delta t}. \tag{77}$$

Any electrical system which is capable of holding or storing an electrical charge when a potential difference is applied to the system is called a *capacitor*. *The amount of charge it can hold for a certain fixed potential difference (one unit) is called its capacitance.*

The unit in which we measure capacitance is the *farad*, or more commonly the *microfarad* (10^{-6} farads), in the practical system of units. In the absolute system of units (esu) we use a unit called the *centimeter*.

A capacitor will have a capacitance of 1 farad when a potential difference of 1 volt will store in it a charge of 1 coulomb. A capacitor will have a capacitance of 1 centimeter if a unit charge (esu) will raise its potential by 1 unit (esu). The relation between the farad and the centimeter is that

$$9 \times 10^{11} \text{ cm} \approx 1 \text{ farad}$$
or $$9 \times 10^{5} \text{ cm} \approx 1 \text{ microfarad}$$
or $$0.9 \text{ cm} \approx 1 \text{ micromicrofarad}$$

In practice, capacitors mostly consist of two parallel metal plates separated by a dielectric, such as, for example, air, mica, waxed paper, etc.

If several of these are connected in series as shown in Figure 158, it can easily be shown that the total capacitance is less than the capacitance of even the smallest capacitor, in fact:

$$\frac{1}{C} = \frac{1}{C_1} + \frac{1}{C_2} + \frac{1}{C_3}. \tag{78}$$

If the capacitors are connected in parallel or multiple as shown in Figure 159, then the capacitors may be shown to give a total capacitance

$$C = C_1 + C_2 + C_3. \tag{79}$$

In tne above discussion of capacitors we are interested mainly in the resultant charge required. Another very important class of measurement of electric charges which flow for a very short time occurs when dealing with induced currents. Suppose, for example, we have a closed coil of wire through which we pass, very rapidly, one pole of a bar magnet. A current is induced in the coil, the time

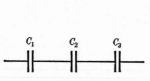

Fig. 158. Capacitors connected in series.

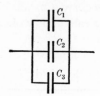

Fig. 159. Capacitors connected in parallel.

for which the current flows being perhaps of the order of $\frac{1}{100}$ second. It is difficult to find out what the current was at every instant. But it is relatively simple to find out, experimentally, how much total charge has passed. Then knowing how much charge has passed, we can calculate the strength of the magnet. Methods of this type are therefore most important in connection with measuring the strength of magnets or magnetic fields and also measuring the inductance of coils.

In all these measurements, of inductance and capacitance, it becomes necessary to measure a certain quantity of charge, independent of the time for which this charge flows. The instrument which will measure charges of this nature is called a *ballistic galvanometer*.

The construction of a ballıstic galvanometer is exactly similar to the D'Arsonval galvanometer, except that we apply an additional condition to a D'Arsonval galvanometer. This condition is, that all the charge flow through the galvanometer before the coil has moved appreciably from its equilibrium position. The coil then deflects after that, due to the impulse or "kick" which it received initially. It can be shown theoretically that the deflection then is directly proportional to the impulse, and consequently also to the total charge that went through the coil in the beginning. In order to satisfy this necessary condition of use, the current must flow for an extremely short time. If this cannot be assumed, then we must give the coil a very large moment of inertia and consequently a very long period of swing. The coil is usually made very broad so as to help in satisfying this condition. Since a ballistic galvanometer therefore gives deflections proportional to the total charge that has passed through it, we can use it as an instrument for comparison of total charges.

Suppose, for example, we wish to compare the capacitances C_1 and C_2 of two capacitors. We shall apply the same potential difference to each one and so charge them. The total charge each will acquire will be different because their capacitances are different, but the potential difference in this case will be the same. Hence we can write

$$Q_1 = C_1 V$$

for capacitor C_1, and

$$Q_2 = C_2 V$$

for capacitor C_2. Now if the deflections produced, when these two charges are allowed to pass rapidly through a ballistic galvanometer, are d_1 and d_2,

$$Q_1 \propto d_1, \text{ or } Q_1 = Kd_1,$$

and

$$Q_2 \propto d_2, \text{ or } Q_2 = Kd_2,$$

where K is a constant of the particular galvanometer.

Hence we see:

$$\frac{Q_1}{Q_2} = \frac{d_1}{d_2} = \frac{C_1}{C_2},$$

which shows that the ratio between the capacitances is simply the ratio between the deflections produced.

We note in the above case that the constant of the galvanometer, namely, K, does not enter when using a ballistic galvanometer for purposes of comparison. If we wanted to know the magnitude of the charge (i.e., Q_1), then we would have to know K. Note further that K is a constant whose value for different galvanometers would give us some idea of the sensitivity of the galvanometer in terms of the total charge which went through. To be more specific, we define the charge or microcoulomb sensitivity (K) as the charge in microcoulombs (*Note.* 1 microcoulomb = 10^{-6} coulombs) necessary to give a standard deflection (see page 268). Once we know the value of K, therefore, we can find Q very simply from the relation $Q = Kd$, since we observe the deflection.

Calibration of a ballistic galvanometer when measuring a magnetic field or flux   When a ballistic galvanometer is connected to a coil of wire (Fig. 160) the con-

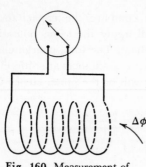

Fig. 160. Measurement of flux.

ditions are not quite the same as when connected to a capacitor. In the latter case the resistance in the galvanometer circuit may be considered to be infinite and hence it makes little difference which capacitor we connect to the galvanometer. When connecting a coil, however, to the galvanometer, the resistance of the circuit of course depends upon the coil, and in most cases this is quite low. Suppose now we produce a magnetic field near the coil, then some lines of force (ϕ) will pass through the coil, and in doing so they will induce an electromotive force in the coil, of amount, $e = -\dfrac{\Delta\phi}{\Delta t}$, for each turn of the coil. This electromotive force will start a motion of charges through the wire and consequently an electric current will flow for a short time. The amount of current that will flow will of course depend upon the resistance of the circuit, consisting of the external coil and the galvanometer coil. The larger each one of these resistances the smaller will be the current. The current now having passed, the coil starts deflecting. As soon as it starts deflecting, however, the induced current set up by the rotating coil, according to Lenz's law, is such as to oppose further rotation. The smaller the external resistance the larger the induced current and so the smaller the deflection. When we calibrate a ballistic galvanometer in terms of flux cut and deflection produced, it will be seen that we do so *for a particular circuit*, consisting, in the above case, of an external coil and a galvanometer coil. Thus, by allowing the flux to cut or pass through the coil, we can measure the amount of flux cut, since the ballistic deflection is directly proportional to the flux change.

We shall discuss one example of the use of the ballistic galvanometer in measuring flux. The problem is to study the nature of
the induced electromotive force in a coil of wire which makes one
complete revolution in a magnetic field. This is done, with the apparatus provided, by allowing the coil
to move rapidly through a very small
angle (θ) as shown in Figure 161 and
then measuring the total charge produced, which, in this case, is proportional to the average induced electromotive force during this small interval.
By measuring the amount of induced

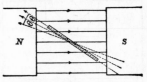

Fig. 161. Rotating coil in a
magnetic field.

electromotive force for all these small steps we can plot the
relative amount of electromotive force induced as the coil rotates
in the magnetic field with reference to the coil position. It will
be seen that the electromotive force induced is a so-called "alternating" electromotive force, reversing its direction every 180°
of rotation. This type of electromotive force or current will be
discussed in detail in Chapter XXVI.

EXPERIMENT 42

COMPARISON OF CAPACITANCES

Part (a) *To measure the charge sensitivity of a galvanometer.*

Part (b) *To compare capacitances of capacitors with a ballistic galvanometer.*

Part (c) *To check the laws of series and parallel connections of capacitors.*

APPARATUS: Ballistic galvanometer, short-circuit key, standard capacitor,
two or three capacitors with unknown capacitances, voltmeter
(0–3 v), charge-discharge key, dry cell.

Part (a) The apparatus is connected as shown in Figure 162.
G is the ballistic galvanometer; k_1 is a key which may be found
useful between measurements for bringing the galvanometer to rest.
Key k_2 is a two-way single-pole switch. The dry cell is connected
at e with a voltmeter across it to measure the potential difference which the battery furnishes for charging the standard
capacitor C. (*Note.* Be very careful to see that your connections at
the key k_2 are correct. It would be better not to connect in the bat-

tery *e* until the instructor has checked your circuit. Failure to do this might burn out the galvanometer coil — *so be over-cautious.*)

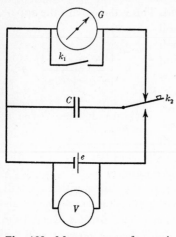

Fig. 162. Measurement of capacitance.

In reading a deflection the procedure is to throw k_2 on the battery side for just a few moments, and then quickly throw it to the galvanometer side of the switch. What is required is the maximum deflection on the scale. If you did not get the first one, repeat the charging and try again. Record all your trials. The zero from which the deflection occurs does not have to be the zero of the scale so long as the zero position is recorded and is steady.* The deflection is the difference between the maximum deflection and the zero reading. Record both these for every trial. Determine the average deflection.

Record also the capacitance of the standard capacitor used, as well as the potential difference of the battery and then calculate the microcoulomb sensitivity.

Part (b) Connect the unknown capacitors in turn into the circuit instead of the standard capacitor *C*. In performing these exchanges always play safe by disconnecting at least one of the battery terminals. Measure the ballistic deflection produced by each capacitor and find their capacitances by comparison with the deflection of the standard. The deflection used in this calculation should not be a single try, but rather the average of several recorded deflections. List finally the measured values of the unknown capacitances.

Part (c) Depending upon instructions connect either two or three of the unknown capacitors in parallel and find the capacitance

---

* Some capacitors with paraffined paper or oil dielectric show the phenomenon of dielectric absorption to a variable degree. Reproducible results can usually be obtained with such capacitors if one allows about 5 seconds for the charging before taking a deflection for the discharge. The capacitor should then be allowed to discharge for at least 10 seconds before charging it up again. Charge-discharge keys are usually so arranged that the capacitor is continuously being discharged except when the key is depressed.

of the combination as accurately as you can. Then compare this measured combination value with the value calculated from the individual measurements in part (b).

Repeat this last part for the unknown capacitors connected in series.

DATA

Part (a)

Value of Capacitance (C)	Voltmeter Reading (V)	Galvanometer		Deflection (d)	Deviation	Remarks
		Zero	Max.			
Average V		Total				
		Mean		$\genfrac{}{}{0pt}{}{+}{-}$		

Per cent of errors =

Capacity.....................±..............%....farads (C)

Potential Difference..........±..............%....volts (V)

Deflection...................±..............%....millimeters

and since

charge $Q = CV$

Therefore charge...........±.............%....coulombs

and   sensitivity ....±...........%....coulombs per mm

      ....±...........%....microcoulombs per mm

Parts (b) and (c)

To record data for these two parts of the experiment make up forms similar to the one shown above.

From part (a) let $Q = Kd = CV$, for the standard capacitor

Then $Q_1 = Kd_1 = C_1V_1$, for one of the unknown capacitors

Hence the ratio:

$$\frac{Q}{Q_1} = \frac{d}{d_1} = \frac{CV}{C_1V_1}$$

and if the experiment is performed in such a way as to make $V = V_1$, we have simply:

$$\frac{d}{d_1} = \frac{C}{C_1}$$

Use this equation to find C_1 when C is known. In a similar way find C_2, C_3, etc. as needed in the carrying out of parts (b) and (c).

Questions

(a) Make a list of the various sources of experimental error, in finding the sensitivity of the ballistic galvanometer.

(b) With the cell provided in your experiment, calculate from your results obtained in part (b) approximately the smallest and largest capacitance that you could measure with your galvanometer.

(c) Do the results you obtained for series and parallel connections check the laws for such connection within experimental error? Discuss this point with reference to your experimental errors.

(d) Suppose you had to measure an unknown capacitance by this method, but with the galvanometer you used in this experiment the deflection was too small to measure. How could you go about it?

EXPERIMENT 43

LENZ'S LAW

Part (a)   *To compare the strength of two magnets by means of a ballistic galvanometer.*

Part (b)   *To demonstrate Lenz's law.*

Part (c)   *To study the direction of the induced electromotive force in another coil mutually coupled with the first.*

Part (d)   *To find the nature of the induced electromotive force (wave-form) when a coil is rotated in a magnetic field (model dynamo).*

APPARATUS: Ballistic galvanometer,* two bar magnets about 8 inches long, a coil with the direction of winding indicated, another iron core coil to fit inside the first, dry cell, contact key, model dynamo.

This experiment is designed to show how a ballistic galvanometer can be used for many purposes in which we wish to investigate either induced electromotive forces produced by coil cutting a known

---

* A portable type of galvanometer is satisfactory if a sufficient number of turns are used in coil through which the flux change is produced.   The one coil in part (c) can contain an iron core in order to increase the flux changes.

magnetic field or else to measure magnetic fields by the use of a coil which is allowed to move in this magnetic field. The three parts of this experiment are independent of each other, and consequently if the apparatus for any of these parts is not available, the remaining parts can still be worked.

The **theory** for this experiment may be summarized by noting that from the equations $q = i\Delta t$ and $e = ri$ (page 249), and $e = -\frac{\Delta \phi}{\Delta t}$ (page 302), one may obtain the equation

$$q = -\frac{\Delta \phi}{r}. \tag{80}$$

If the number of turns on the coil is n and if K is the sensitivity of the ballistic galvanometer, then the deflection (d) of the galvanometer will be, since $q = Kd$,

$$d = -\frac{n\Delta \phi}{Kr}. \tag{81}$$

This equation is true if the time of flow of charge is short compared to the period of the galvanometer.

Part (a) The galvanometer and fixed coil are connected together as shown in Figure 163. When the magnetic field inside the coil is allowed to change, then an induced electromotive force is produced while the change takes place. Note what happens when the N pole of a magnet is thrust quickly into the coil, say from left to right. Measure the deflection produced. Several trials will be necessary to obtain this deflection. Record them all to find the average deflection and error. Repeat for the other magnet and

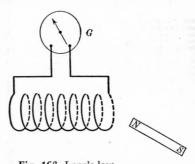

Fig. 163. Lenz's law.

thus compare their pole strengths. Construct your own data form.

(*Note.* In obtaining the deflection of a very sensitive galvanometer it is necessary to read and record the zero reading every time before observing the deflection, the reason being that the galvanometer is usually overdamped when a low-resistance coil is connected to it. This means that the galvanometer takes an enormously long time to come back to its original position, due, of course, to induced electromotive forces being created when the coil tries to come back, these induced electromotive forces opposing this motion. Since we cannot wait for the galvanometer to come back to the same zero, we ordinarily use the position from which it starts its deflection as zero. When using the galvanometer this way, of course, the student should wait long enough so that the zero does not drift very much. There are two other ways of overcoming this effect of overdamping or lag settling back to zero. One way is to open up the circuit somewhere, long enough for the galvanometer to swing back, and then close it as before. A better way sometimes is to induce a small electromotive force in such a direction as to bring it back to zero. This is done very simply with the aid of a small magnet. The student should try any one or all of these methods in obtaining a zero.)

Part (b)   With the same setup as in the previous part, perform the following tests and explain your results, using diagrams. In order to determine the direction of the induced currents from the observed direction of the galvanometer deflections (galvanometers are usually zero-center instruments), it is necessary to know in which direction the galvanometer deflects when current enters at a given binding post. Normally a deflection to the right on the scale means that the current entered at the binding post marked + on the galvanometer. In any case check this point with the instructor. Diagrams should be drawn for each answer.

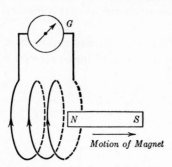

Fig. 164. Direction of the induced current.

1   Push a N pole of a magnet into the coil quickly and note the direction and magnitude of the deflection (the pole only is pushed through and not the whole magnet). After having determined the direction of the winding on the coil draw a diagram similar to that in Figure 164 to represent your observed results.

2   Pull out the N pole of the magnet rapidly (after having inserted it as in (1) and observe the direction and magnitude of the swing.

3   Push in the S pole — observe as before and show diagrammatically the direction of current flow.

4 Pull out the S pole and explain as in (3).

5 Having inserted the N pole as in (1), pull it out with various speeds, noting the deflection in each case. Record and explain your results.

6 If the apparatus will allow this, pull the whole magnet (both poles) through very rapidly and observe.

Part (c) For this part of the experiment we will place another coil inside the one used in parts (a) and (b). This second coil will take the place of the magnet. The direction of the winding on this coil is indicated and the iron core is inserted to increase the flux when a current is sent through the coil. For simplicity in Figure 165, these coils are represented as being next to each other, instead of inside one another.

1 Determine the direction of the induced electromotive force in the galvanometer coil when the switch is closed and show the direction in a diagram such as in Figure 165.

2 Repeat for the conditions when the switch is opened. Mark on your diagram whether the switch is being opened or closed and the current directions in both coils.

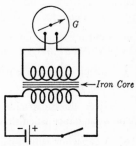

Fig. 165. Mutual induction.

Part (d) Connect the model dynamo to the ballistic galvanometer. Note the mechanism for rotating the coil through 10 degrees at a time (in Fig. 161, $\theta = 10°$). The spring tension should be kept always about the same. Arrange to start your readings from the position in which the plane of the rotating coil is at right angles to the magnetic field produced by the poles of the magnets. Record your ballistic deflection every 10 degrees, for a complete revolution (360 deg). Plot your results on a graph with degrees as abscissa and electromotive force or deflection as ordinate. Draw a smooth curve through as many of the points as possible.

Questions

(a) In measuring flux with a ballistic galvanometer, why is it essential that the magnet in the experiment [part (a)] be pulled out quickly?

(b) Given a magnet with a pole strength of 25 units (cgs) what is the flux sensitivity of the galvanometer if the coil through which the magnet was thrust had 50 turns? Assume a deflection of 30 divisions.

(c) Explain the results of part (c) in terms of Lenz's law.

(d) If the coil in part (d) is rotated, continuously, what would be the nature of the emf produced by this coil?

PROBLEMS

Experiment 42

1   Given that two similar charges, each of magnitude 300 esu, when separated in a medium by a distance of 13 cm are repelled with a force of 50 dynes, find the dielectric constant of the medium, and then from a book of physical tables find approximately the material of which the medium consists. *Note:* 300 statcoul. $\approx 10^{-7}$ coul.; 50 dynes $\approx 5 \times 10^{-4}$ newton.

2   Calculate the amount of charge which flows into a capacitor of capacitance 8 μf when charged to a potential difference of 100 v. Express your result in coulombs.

3   Find the capacitance (in f, μf, $\mu\mu$f, and cm) if a potential difference of 2 v produces a charge in the capacitor of 3 microcoulombs.

4   Calculate the current in problem 2 if the capacitor could charge up uniformly in 0.001 sec.

5   Given three capacitors of capacitances 0.30, 1.5, and 2 μf, find the total capacitance when they are connected (1) in parallel and (2) in series.

6   A capacitor with a capacitance 2 μf is connected to a dry cell giving 1.5 v. When discharged through a ballistic galvanometer, the deflection is 15 cm. Find the microcoulomb sensitivity. If another capacitor is charged from the same battery and produces 3 cm deflection, find the capacitance of the second capacitor as well as the amount of charge which this second capacitor had.

7   Distinguish carefully between the use of a ballistic galvanometer and a constant-current galvanometer, pointing out their similarities and differences in construction and use. Under what conditions could an ordinary D'Arsonval galvanometer be used for both purposes?

Experiment 43

1   A coil having 300 turns is connected to a ballistic galvanometer. It is known that 3000 lines of force are made to pass through this coil in 0.0005 sec. Find the emf induced in the coil.

2 Draw diagrams to illustrate Lenz's law and current flow in the following cases:

    (a) a north pole is thrust into a coil.

    (b) a south pole is withdrawn.

    (c) a current is made to flow in one circuit and induces a current in the second.

    (d) a current is broken in the first circuit.

3 Derive an expression for the emf induced in a coil when it rotates in a uniform horizontal magnetic field.

4 A magnetic flux of 0.00003 weber is known to have passed through the coil of a ballistic galvanometer in 0.0006 sec. If the coil had 360 turns, what emf was induced in the coil?

INTRODUCTORY RELATIONSHIPS

Generation of an alternating electromotive force in a wire is the result of relative motion between a magnet (or electromagnet) and the wire. The wire is usually in the form of a rectangular coil. The coil may be stationary as in many large generators, and the electromagnets rotating, or the magnets may be stationary and the coil (or coils) rotating as in Experiment 43.

In Figure 166 the mid-section of a single coil of wire is shown rotating clockwise between the poles of a magnet. Fleming's rule

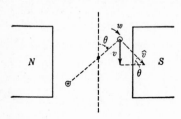

Fig. 166. A coil rotating in a uniform magnetic field.

applied here will show that the current is coming out from the paper on the right, and the conservation of energy formula will show that the instantaneous voltage developed will be $e = Bvl$ where v is the component of velocity perpendicular to the lines of flux and l is the length of the wire that is cutting the flux. Both the left and the right sides of the coil cut the lines of flux of density B gausses (i.e., lines of flux per square centimeter).

Since a summary of alternating current theory sufficient for the experiment only will be given, considerable reference to the lecture text will be needed for proofs of many of the relationships introduced and for the meaning of many terms.

The instantaneous velocity v of Figure 166 is related* to the

---

* The following letter notations will be used, illustrated by use of appropriate symbols for voltage: Instantaneous magnitude, e; root mean square (rms) magnitude, E; average magnitude, $\bar{E}$; peak (or maximum) magnitude, $\hat{E}$. We will further assume that we are to deal with simple harmonic motion only. The peak value for velocity will be given as $\hat{v}$ and the instantaneous value as v.

maximum velocity by the equation $v = \hat{v} \sin \theta$. Hence one may write

$$e = Bvl = B\hat{v}l \sin \theta = \hat{E} \sin \theta \qquad (82)$$

where $\hat{E}$ is the maximum electromotive force developed. Figure 167 illustrates the form of sinusoidal curve for instantaneous values of e versus θ or time (i.e., $\theta = \omega t$).

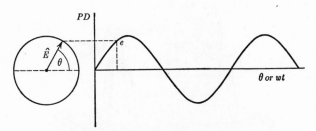

Fig. 167. Induced electromotive force developed in a coil rotating with constant angular speed in a uniform magnetic field.

If a resistance R only is in the circuit, the instantaneous magnitude of current will be likewise

$$i = \frac{e}{R} = \frac{\hat{E}}{R} \sin \theta = \hat{I} \sin \theta \qquad (83)$$

Reference to Figure 167 shows that we may consider $\hat{E}$ as a rotating voltage vector because of the sinusoidal relationship. In a similar manner $\hat{I}$ may be considered a rotating current vector.

Ammeters (also voltmeters) are calibrated to read $1/\sqrt{2}$ of the peak values for alternating current, and the alternating current ampere is defined as giving the same heat effects in a resistor as a direct current of the same magnitude. The magnitude $\hat{I}/\sqrt{2}$ is called the effective (or root mean square) current (I). That is $I = 0.707 \, \hat{I}$, and similarly, $E = 0.707 \, \hat{E}$. The reason for the root mean square relationships may be understood by noting that heat effects due to currents are proportional to the current squared. If a large number n of instantaneous current values (i_1, i_2, i_3, etc.,) equally spaced are squared, added, and then divided by n, we will get the average squared value of I used in the equation $P = I^2R$, where P

represents the power expended. One may show by appropriate figuring that

$$I = \sqrt{\frac{i_1^2 + i_2^2 + i_3^2 + \cdots i_n^2}{n}} = \frac{\hat{I}}{\sqrt{2}} = 0.707 \, \hat{I}.$$

Alternating current is led out of the coil to the external circuit by means of slip rings. In the simple alternator used in the experi-

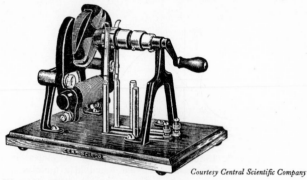

Courtesy Central Scientific Company

Fig. 168. Miller-Cowen dynamo-electric machine.

ment there is one rotating coil. Each of the two ends of the coil are attached to a slip ring. Hence our alternating current generator has two slip rings and a field externally excited by direct current (Fig. 168). A spring, called a brush, rubs against each ring. The external circuit is connected to the two brushes.

DIRECT CURRENT GENERATORS

The same generator as used above (Fig. 168) may be used to generate direct current by connecting the two ends of the coil to a single ring which has been divided into two equal semicircles and insulated. Such a device is called a commutator. When the two brushes are properly placed relative to the coil and the two segments of the ring, direct current flows in the external circuit that is con-

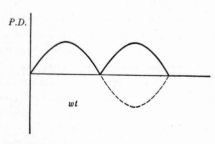

Fig. 169. Commutation of the electromotive force.

nected to the brushes while an alternating electromotive force is still induced in the rotating coil. Each half-cycle, therefore (Fig. 169), is reversed in direction to give a pulsating current. In commercial generators, the pulsating effect is minimized by use of multiple coils. The commutator consists of several segments, and there are usually more than two electromagnets.

Our direct-current generator has an advantage in that the current generated by the machine may be used to energize the magnets

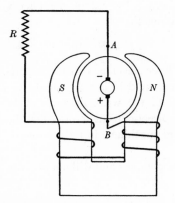

Fig. 170. Series wound self excited d-c generator.

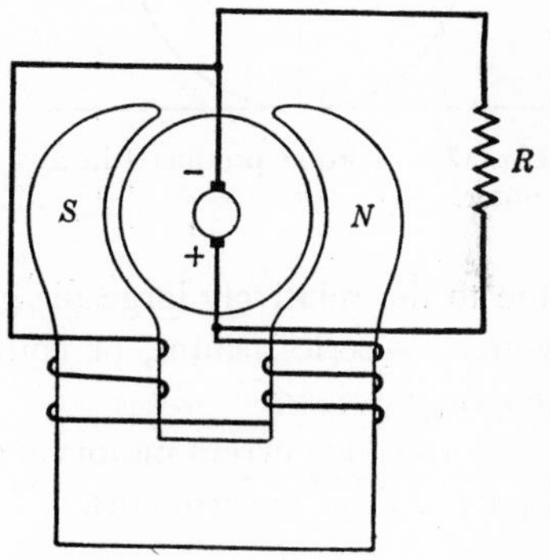

Fig. 171. Shunt wound self excited d-c generator.

also. If the coil, field, and external circuit are connected in series (Fig. 170), the generator is called series wound. In this case, the field will be wound with a few turns of large wire. If the coil and field with many turns of small wire are in parallel (Fig. 171) with the external circuit, the generator is said to be shunt wound. For more constant voltage under wide ranges of resistance (i.e., large load variations), a compound winding is used. A compound-wound generator has a combination of series and shunt windings. Such a winding may be visualized by winding the field of the generator in Figure 170 with a large number of turns of small wire and connecting the two ends of this coil to A and B.

DIRECT CURRENT MOTORS

If in Figure 172 an external current is forced through the coil in the same direction as in Figure 166, in which case an external torque was applied, a torque will now be produced which will tend to spin the coil in the opposite direction (i.e., counterclockwise). This torque (τ) is due to the force F developed as a result of the external current $\hat{I}$ forced through the coil and has the magnitude $\tau = dF \sin \theta$ where d is the distance between the active conductors of the coil. One may prove by use of the energy equations that

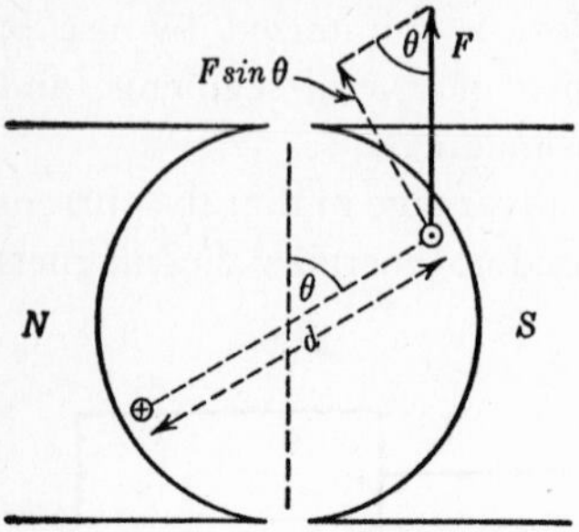

$$F = B\hat{I}l/10. \qquad (84)$$

Fig. 172. Torque produced in a motor.

The force developed in the experimental models is very small because of the weak magnetic field due to the relatively large air gaps. Direct-current motors may be wound as series, shunt, or compound machines, just the same as generators.

Alternating-current motors are more complex and will not become a part of these experiments.

IMPEDANCE

As long as resistance only constitutes the load (Fig. 174), the voltage and current remain in phase and assume zero, or maximum, values at the same instant. When reactive voltages constitute a part of the load, as for example when inductances and capacitances are in the line, additional opposition to the flow of alternating current is encountered and the current is thrown out of phase with the voltage. Figure 173 illustrates

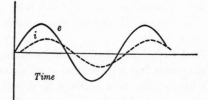

Fig. 173. Current and voltage are out of phase.

a case where the current lags behind the voltage, typical of a circuit containing resistance and inductance in series.

The total opposition to the flow of alternating current is called *impedance* and is designated by the letter $\mathcal{Z}$. In alternating current circuits $\mathcal{Z}$ replaces R, and $\mathcal{Z}$ is defined by the equation

$$\mathcal{Z} = \frac{E}{I}. \tag{85}$$

The relation between $\mathcal{Z}$ and R will be given later.

Resistance only in circuit If the circuit contains resistance only (Fig. 174) then

$$e = \hat{E} \sin \omega t;$$

also

$$i = \frac{e}{R} = \frac{\hat{E}}{R} \sin \omega t = \hat{I} \sin \omega t,$$

and

$$\mathcal{Z} = R = \frac{E}{I}.$$

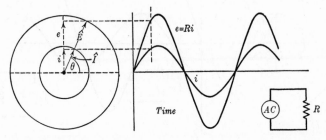

Fig. 174. Representation of current and electromotive force when the circuit contains resistance only. The current is in phase with the voltage across R.

Inductive reactance only in circuit When an "ideal" coil with inductance only is in the circuit, the opposition (i.e., impedance) to the flow of current is determined by the rate of change of current which sets up an opposing electromotive force. The ratio of the back electromotive force (in volts) to the rate of change of current (in amp per sec) is defined as the inductance $\left(\text{i.e., } L = -\dfrac{e_\mathrm{b}}{\dfrac{\Delta i}{\Delta t}} \right)$. The unit of inductance L defined this way is the henry. The generated electromotive force e therefore has the instantaneous magnitude $e = L \, \Delta i / \Delta t$. Note that when the current i has an instantaneous value 0, then e is a maximum, since the slope of $\Delta i / \Delta t$ is a maximum (Fig. 175). This relationship between instantaneous values of e and i can exist only if the current vector $\hat{I}$ is behind the voltage vector $\hat{E}$ by 90 degrees. The figure shows that

$$e = \hat{E} \sin \omega t$$

$$i = \hat{I} \sin (\omega t - 90°) = \frac{\hat{E}}{Z} \sin (\omega t - 90°).$$

Z may be shown to have the value

$$Z = X_L = \omega L = 2\pi f L, \qquad (86)$$

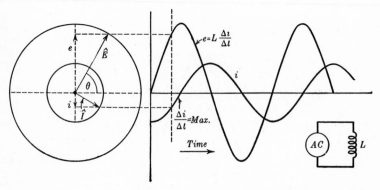

Fig. 175. Circuit contains only "pure" inductance. The current lags the voltage by 90°.

where f, L, and Z represent, respectively, the frequency in cycles per second, inductance in henries, and inductive reactance in ohms. The symbol X_L is used commonly to represent the reactance in ohms due to inductance. There is actually no dissipation of energy in a "pure" inductor for the current and voltage are out of phase by 90 degrees.

Inductance and resistance only in the circuit Every inductor has some resistance because of the wire making up the coil. Let this resistance be R_c. Now place a lamp of resistance R_b in series with the inductor. The total noninductive resistance will be $R = R_c + R_b$. For purposes of calculation, we consider the two elements (i.e., noninductive and inductive) opposing flow of current by themselves.

The current through R is I, and the potential drop across R is IR. The potential drop across the "pure" inductor is IX_L. Since the voltage and current are out of phase by 90 degrees in the inductor, a proper voltage relationship between the two elements and the applied line voltage may be obtained by constructing a vector diagram (Fig. 176) with voltage ($\hat{E}_L$) across the pure inductor

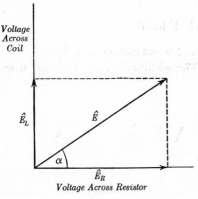

Voltage Across Coil

$\hat{E}_L$ $\hat{E}$

α

$\hat{E}_R$

Voltage Across Resistor

Fig. 176. Vector representation of the voltages for a circuit containing L and R.

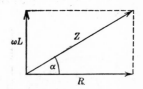

ωL Z

α

R

Fig. 177. Impedance representation for the same circuit showing the resistive (R) and the reactive (ωL) components of the total impedance (Z).

placed on the vertical (up) axis, and the voltage ($\hat{E}_R$) across the total noninductive resistor R located on the horizontal axis, the current being in the phase with $\hat{E}_R$. Experiment and theory show that the resultant voltage $\hat{E}$ will be

$$\hat{E} = \sqrt{\hat{E}_R^2 + \hat{E}_L^2} = \sqrt{(\hat{I}R)^2 + (\hat{I}\omega L)^2} \tag{87}$$

Note that the scalar addition of the voltage across the resistor (or resistors) and the inductor will not give the voltage across the generator. If R_c is very small compared to R_b, the voltage relationship of equation (87) may be readily checked on the a-c 60-cycle line, by reading an ammeter placed in the circuit and a voltmeter placed across the line, the inductor, and the lamp, respectively. We get $Z = E/I$ and the approximate relationships $R = E_b/I$, and $X_L = E_L/I$, where E_b and E_L are the voltages developed across the lamp and the inductor, respectively.

The angle of lag of the current through the circuit compared to the generator electromotive force is now α and is less than 90 degrees. The equations representing the instantaneous voltage and instantaneous current are (Fig. 178).

$$e = \hat{E} \sin \omega t$$

$$i = \hat{I} \sin (\omega t - \alpha)$$

The impedance of this circuit, defined as $\mathcal{Z} = E/I$, is found by reference to equation (87) to be

$$\mathcal{Z} = \sqrt{R^2 + (\omega L)^2}. \tag{88}$$

That is, the impedance consists of a dissipative part R, and a reactive, nondissipative part ωL. The addition is seen, therefore, from

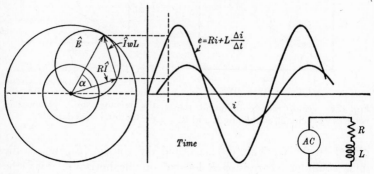

Fig. 178. Alternating current flowing in a circuit containing inductance and resistance.

equation (88) to be similar to that for the component voltages, and is represented by Figure 177. The nondissipative part of an impedance limits the current flow because of the out-of-phase relationship between voltage and current.

Capacitative reactance only in the circuit When only a capacitor is connected to an alternating electromotive force theory shows that the current vector $\hat{I}$ is ahead of the voltage vector $\hat{E}$ by 90 degrees. The equation which shows this may be simplified by reference to the charging of a capacitor with a dry cell of voltage E. If the charging time is t, usually a very small fraction of a second, the charge Q on the capacitor after the time interval t is $Q = \bar{I}t = CE$, where $\bar{I}$ is the average magnitude of the current in the time t, C

being the capacitance. Hence, $\overline{I} = C(E/t)$, and for any infinitesimal time interval Δt, in which the voltage changed by the infinitesimal value Δe, the instantaneous magnitude of current will be

$$i = C \frac{\Delta e}{\Delta t}. \qquad (89)$$

The above equation shows that i is a maximum when the voltage is changing most rapidly (i.e., when its slope is maximum.) Hence,

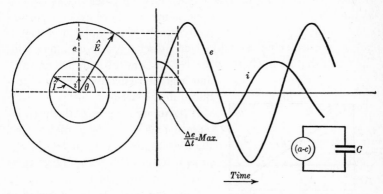

Fig. 179. Alternating current flowing in a circuit containing only capacitance.

the current vector $\hat{I}$ is 90 degrees ahead of the voltage vector as pictured in Figure 179. The equations for the instantaneous values of current and voltage will be

$$e = \hat{E} \sin \theta = \hat{E} \sin \omega t$$

$$i = \hat{I} \sin (\omega t + 90°) = \frac{\hat{E}}{Z} \sin (\omega t + 90°)$$

where Z, which is the impedance for this particular case, may be shown to have the magnitude

$$Z = \frac{1}{\omega C}. \qquad (90)$$

The impedance for a capacitor only is commonly called capacitive reactance, hence $Z = X_c = \frac{1}{\omega C} = \frac{1}{2\pi f C}$, where Z is in ohms when C is measured in farads.

An alternating current flowing in the wires leading to the two plates of a condenser changes in magnitude and direction depending upon the rate at which charge is accumulating or flowing off the plates. An ammeter that is not sensitive to change in direction of the current deflects just as though a certain continuous current were passing through it, and although there is no direct electrical connection from one capacitor plate to the other, we may regard the phenomenon as an alternating current passing through the capacitor. If the capacitor is one of large capacitance a greater charge goes on its plates each time it charges and hence a greater average current exists in the circuit. Also, if the frequency of the applied voltage is larger, the capacitor is charged and discharged more often, with the result that more charge per second is sent through the ammeter and a greater effective current is produced in the circuit.

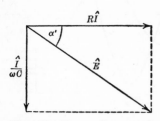

Fig. 180. Vector diagram of voltages in a circuit containing C and R.

A resistance in series with the capacitance makes the angle of lead less than 90 degrees. The angle will approach zero as R becomes large compared to the value of $1/\omega C$.

Since the peak current is ahead of the peak voltage by 90 degrees when a capacitance only is in the circuit, the resultant voltage across a capacitor and a resistor in series may be represented by a vector diagram as shown in Figure 180 where the peak voltage across the capacitor is placed on the vertical (down) axis and the peak voltage across R is placed along the horizontal axis. The line voltage (either peak or effective) will be related to the component voltages (either peak or effective) by the relationship

$$E = \sqrt{(IR)^2 + \left(\frac{I}{\omega C}\right)^2} = I\sqrt{R^2 + \left(\frac{1}{\omega C}\right)^2} \qquad (91)$$

The impedance diagram of this circuit is represented by the equation

$$\mathcal{Z} = \frac{E}{I} = \sqrt{R^2 + \left(\frac{1}{\omega C}\right)^2} = \sqrt{R^2 + X_c^2} \qquad (92)$$

Resistance, capacitance and inductance in series   The above description of the current and voltage relationships with capacitors

and inductors used separately, indicate that the peak current and
the peak voltage may be considered as rotating vectors, and that
the resultant magnitude of the voltage across the lamp, coil, and
capacitor may be obtained by a proper "addition" of the voltages
across each of the three elements L, C, and R (Fig. 191), where R
is made up of the resistance R_b of the lamp and the resistance R_c
of the coil.

When the circuit contains L, C, and R in series and an alternating
current is flowing through them, then the method used for additions
of the component voltages is shown in the two-dimensional diagram
of Figure 181. The voltage ($\hat{E}_L = \hat{I}\omega L$) across the inductor is plotted

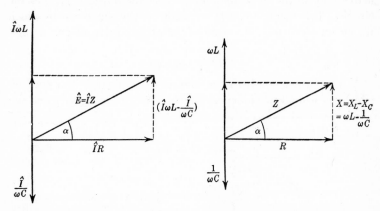

Fig. 181. Circuit containing inductance,
capacitance and resistance—vector diagram of voltages.

Fig. 182. Circuit containing L, C,
and R.—Impedance diagram.

on the vertical (up) axis, the voltage ($\hat{E}_C = \hat{I}/\omega C$) across the capacitor is plotted on the vertical (down) axis, and the voltage across
the resistor is plotted along the horizontal axis. The resultant peak
generator voltage ($\hat{E}$) in terms of the peak voltages across the
different parts of the circuit is

$$\hat{E} = \sqrt{\hat{E}_R{}^2 + (\hat{E}_L - \hat{E}_C)^2} = \hat{I}\sqrt{R^2 + (\omega L - 1/\omega C)^2}$$
$$= \hat{I}\sqrt{R^2 + (X_L - X_C)^2} = \hat{I}\sqrt{R^2 + X^2} \qquad (93)$$
$$= \hat{I}Z.$$

The corresponding impedance diagram is shown in Figure 182, where the magnitude of Z is given* by

$$Z = \sqrt{R^2 + (\omega L - 1/\omega C)^2}; \quad \tan \alpha = \frac{\omega L - 1/\omega C}{R} \qquad (94)$$

Resonance, or maximum current, is obtained when $\omega L = 1/\omega C$ (i.e., $f = 1/2\,\pi\sqrt{LC}$). Then our equations simplify so that

$$\alpha = 0 \text{ and } Z = R.$$

Of the three impedance elements, resistance is the only one that dissipates power (i.e., liberates heat when a current flows). The other two elements, namely inductance and capacitance, are reactive only in the sense that they reflect the power back into the circuit. Their reactive effects are indicated by the extent to which the current is thrown out of phase with the source voltage.

TRANSFORMERS

A transformer consists of a continuous laminated iron core on which are wound two independent coils, called the primary and the

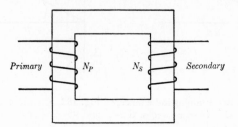

Fig. 183. Transformer.

secondary (Fig. 183). The object of the transformer is to transfer the impressed alternating potential difference from the one coil (the primary) to the other (the secondary) by means of changes of

---

* Use of vectors or complex numbers leads to a much clearer understanding of the phenomena, and either method is a more powerful mode of attack. In complex number notation, the impedance may be written as

$$Z = R + jX = |Z|e^{i\alpha}$$

where $\qquad |Z| = \sqrt{R^2 + X^2},\ X = X_L - X_C,\ \tan \alpha = \dfrac{X_L - X_C}{R}$

and $e^{i\alpha} = \cos \omega t + j \sin \omega t$. As used here $|Z|$, the absolute value of Z, is the same as the Z used in the text.

flux through the common iron core. Neglecting the resistance of the wire, the instantaneous voltage e_p in the primary is, by definition, $e_p = N_p \Delta\phi/\Delta t$, while the instantaneous voltage e_s induced in the secondary is $e_s = N_s\Delta\phi/\Delta t$, where N_p and N_s are the numbers of turns of wire in the primary and secondary, respectively, and where $\Delta\phi$ is the change of flux during the time interval Δt. If we assume, for simplicity, that we are dealing with a perfect transformer, the instantaneous power input $e_p i_p$ will be equal to the instantaneous power output (i.e., $e_p i_p = e_s i_s$). We may write therefore the following important ratios:

$$\frac{e_p}{e_s} = \frac{N_p}{N_s} = \frac{i_s}{i_p}. \tag{95}$$

In actual commercial practice the coils have resistance, and induced currents are produced in the iron. Both of these effects produce unnecessary heat and consequently decrease the efficiency of the transformer. A careful study of these losses is necessary in designing a transformer. Such matters are discussed in textbooks on the subject. We will assume for the purposes of the experiment that these losses are negligible.

EXPERIMENT 44

GENERATORS AND MOTORS

Part (a) *To connect and operate a simple a-c dynamo.*

Part (b) *To operate a simple externally excited d-c dynamo.*

Part (c) *To connect and operate a simple form of series, shunt, and compound wound d-c dynamo.*

Part (d) *To connect and operate a simple form of d-c motor.*

APPARATUS: Demountable generator, small rheostat of about 20 ohms, portable galvanometer of rather low sensitivity, storage battery of about 6–8 volts.

Before commencing the work outlined below, study the instrument (Fig. 168) itself. Note the relation of the different parts to the whole. Trace the electric circuit from the armature coil through the split commutator or collecting rings to the brushes and binding posts.

The rings and sections of commutator should be clean, and it is well to occasionally polish them with very fine sandpaper, as imperfect contact with the brushes will give poor results, especially in

the experiments in which the iron is left out of the armature, since
the electromotive force generated is small.

Part (a)   The more insensitive form of setup for the a-c dynamo
is made by removal of the laminated iron core from the armature
coil. After removal of this laminated iron core, (1) connect the field
winding to the 6–8 volt source through the rheostat so that a small

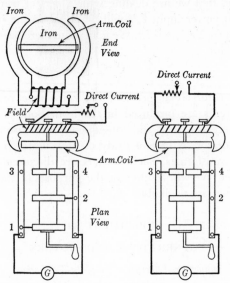

Fig. 184. Separately ex-   Fig. 185. Separately excited a-c generator.   cited d-c generator.

current of 0.5 to about 2 amperes flows, (2) attach the brushes so
that they will make contact with the collector rings (1 and 2), (3)
connect the galvanometer (see Fig. 184).

Turn the armature coil slowly. Note movement of the galvanometer needle. Does the needle move continuously in one direction, or does it move first in one direction, then in the reverse
direction?

Note the relation of the position of the armature coil to the field
magnet at the time of change in the current direction. Turn the
armature coil sharply one-quarter turn in one direction and note
movement of galvanometer needle. Move armature coil back to
original position by another sharp turn. What connection is there
between change of polarity in the armature coil and change of

direction of the current? Why is the current produced called an alternating current? Note the magnitude of change in frequency as the coil is rotated more rapidly.

Replace the laminated iron core in the armature coil. Follow same steps as above. What effect has iron in the armature coil upon strength of current?

Part (b) Now attach the brushes to 3 and 4 (Fig. 185) so that they make contact with the commutator. Turn the armature at a moderate speed. Observe the movement of the galvanometer

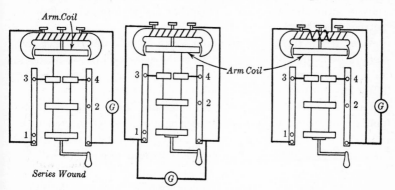

Fig. 186. Series wound d-c generator.

Fig. 187. Shunt wound d-c generator.

Fig. 188. Compound wound d-c generator.

needle. How is this current different from that observed above? Why is it known as direct current?

Describe the commutator. Note how it is connected to the armature coil and its relation to the brushes as the armature coil is rotated. Rotate the armature coil slowly and test the polarity of the ends as the brush contact changes on segments of the commutator. What is the function of the commutator?

Rotate armature coil at different speeds. How does the speed of rotation affect the strength of the current?

Note that in Figures 184 and 185 the armature coil is not electrically connected with the field coil. Why would apparatus of this class be known as *separately excited* dynamos?

Part (c) How do the connections of Figures 186, 187 and 188 differ from those of Figures 184 and 185? Why is a power supply unnecessary? Your conclusion should give you the definition of a self-excited dynamo. Why are many large alternating-current dynamos of the separately excited type? Why are practically all direct-current dynamos self-excited.

Connect apparatus as in Figure 186. How is the field excited? What form of connection is this? Why does such an arrangement show a series dynamo? What effect has this winding upon flow of current generated?

Connect apparatus as in Figure 187. How is the field coil excited? What form of connection is this? Why does such an arrangement show a shunt dynamo? What effect has this winding upon flow of current generated?

Wind a few turns of wire about the field coil and connect the apparatus as in Figure 188. How is the field excited? Why does such an arrangement show a compound wound dynamo? What effect has this winding upon flow of current generated?

Part (d)   A well-designed dynamo of the shunt, series, or compound type will usually operate as a motor when connected to a source of electrical energy having sufficient power. Its speed of rotation will be fixed, for in rotating, the armature generates an electromotive force just the same as though it were turned mechanically. The current actually supplied by the outside source to this motor will be determined by the numerical difference between the applied electromotive force and the generated back electromotive force. The latter depends upon the speed. Hence if the load (and other frictional losses in the motor) tend to lower the speed, the difference between these two electromotive forces becomes greater and consequently the actual current taken from the supply line will increase.

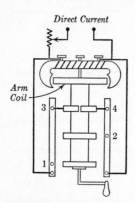

Fig. 189.   Shunt wound d-c motor.

The apparatus connected as in Figure 189 shows the dynamo run as a motor. Explain the operation. What is the direction of the current flow from the outside source? Disconnect and determine the direction of current flow when the armature is turned by hand in the same direction as for the motor. Are these currents opposed to each other or do they flow in the same direction? What effect would this have on the rotation of the armature?

Questions

(a) What is the object of a commutator?

(b) Some dynamos are classified as separately (or externally) excited. Why?

(c) Why are a-c dynamos separately excited?

(d) Why are the more complicated compound motors useful?

(e) Does the current go the same way through the coil when turning in the same direction both as a motor and as a generator?

(f) Which type of motor will have the larger field coil resistance, a series or a shunt wound motor? Why?

EXPERIMENT 45

ALTERNATING CURRENT AND IMPEDANCE

Part (a) *To determine the resistance of a lamp, of a coil, and of a condenser with d-c and a-c circuits.*

Part (b) *To measure the resistance (impedance) of a lamp, coil, and capacitor in series.*

Part (c) *To determine the inductance of a coil necessary to produce resonance on the 60-cycle a-c line with the fixed capacitor provided, when the lamp, coil, and capacitor are all in series.*

APPARATUS: Impedance board* consisting of an inductor with removable iron core, capacitor, one 100-w lamp, two a-c ammeters (0–1 and 0–3 amp), two a-c voltmeters (0–50, 0–500 v), 110-v d-c line, 110-v a-c line, pair of prods with phone tips and connecting wires for measuring potential differences.

The apparatus is illustrated in Figure 190. In this apparatus, the lamp cannot be shunted out since it is in a lamp socket. (If your apparatus is made so that each of the elements may be shunted out, a 0–10 ammeter must be used when the 110-volt d-c line is placed across the inductor. The inductor will heat considerably, and there-

---

* A convenient form of apparatus consists of an inductor wound with #16 wire having about 0.5 henry inductance without the iron core, in series with a capacitor of capacitance about 10 to 12 μf and a lamp of about 100 ohms. Switches and terminals should be provided to insert an ammeter and to shunt out, at will, either the inductor or the capacitor or both. A larger-wattage lamp will give sharper resonant peaks, but the voltages may become highly excessive. If your apparatus allows shunting of the lamp also, a higher range ammeter will be required, i.e., 0–10 amperes.

fore change its resistance easily by 10 to 15 per cent in the process of making the measurement.)

Part (a) Connect the inductor and the lamp in series and throw the double-pole double-throw switch to the d-c line. Measure the

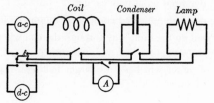

Fig. 190. Circuit containing inductance, capacitance and resistance.

current through the inductor and the voltage across it (with and without core). Repeat these measurements for the lamp. The larger-range ammeter should be tried first. Calculate the impedance of the inductor and of the lamp $\left(\text{i.e., } Z = \dfrac{E}{I}\right)$ using the larger-range voltmeter first. Now connect the capacitor and the lamp to the d-c line. Measure the currents and voltages as previously. Calculate the impedance of the capacitor and the lamp.

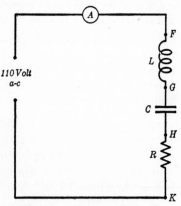

Fig. 191. An inductor, capacitor, and resistor connected in series.

Make similar measurements as above with the a-c line. Calculate the impedance of the coil (with and without core), the capacitor, and the lamp when alternating current is used. Also calculate the capacitance C of the capacitor.

The ammeters and the voltmeters you are using are a-c instruments and therefore may be used on either alternating or direct current.* Direct-current instruments are usually made to operate on d-c lines only.

Calculation of the inductance (L) of the coil   From the above experiments on the impedance of the coil when connected to the

* This does not apply if the test instrument includes a rectifier.

60-cycle a-c line, calculate its inductance, with and without the core, by use of the formula $Z = \sqrt{R_c^2 + X_L^2}$. In this formula, R_c is the d-c resistance of the coil, and $X_L = \omega L$, where $\omega = 2\pi60 = 377$. The value of L will be in henrys.

Part (b) Connect the inductor (with core), the capacitor, and the 100-watt lamp in series as shown in Figure 191. Measure the current through the series combination, also the potential drops across FK, FG, GH, and HK. Note that the sum of the voltages across FG, GH, and HK do not add up to be equal to that across

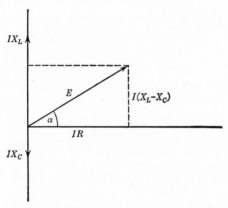

Fig. 192. Vector addition of voltages in the circuit of Fig. 191.

FK. An approximate calculation for the voltage across the 110-volt a-c line in terms of the impedance elements of Figure 181 is obtained by use of the equation

$$E = \sqrt{(\text{Voltage across } HK)^2 + (\text{Voltage across } FG - \text{Voltage across } GH)^2}$$

What is the error when added this way?

The proper addition in accordance with Figure 192 will be obtained if we recall that the coil (see page 323) has some resistance R_c that must be added to the resistance R_b of the lamp, and that the voltage drop across that part of the coil which can be supposed to have pure inductance only is IX_L. Hence, the voltages are properly added as follows

$$E = I\sqrt{(R_c + R_b)^2 + (\omega L - 1/\omega C)^2}$$

where I is the current as read by the ammeter. The magnitudes of L and C have been determined previously. Recalculate the voltage across the a-c line in terms of the impedance elements of the above equation.

Fig. 193. Resonance conditions in the series circuit.

Part (c) With the same connections as in part (b), it should be possible to find a maximum current for a certain adjustment of the core (and possibly of the capacitor if variable). Measure this maximum current. For this maximum current condition the circuit is said to resonate to the frequency of the impressed voltage. Having obtained this resonance, measure the voltage across the inductor, the capacitor, and the lamp. Note that they not only do not add algebraically to give the applied electromotive force, but that the voltages are high across the inductor and the capacitor and of about the same magnitude.

They can be added only vectorially as suggested in part (b), and shown in Figure 193. From your measurements how do the voltage drops across the inductor and across the capacitor compare? Also, how does the sum of the potential differences across the resistances (i.e., lamp and coil) compare with the line voltage? Note also at this resonant condition that $\omega L = 1/\omega C$. If C is known, the value of L to cause resonance can be calculated.

Questions

(a) Does a current flow through a capacitor continuously when connected to alternating current?

(b) What is the resistance of a capacitor on direct current?

(c) In what way does Lenz's law apply to this experiment for (1) a d-c source, (2) an a-c source?

(d) Calculate the value of L needed to cause resonance at 60 cycles per sec in part (c).

(e) What is the magnitude of $I\omega L$ in part (b)? How does this compare with the voltage across the parts FG?

(f) What is meant by a reactance? What electrical element, or elements may be found in a reactance.

(g) Compare the impedance of the lamp on alternating current with that on direct current. Make similar comparisons with the coil, the capacitor.

EXPERIMENT 46

THE TRANSFORMER

Part (a) *To study the magnitude of magnetic flux changes associated with primary coils when direct current is used.*

Part (b) *To study the magnitude of magnetic flux changes associated with primary and secondary coils that surround a **U**-shaped core when direct current is used.*

Part (c) *To study the magnetic effect on a third coil used as a load when direct current is used, the setup otherwise as in part (b).*

Part (d) *To study the load characteristics when lights are substituted for the coil and a source of alternating current is used in place of direct current.*

APPARATUS: Three Gilley coils,* one having fewer turns than the other two, one soft iron **U**-shaped core, soft iron armature, soft iron core, d-c and a-c voltmeters of 10-v range; d-c millivoltmeter or a three-button portable galvanometer, two test prods with wire leads, magnetic compass, two 3.8-v (approximate) bulbs of unequal current rating, source of direct voltage of about 2–3 v, source of alternating voltage of about 6–7 v, switch.

Part (a) Connect a low direct voltage source of about 2 to 3 volts in series with a switch and one of the coils, (Fig. 194). Close the switch and place the compass at *A*. Observe whether end *A* of the coil has a north or south polarity. Repeat for position *B*. Open the switch and reverse the battery. Repeat the observations at *A* and *B* with the magnetic compass. *Do not keep the switch closed longer than necessary.*

Part (b) Connect the two Gilley coils and the soft iron **U**-shaped core to the battery of 2 and 3 volts as shown in Figure 195. Close the switch and observe the polarity at *A* and *C* with the magnetic compass. Connect the d-c voltmeter by means of the test leads first

---

* Form-wound coils mounted on a base with binding posts or clips. They are made so that the coils may be placed close together.

to the terminals P_1 and P_2 and then to the unconnected terminals P_3 and P_4. Record the voltages.

Open the switch and reverse the battery connections. Then close the switch, observe the polarity at A and C, and repeat the above voltmeter readings.

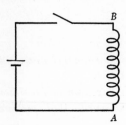

Fig. 194. Magnetic effect produced by current flowing in a coil.

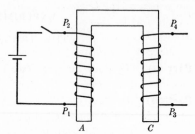

Fig. 195. Effect of iron on the magnetic flux.

Close the opening in the soft iron **U**-shaped core with the soft iron armature. Next close the switch and take readings with the voltmeter at P_1 and P_2, also P_3 and P_4 as above. Do you observe any sparks upon opening the switch. What is the cause of the sparks?

Connect a d-c millivoltmeter to the terminals P_3 and P_4. Open and close the switch with and without the soft iron armature in place across the gap in the **U**-shaped core. Record the magnitude and direction of the current on make and break of the circuit in both instances. What is the voltage after the circuit has been closed more than about 1 second?

Trace for any given instant the direction of the current from the battery and of the flux in the core. Make any necessary assumptions.

Part (c) Connect the three Gilley coils and the soft iron **U**-shaped core as shown in Figure 196. Close the switch and observe

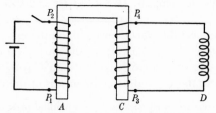

Fig. 196. Induced effects in the secondary coil.

the polarity at C and D (if any). Observe if there is more polarity at D when the switch is just opened or closed. *Coil at D should be a foot or more from either of the other coils.* Coil D should be placed so that the least possible deflection may be noted.* Connect the d-c voltmeter by means of the test leads first to the terminals P_1 and P_2 and then to the terminals P_3 and P_4. Does the voltmeter deflect as much and in the same way as in part (b) under similar circumstances?

Place the soft iron armature on the soft iron **U**-shaped core. Does the magnetic compass deflect more now at D when the switch is just opened or closed?

Part (d)   Connect a source of 6–7 alternating volts, a soft iron **U**-shaped core, two Gilley coils, a 3.8-volt flashlight, and a switch

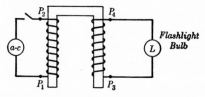

Fig. 197. Transformer action.

as shown in Figure 197. Close the switch and observe the brightness of the light. Read the voltage with the a-c voltmeter across P_1 and P_2, also P_3 and P_4.

Now place the soft iron armature across the opening of the soft iron **U**-shaped core. Observe the brightness of the bulb. Measure the voltage again across P_1 and P_2, also P_3 and P_4. Repeat, using a secondary coil of lesser number of turns and observe the brightness and voltage across P_1 and P_2, also across P_3 and P_4.

Now place a second flashlight in parallel with the first. Has the brightness decreased? If it has, explain. Measure the voltage across P_1 and P_2, also across P_3 and P_4. Try loosening the light that draws the lesser current, if there is any difference in current carrying capacities, and then the light that draws the larger current. Explain any differences noticed.

* Because of the magnetic effect of the **U**-shaped core.

Questions

(a) What advantages, if any, are there in use of a laminated iron core for the transformer? (*Note.* A laminated iron core was not furnished for the above experiments.)

(b) Will a transformer work on direct current? Explain your answer.

(c) How are *direct* voltages changed from lower to higher and from higher to lower values?

(d) What are some of the causes for lights in a house to dim sometimes when a heavy-duty electric iron is connected into the convenience outlet?

(e) An alternating current voltmeter of the iron vane type was furnished for the experiment. On what parts of the above experiment will a moving-coil permanent-magnet type of voltmeter work?

(f) Draw an enlarged picture of the setup of Figure 196 that will indicate clearly the way the wire is wound in all three coils. When the switch is just closed so that the current is increasing in the direction from the positive battery terminals towards the terminal P_2, label the directions of the current around all coils and the direction of the increasing flux through all coils.

(g) Why must the iron core used in a transformer be continuous?

PROBLEMS

Experiment 44

1 An experimental motor has a rectangular armature coil of 50 turns. The length of each wire perpendicular to the magnetic field is 5 cm. If the plane of the coil is parallel to the field, what will be the magnitude of the flux density if a current of 2 amp flowing in the conductors produces on the periphery at one end of the coil in a direction perpendicular to the flux density a force of 5000 dynes?

2 Assume the rectangular coil of Figure 166 has 75 turns, and has dimensions 8 by 3 cm, the narrow sides being perpendicular to the field. If the flux density is 100 gausses, what will be the instantaneous voltage developed when turning at the rate of 4 rps and θ is (a) 90°, (b) 60°.

3 Derive the expression $F = B\hat{I}l/10$, in equation (84) page 316. Refer to some lecture text for details.

4 What will be the torque on the coil in problem 1 if the side of the coil parallel to the field is 10 cm.

5 What will be the torque on the above coil after it has turned 30° from the position as given in problem 1.

Experiment 45

A resistor, an inductor of negligible resistance, and a capacitor are connected to a 60-c a-c line as shown in Figure 198. The emf's across the elements are measured by an a-c voltmeter and found to be 80 v across the resistor, 90 v across the capacitor, and 30 v across the inductor. The current was found to be 0.25 amp.

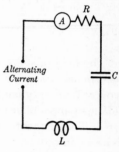

1 Draw a vector diagram representing the rms voltages across the separate elements.

2 What is the voltage across the a-c line?

3 What is the reactance of the capacitor?

4 What is the capacitance of the capacitor?

5 What is the reactance of the inductor?

6 What is the coefficient of self inductance of inductor?

Fig. 198.

7 What is the resistance of the resistor?

8 What is the resultant reactance of the capacitor and inductor?

9 What is the total impedance of the series circuit?

10 At what frequency would there be current resonance in the circuit?

Experiment 46

1 The power lines under the sidewalks of a certain campus are operated at 2300 v and are transformed to 120 v by a transformer at the entrance, or near the entrance, to each of the larger buildings. What will be the ratio of turns of primary to secondary, provided there are no power losses?

2 If there are no power losses, $V_1I_1 = V_2I_2$ where V_1 and I_1 are the effective voltage and the effective current respectively in the primary. If 200 amp are being used in a certain building, what will be the current in the primary when the voltage is 2300? Secondary voltage is 120.

3 What is the magnitude of power consumed in the above problem if the voltage is 120?

4 If the primary of a doorbell has 4400 turns, how many turns must the secondary have if the bell is to be operated at a difference of potential of 5 v when the primary voltage is 110?

CHAPTER XXVII

FUNDAMENTALS OF VACUUM TUBES AND RADIO

The field of study involving radio tubes of all kinds is of course enormous and in an experimental *physics* course one can hope to cover only a very small portion. The simplest radio tube consists of a filament and a plate sealed into a glass envelope which is then evacuated. The filament is usually made of tungsten wire (similar to the wire in an ordinary electric light bulb). The function of this wire is to act as an emitter of electrons if the temperature is high enough, or to act as a heater for an oxide-coated metallic surface which has the property of making it easier for the electrons in the metal to escape through the surface. In all cases the filament has to be heated so that it, or else some oxide-coated conductor nearby, will act as a source of free electrons (the cathode) inside the evacuated bulb. The part called the plate is usually in the form of a cylindrical or oval-shaped metallic electrode which surrounds the cathode and has a potential applied to it that is positive with respect to the cathode. Once the electrons have been evaporated from the cathode they will be attracted by the positive plate. This electric current is referred to as the plate current. Note that the electron flow is opposite in direction to the conventional current direction. Electrons will continue to flow as long as they are returned back to the cathode and the latter keeps on emitting electrons. As a matter of fact in their passage through the tube from cathode to plate the electrons are accelerated and, as we know, when the plate potential (and consequently electric field) becomes high enough, X-rays are produced at the plate (or target). In radio use, however, this condition is not reached because the plate voltages are in the order of a few hundreds of volts instead of the thousands of volts used in X-ray work. Such two-electrode tubes are used in radio applications for power rectifiers (to change alternating current to direct current) and detectors (to separate the audio frequencies from the modulated radio-frequency waves that are produced in the antenna system).

The three electrode vacuum tube, i.e., triode   When the tube is to be used for purposes of amplification, oscillation, etc., it is customary to introduce one or more grids. We shall confine ourselves to one grid only. This makes it a so-called 3-electrode vacuum tube. Two of these, the cathode and plate, are similar to those described for the diode. The grid is a loosely wound wire electrode placed between the cathode and plate. In tetrodes and pentodes instead of one grid there are two and three grids, respectively.

When the cathode is emitting electrons and the plate voltage is not too high there will be a "cloud" of electrons always in the vicinity of the cathode. Some of the electrons leave the cloud and go to the plate (forming the plate current) whereas others will be entering the cloud from the cathode. Some low-velocity electrons leave the cathode but, due to the repulsion of the cloud (or negative space charge as it is called), will move back to the cathode. From this action it will be seen that if a very open grid structure is placed where this space charge exists it will have a relatively very large effect on the number of electrons reaching the plate. By controlling the space charge the grid can act as a valve in determining the amount of plate current. In order that the electrons shall not flow to the grid instead of the plate, the potential of the grid is always kept negative with respect to the cathode.

The effects of a change in the grid voltage on the plate current, and of a change in the plate voltage on the plate current when other quantities are kept constant, are usually represented by characteristic curves. These curves are of fundamental importance in designing circuits in which such tubes are to be used.

In the time available we will confine ourselves to two fundamental characteristics: the transfer characteristic E_g vs. I_p, and the amplification factor of a triode.

The transfer characteristics show the effect of grid voltage E_g on the plate current I_p. A transfer curve for a common three-electrode tube (type **6J5**) is shown in Figure 199. Although tube designations are still somewhat confused, the 6 stands for 6.3 volts commonly applied to the heating filament.

As mentioned before the grid should not be allowed to become positive. Should it be made positive, it will attract electrons, become overheated, and outgas, thus spoiling the vacuum in the tube (the tube is then said to become soft).

The point A on any curve when $I_p = 0$ is called the cutoff point. The three curves shown in Figure 199 represent three different fixed plate voltages E_p.

The amplification factor of the tube is another very important quantity in connection with the use of the tube as an amplifier.

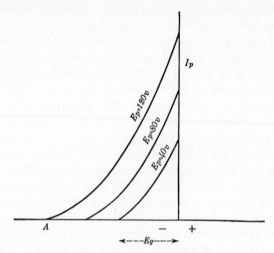

Fig. 199. Transfer characteristics Eg vs Ip.

Small signals applied to the grid will be amplified and appear as larger voltage across a resistance in the plate circuit. The amount of voltage amplification is important. In proper design and use it is necessary to know how much this amplification is, and under what conditions it will be a maximum. Also just as important in connection with telephone voice current amplification is a knowledge of the amount of nonlinear amplification (distortion). The voltage amplification factor is defined as:

$$\mu = \frac{\Delta E_p}{\Delta E_g}\bigg]_{I_p = \text{const.}}$$

and is the ratio between the change in plate voltage and the change in grid voltage necessary to produce the same change in plate current. Or, in other words, if the grid potential is increased slightly (by an amount ΔE_g that will produce a slightly increased current), and the plate voltage decrease necessary to bring the plate current back to the same value is ΔE_p, then $\mu = \Delta E_p/\Delta E_g$.

Suppose for example that the voltage amplification of a single triode is 10; if a signal of 10 μv is introduced on the grid of this tube, the output plate signal voltage will be 100 μv. Another tube could be used to amplify 10 times again, etc., so that 5 tubes would bring the signal up to 1 volt.

Radio reception   The incoming electromagnetic waves from the transmitting station have a very high frequency (e.g., 880,000 cycles per sec — called radio frequency), but the envelope is modulated with a superimposed audio frequency which represents the music or speech that entered the microphone. The radio set has to be capable of amplifying (radio-frequency voltage amplification) these very small voltages induced in the receiving antenna, and then in order to make the music or speech intelligible it is necessary to separate the audio from the radio frequencies (detection), and finally the audio frequencies must once more be amplified (audio-frequency power amplification) sufficiently to operate a loudspeaker.

In order to get sufficient voltage in the receiver from the antenna a resonant circuit is used which must be tuned exactly to the incoming frequency. The resonant circuit has a fixed inductance L and a variable capacitance C as shown in Figure 200. This L C circuit is resonant to a frequency $f = 1/2 \pi \sqrt{LC}$ which can be varied

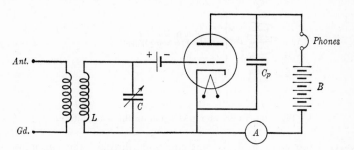

Fig. 200. A simple radio receiver.

(tuned) by changing C. Only when the resonant circuit is in tune with the incoming frequency between antenna and ground will sufficient voltage be induced on the grid of the triode. This triode will amplify the signal. We wish however to hear the audio-frequency part. In order to do this it is necessary to have the tube function also as a rectifier or nonlinear detector.

This it will do if a grid voltage $-E_g$ is applied to keep the average operating potential of the grid, a of Figure 201, on the curved portion of the transfer characteristic. Because of this non-linearity the incoming symmetrical amplitude modulated radio frequency signal on the grid becomes distorted so that the plate current will have in it the required audio frequency component (Fig. 201). This audio-frequency component flows through the phones. The radio-frequency

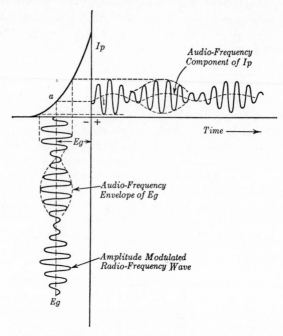

Fig. 201. Effect of a grid signal on the plate current.

part of the current finds that the path through the capacitor C_p (Fig. 200) has a much lower impedance and thus will not go through the phones. When the curved part of the transfer characteristic is used for detection (also called demodulation) this is called square-law detection. In such cases therefore a steady negative grid bias of $-E_g$ is required to keep the average grid operating point at a.

Another type of square-law detector which works well but does not require a battery to supply the bias $-E_g$ is shown in Figure 202 and can be referred to as a grid-leak detector. In this case a negative audio-frequency voltage is built up across the grid-leak resistance by the modulation in the incoming wave, and since this voltage exists between cathode and grid it will be amplified. Of course the

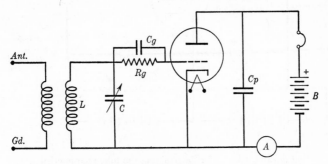

Fig. 202. Grid leak detector.

radio frequency will also be amplified but it can be by-passed as before through the capacitor C_p, which should have a capacitance of approximately 0.001 μf.

EXPERIMENT 47

SOME STATIC CHARACTERISTICS OF A TRIODE

Part (a) *To determine the transfer characteristics of the tube.*
Part (b) *A determination of the voltage amplification factor of the triode.*

APPARATUS: A 6J5 tube mounted,* d-c milliammeter (0–20 ma range), d-c voltmeter (range 0–15 v), d-c voltmeter (range 0–150 v), 500-ohm potential divider, 5000-ohm potential divider, B battery (or d-c line) of at least 120 v, C battery of $22\frac{1}{2}$ v.

It will be seen from the diagram (Fig. 203) that two sources of potential will be necessary, one for the grid and one for the plate. When these potentials are supplied by batteries they are usually referred to as the "C" and "B" batteries respectively. These potentials can be supplied by power lines, in which case you must pay special attention to the advice from the instructor on the proper and safe use of such lines. The potential dividers enable you to change the grid and plate potentials. Note that the grid potential will always be negative and the plate potential positive.

* See footnote on the next page.

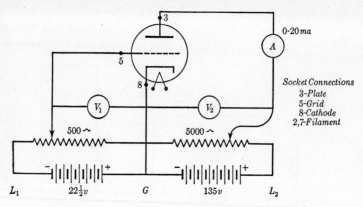

Fig. 203. Circuit for determining the tube characteristics.

Construct a table for data:*

$E_p = 40\ v$		$E_p = 80\ v$		$E_p = 120\ v$	
E_g	I_p	E_g	I_p	E_g	I_p
0		0		omit	
-2		-2		-2	
-4		-4		-4	
..		..		..	
..		..		..	
..		..		..	
-12		-12		-12	

(*Note.* The magnitude of I_p for $E_g = 0$ is missing in the 120-v table. *Avoid this setting very carefully since it will damage the tube*).

Plot on millimeter cordinate paper, grid voltage as abscissa and plate current as ordinate. Plot all the data recorded in the table.

Note that the points for each of the three plate voltages form a smooth curve. Draw these three curves. They are known as the

* If a three-electrode tube of the 12A type is used, the potential on the grid may be made positive up to about 5 to 10 volts depending upon the plate voltage used. Figure 204 represents an alternative set up for use of such a tube. The table for the data may be altered to include positive voltages. However do not exceed the milliampere rating for the meter, or for the tube, depending upon which is the larger. Consult the instructor if in doubt.

transfer characteristics of the tube. Compare them with published data for this type of tube.

Part (b) Set the plate voltage at some high value such as 115 volts, and the grid voltage at −5.0 volts. Read the plate current milliammeter after having set the voltmeters as accurately as you can. Now change the grid voltage to −4.5 volts exactly. This will increase the plate current. Reduce the plate voltage until the original ammeter reading is obtained once more. Read the new plate voltage very carefully. The quotient of the plate voltage change by the grid

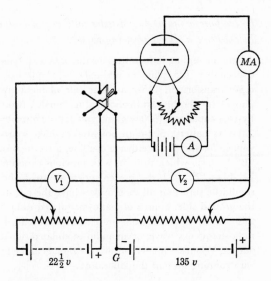

Fig. 204. Alternate circuit for applying either positive or negative grid potentials.

voltage change (0.5 volts) is the "amplification factor" of the tube. Note that the plate current is the same before and after the two voltage settings. Repeat, using slightly different values of E_p and E_g. Construct your own data form and compare your value with those given in a handbook.

Questions

(a) Why are the plate current readings zero for some pairs of values of plate voltage and grid voltage?

(b) Assuming that the amplification factor is constant, if the grid voltage change from -5.0 v to -4.5 v had been made with 200 v on the plate, what plate voltage change would have been necessary to restore the plate current to its original value.

(c) Does the plate circuit of the tube seem to obey Ohm's law? (Examine at constant grid voltage.)

EXPERIMENT 48

TRIODE DETECTION AND TUNING OF AN LC CIRCUIT

Part (a)   *To compare a square-law detector with a grid-leak detector.*
Part (b)   *To calibrate a simple receiving circuit.*

APPARATUS: Antenna coupling inductances for the broadcast band, variable capacitance (23 plate — 365 $\mu\mu$f), 6J5 tube, octal socket, 6.3-v transformer, 115-v a-c line (for filament transformer), phones (preferably with concealed terminals), two 0.001 mica by-pass capacitors (500 working volts), d-c voltmeter (0–15 v), $22\frac{1}{2}$-v C battery, 500-ohm potential divider, source of direct voltage for the plate (either a d-c line, a rectified supply, or a "B" battery, which to fit in with previous experiment should be about 120 v). If d-c power outlets are used, the instructor should be sure that all such outlets have the negative pole on the ground side. Source of audio-modulated radio frequency; this can be obtained from an aerial, an amplified broadcast radio-frequency wave, or an audio-modulated signal generator output. When set up even-front, the signal can be applied to a wire running around the laboratory.

Part (a)   1   Connect as shown in Figure 205. Be sure to get details on the available power sources or batteries and have the instructor check your circuit before applying any voltages. If the power supply outlets are used be careful not to ground or get across the live wire side and ground. In this first part we will test for maximum loudness (i.e., efficiency of detection and amplification) in the phones. Adjust the grid bias voltage to a maximum of -12 volts. Tune the capacitor C so that the signal comes through as loud as possible. Keeping capacitor C fixed at this value, reduce the value of grid bias but do not go above -2 volts.

Note what happens to the signal and record which bias voltage gives best results. Repeat for another applied frequency.

Part (a)   2   Disconnect the batteries from the circuit and replace the grid battery and voltmeter with the grid-leak and grid-capacitor combination shown in Figure 202. Reconnect the "B" battery. Tune in the signal again and compare this signal strength with what you observed when using a grid-bias battery as in part (a) 1 above. Repeat for another applied frequency.

Part (b)   The purpose of this part is to calibrate the capacitor dial in terms of the incoming applied frequencies. This will have to

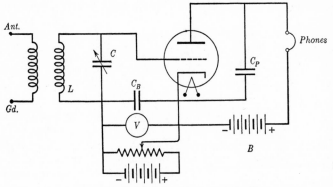

Fig. 205. Calibration of a tuned circuit.

be done in unison with other groups connected to the same source of radio frequencies. If the source is a broadcast transmitter, record the frequency of the transmitting station (in kilocycles) and the reading on the capacitor dial for loudest signal. Plot a curve of station frequency as abscissa against capacitor setting as ordinate. If the source is a modulated signal generator the instructor will announce the radio frequency being used and this frequency will be recorded and plotted against capacitor dial setting.

Questions

(a) Explain the variation of observed signal loudness with location of the operating point on the grid bias-plate voltage curve.

(b) What is the purpose of the capacitors C_B and C_p in Figure 205?

(c) Which type of detector gives the loudest signal?

(d) Which type of detector gives the sharpest tuning?

(e) From a practical standpoint which arrangement is better — Figure 200 or Figure 202?

PROBLEMS

Instead of working numerical problems the student should consult a physics textbook in regard to the following related subjects:

1   Electron tubes
2   Use of a tube as a detector
3   Use of a tube as an amplifier
4   Radio receiving sets
5   Electric oscillations and waves.

PART 6 LIGHT

CHAPTER XXVIII

PHOTOMETRY

Photometry is the science that deals with measurement of intensity of light sources and of illumination produced on absorbing and reflecting surfaces.

These measurements are usually relative and are made by comparison with some standard source such as the standard Hefner lamp, which is a lamp burning amyl acetate at a certain definite rate, with a definite height of flame and definite conditions of air, pressure, humidity, etc. This Hefner standard of light intensity is found to be 90 per cent of the international candle. The National Bureau of Standards has standardized certain incandescent lamps for routine testing. Maintenance of standards is no easy task.

Instruments used to compare intensities of light sources are called photometers. The Bunsen and Lummer-Brodhun photometers are representative of the simpler type, while the flicker and integrating photometers are examples of the more specialized forms.

The theory of our experiment is based on the fact that the light is assumed to be radiating from a "point" source out upon an expanding spherical surface. Hence, the luminous flux falling on one square foot of a surface becomes less when the surface is further removed from the source — in other words, the illumination of the surface becomes less. Now it is a general law, in connection with radiation of energy from a point source, that the energy passing normally through 1 sq cm falls off inversely as the square of the distance from the source, and hence the illumination produced on a screen by a point source of light falls off inversely as the square of the distance between source and screen.

If we should place two point sources of light consecutively at a given location in front of a screen and each produced the same illumination, as observed by the eye, then we would conclude that the two sources have the same strength or intensity. On the other hand, if one were four times as intense, according to the above it would need to be placed at twice the distance from the screen.

Suppose we wish to compare the strength of two point light sources C_1 and C_2. They are placed as shown in Figure 206 so as to illuminate a screen at B_1 and B_2. The illuminations on the two sides can be observed visually. Now if C_1 is the brighter source, it will have to be

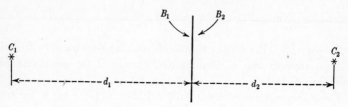

Fig. 206. Comparison of two point sources of light.

placed further from the screen than C_2, since the illumination falls off inversely as the square of the distance from the source. Suppose that when C_1 and C_2 are in the positions shown the illumination on B_1 is the same as that on B_2.
We can then write

$$\frac{C_1}{C_2} = \frac{d_1^2}{d_2^2}.$$

Knowing the luminous intensity of one of the sources, for example C_1, and measuring d_1 and d_2, one can calculate the luminous intensity of the source C_2. Note that these intensities of sources are measured in terms of the standard candle. The *luminous intensity* of a lamp or source of light is usually given in candlepower, which simply means the equivalent of so many standard international candles.

Luminous flux and illumination on a surface   When one is concerned with the amount of light falling on a surface it is customary to think in terms of luminous flux. By definition the total amount of *luminous flux* from a standard candle is 4π lumens. From a point source of light this flux is given off symmetrically in all directions. The amount of light flux falling normally on a unit area is called the *illumination* (E) of the surface. If one considers that a point source of light having a luminous intensity of C candlepower gives out a total flux $F = 4\pi C$ lumens, a little consideration will show that the amount of flux falling on a *unit* area becomes less as the area is taken farther away from the source. Consider a spherical surface, around C, having a radius d. The illumination on this surface is $E = F/4\pi d^2$. If d is measured in feet and F in lumens, the units for E will be lumens per square foot.

But since $F = 4\pi C$ lumens, the illumination can also be expressed as:

$$E = \frac{4\pi C}{4\pi d^2} = \frac{C}{d^2}. \tag{96}$$

The illumination on a spherical surface at a distance of 1 foot from a standard candle is called a *foot-candle*. This is a very common unit used in practical work. The student should be able to prove that a foot-candle of illumination is equivalent to 1 lumen per square foot.

The instruments used to measure the illumination of a surface are usually referred to as foot-candle meters. Of course, if the intensities of all sources of illumination were exactly known — and furthermore that they were point sources — and if their exact locations were given and no stray reflected light fell on a given surface, it should be possible to calculate the normal light flux falling on the surface. All these facts are hardly ever known and such special conditions very seldom occur in practice. Yet it is desirable to *measure the illumination* falling on a surface, and many different types of instruments have been developed for this purpose.

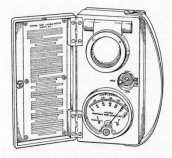

Fig. 207. Foot-candle meter. Courtesy Weston Electrical Instrument Company.

In one of these instruments a white opaque surface has a series of translucent circular spots arranged along a line. These spots are illuminated from below with gradually increasing amount of light. The amount of illumination in these spots is standardized by regulating the current supplied to the illuminating lamp. A scale marked off in foot-candles is placed along the series of spots. In using the instrument the current is first standardized and then the instrument is placed on the surface on which we wish to know the degree of illumination. When the illumination on the opaque section of the scale equals that of the translucent hole, then the outline of the hole will disappear. This illumination is then read off on the foot-candle scale next to the row of spots.

Another foot-candle meter (see Fig. 207) which is still easier to use consists of a photovoltaic cell (also called a "photronic" cell) connected to a microammeter. Such a photoelectric cell has the property that the current produced by the action of the light is almost exactly proportional to the illumination falling on the surface. This is the same principle used in the photoelectric type of photographic exposure meter. The scale can be directly calibrated to read foot-candles of illumination. No battery is needed. To cover the tremendous ranges of illumination encountered in practice the meter can be shunted and thus several scales obtained.

EXPERIMENT 49

THE PHOTOMETER

Part (a) *Variations of luminous efficiency of a source of light with voltage.*
Part (b) *To measure the illumination falling on a surface.*

APPARATUS: Photometer, standard incandescent lamp, two incandescent lamps of unknown candlepower, rheostat, ammeter, voltmeter, food-candle meter.

The apparatus (Fig. 208) is a modified form of a Joly photometer. You will find the apparatus connected as shown in Figure 208.

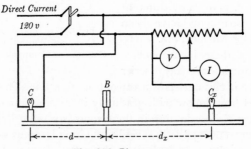

Fig. 208. Photometer.

Check the circuit. The device B, used to determine the degree of illumination on a surface consists of two thin rectangular pieces of paraffin separated by a strip of tinfoil (or aluminum foil) and mounted on a bench between two lamps. In our experiment, the lamps are kept at a fixed distance from each other, usually 100 cm. With the switch open, insert the plug in the 120-volt circuit. The standard lamp of candlepower C will light brightly. Now adjust the rheostat, acting as a potential dividing device, so that little or no voltage will be across the lamp whose candlepower C_x is to be determined. After the instructor has checked the wiring, close the switch to see if the polarity through the voltmeter and ammeter is correct. If not, withdraw the plug and reverse. Then adjust the rheostat for maximum voltage through the lamp.

For our purpose we shall take the *candlepower per watt* as a measure of the relative light efficiency of lamps because greater efficiency is associated with greater candlepower per unit power consumption. With the rheostat set for maximum voltage through the lamp, the procedure is to adjust the comparing device B so that it is illuminated equally on both sides of the aluminum foil when viewed from the side (i.e., perpendicular to the plane of the aluminum foil). The reflected light will be scattered in the paraffin blocks and their degree of illumination compared by observation from the front. When this is done, the illumination on both sides of B from the two sources is the same. Record the distances d and d_x. If a Bunsen photometer is used, the illuminated spots will be viewed simultaneously by reflecting the light from mirrors.

Then assuming the inverse square law and point sources, we have

$$\frac{C}{C_x} = \frac{d^2}{d_x^2}$$

Reduce the voltage, approximately in steps of 10 volts, keeping the distance between the lamps constant, and repeat the above measurement in every case until the low luminosity or difference in color of the lights makes further measurements meaningless. The uncertainty of matching light intensities due to color differences may be minimized by averaging the extreme distances in either direction for which you are sure that no intensity match exists.

Repeat, using the other lamp.

Part (b) Study the construction as well as the instructions for operating the foot-candle meter supplied to you. Then measure and record the illumination at the several locations in the rooms suggested by the instructor. Compare with recommended values as pub-

Data for one lamp:

V (volts)	I (amperes)	VI (watts)	d	C_x (calculated)	Candlepower per watt

$C =$

$d + d_x =$

lished by the Illuminating Engineering Society (see any standard Handbook on Electrical Engineering).

Questions

(a) Draw a graph with the candlepower per watt as ordinates against V as abscissas.

(b) Calculate from your data or graph (question a) the per cent decrease of the efficiency from its value at the maximum voltage, for voltages of 10, 20, and 30 less than the maximum value.

(c) At what voltage would you operate the lamp for greatest light efficiency and economy?

PROBLEMS

Experiment 49

1   One electric lamp of 20 cp is separated from another of 55 cp by 150 cm. At what distance, or distances, on a line joining the two lamps, will the illumination from the two lamps be the same? Calculate the distance from the lamp of smaller candlepower. Calculate also the illumination in foot-candles at this point of balance.

2   Two sources of light, each of 6 cp, are placed at distances of 3 ft and 5 ft, respectively, on the same side of the paraffin block. At what distance must a source of 12 cp be placed on the other side so as to produce equal illumination on both sides of the paraffin block?

3   What is meant by candlepower and what is meant by foot-candle? What does each measure? If the intensity of illumination produced on a screen 25 m from an arc lamp is equivalent to that produced by a standard Hefner lamp at 1 m, what is the candlepower of the arc lamp?

CHAPTER XXIX

REFLECTION AND REFRACTION AT PLANE SURFACES

When a beam of light strikes a surface of different optical density, we notice that some of the light is reflected and the remainder transmitted through the separating boundary. The relative amounts depend upon the optical conditions at the surface. In this chapter, we are interested only in the paths taken by a reflected or a transmitted beam of light in an isotropic medium.

REFLECTION OF LIGHT AT A PLANE SURFACE

Consider the reflection of light, coming from a source S, and striking a plane mirror as shown in Figure 209. Let SO and OR represent the paths of the incident and reflected ray, respectively, and let ON be the normal to the plane at the point of incidence. The following two laws may be proved experimentally:

1 *When a ray of light strikes the surface of the mirror at any point O, the angle of incidence i is equal to the angle of reflection r.*

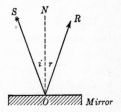

Fig. 209. Angles of incidence and reflection.

2 *The incident ray, the normal, and the reflected ray lie in the same plane.*

Applying these two laws to all the rays coming from an object and being reflected at the surface leads to the important result that the image I of an object S will appear as far behind the mirror as the object is in front of the mirror. That is, referring to Figure 210.

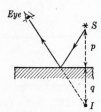

Fig. 210. Image of a point source in a plane mirror.

$$q = p.$$

Very frequently it becomes necessary to locate the position of an image. The method of parallax is useful in such cases. Place a pin, which may be seen over the top of the mirror, at the point I where you think the image is located. Now move your eye back and forth in a direction perpendicular to the plane defined by the pin and a line connecting the image and source. This is called locating an image by parallax. *Parallax* is defined as the apparent angular separation of two objects due to a real displacement of the observer. Thus in Figure 211 (a) there is parallax when the eye is moved from the point A to the point B. In Figure 211 (b) there is negligible parallax, which vanishes entirely when the pin and image coincide.

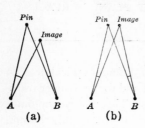

Fig. 211. Parallax.

It will be seen in Figure 211 (a) that the angular separation of the image and the pin at point A is greater than at point B. There is no such difference in the angles at points A and B in Figure 211 (b), and hence in this case the parallax is not noticeable.

REFRACTION OF LIGHT AT A PLANE SURFACE

When light travels from one transparent and isotropic* medium into another with different density, the light is said to be refracted. There are two important laws, often known as the laws of refraction, which can be verified by experiment:

1 *The incident ray, the normal, and the refracted ray lie in one plane.*

2 *The ratio of the sine of the angle of incidence to the sine of the angle of refraction is a constant quantity.* It does not vary with the angle of incidence.

The path of a light ray from a medium (1) into a medium (2) is shown in Figure 212. The value of the ratio of the sine of the angle of incidence to the sine of the angle of refraction depends upon the nature of the two media and upon the wave

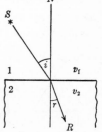

Fig. 212. Refraction at a plane surface.

---

* An isotropic medium is one that has the same optical properties in all directions.

length of the light used. It is usually referred to as the *refractive index* of the second medium with respect to the first. It may be shown that the angles i and r are such that

$$\frac{\sin i}{\sin r} = \text{constant} = {}_1n_2 = \frac{v_1}{v_2}$$

where ${}_1n_2$ represents the refractive index of medium (2) with respect to medium (1), and v_1, and v_2 represent the velocity of light in each medium respectively. If the velocity of light in a vacuum is c, then the absolute index of refraction of light entering the first medium is $n_1 = \dfrac{c}{v_1}$ while that of the light entering the second is $n_2 = \dfrac{c}{v_2}$. In an experiment we usually determine the index of refraction by measuring any angle of incidence i and the corresponding angle of refraction r, and calculate the ratio $\dfrac{\sin i}{\sin r}$, which by definition is n.

A SIMPLE REFRACTOMETER

A refractometer is an optical device for determining the index of refraction of a substance. Unless the two media involved are

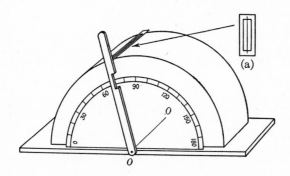

Fig. 213. A simple refractometer.

specifically stated it is usually assumed that the value given for this quantity refers to the ratio between the velocities when the light is traveling from air (or vacuum) into the medium. Many forms of refractometers have been designed depending upon the nature of the sample to be tested. The apparatus which is described below and used in Experiment 51 is a very simple form which is convenient for measuring the refractive index of small amounts of liquids.

The apparatus, which is shown in Figure 213, consists essentially of a semicircular disk of glass resting on a metal platform. The latter has a sharp line (O–O in the figure) ruled on it and the disk is so held that the line O–O is at the center. It is possible to see this line by looking through the cylindrical surface from certain directions.

The principle underlying this experiment will be understood more clearly by referring to Figure 214. Consider a narrow beam of light

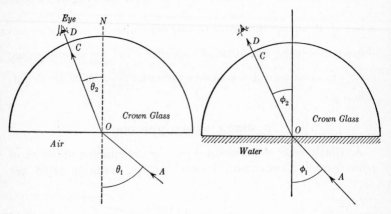

Fig. 214. A narrow beam of light travelling from air into glass.

Fig. 215. A narrow beam of light travelling from water into glass.

entering the eye at D after traveling upwards in the direction AOC. Such a ray will be bent towards the normal at O, and when it leaves the glass at C it will be traveling normally to the cylindrical glass surface, and therefore suffers no further deviation.

The index of refraction ($_an_g$) from air to glass is

$$_an_g = \frac{\sin \theta_1}{\sin \theta_2} = \frac{v_a}{v_g}$$

At the critical angle (θ_c), when θ_1 has its maximum value of 90 degrees,

$$_an_g = \frac{1}{\sin \theta_c} \tag{97}$$

Equation (97) shows that as the eye is moved down the edge away from ON there will be a maximum value of θ_2 after which no light beam AO can travel from the lower air surface and into the glass.

If a thin film of water (the thickness of this film is much exaggerated in Figure 215) is placed beneath the semicircular plate of glass, the ray of light from A will take the course $AOCD$ shown in Figure 215.

The index of refraction from water to glass is

$$_wn_g = \frac{\sin \phi_1}{\sin \phi_2} = \frac{v_w}{v_g} \tag{98}$$

and if we once more consider the critical case ($\phi_2 = \phi_c$) when $\phi_1 = 90°$, then

$$_wn_g = \frac{1}{\sin \phi_c} \tag{99}$$

Finally to find from these two indices of refraction the index for light traveling from air to water we have that

$$_an_w = \frac{v_a}{v_w} = \frac{v_a/v_g}{v_w/v_g} = \frac{_an_g}{_wn_g}$$

$$= \frac{\sin \phi_c}{\sin \theta_c} \tag{100}$$

EXPERIMENT 50

THE BEHAVIOR OF LIGHT AT A PLANE SURFACE

A study of the laws of reflection and refraction of light at plane surfaces.

Part (a) *To show that the angle of incidence (i) is equal to the angle of reflection (r), and that the image and object are at equal distances from the mirror.*

Part (b) *To show that for light passing from one medium to another*

$$\frac{\sin i}{\sin r} = \text{constant} = n$$

Part (c) *To obtain the index of refraction of a prism by measurement of the prism angle and the angle of minimum deviation.*

APPARATUS: Mounted mirror, four pins about 2 to 4 inches in length, one rectangular piece of plate glass with two of the narrow opposite sides polished, glass prism, ruler, protractor, drawing board and thumbtacks.*

Part (a)   Tack a sheet of paper to the drawing board. In the approximate center of the sheet draw one thin line XX' and locate

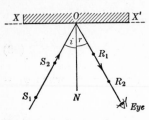

Fig. 216.   Reflection from a plane mirror.

the reflecting side of the mirror exactly along this line. Place two pins S_1 and S_2 (Fig. 216) in front of the mirror. Insert two more pins R_1 and R_2 in line with the two images of S_1 and S_2 as seen in the mirror. Remove the mirror, and at the point O of intersection of S_1S_2 with R_1R_2, erect a normal to the surface (whose trace is XX'). Measure i and r with a protractor. Repeat this experiment two or more times using different values of angle i. Find the per cent of error from the mean of i and r for each experiment.

Find the distance q of the image from the mirror by using the parallax method described above and repeat two or more times, varying the distance p of the object from the mirror. Find the per cent of error from the mean of p and q for each experiment.

ANGLES		Per Cent Error from Mean	DISTANCES		Per Cent Error from Mean
i	r		p	q	

Part (b)   Place the glass plate (Fig. 217) on your data sheet and outline the edges ($XX'Y'Y$) with a pencil. Place a pin at each of the

* If a source of light such as is described in Chapter XXXIV (page 412) is available, the narrow beam of light can be made to fall on the mirror, or to pass through the glass plate or prism. The path of the beam can then be traced on a sheet of paper below the beam.

points marked P and O. Now with the eye brought close to the paper, sight through the glass so as to bring the pins O and P in line with each other. Place another pin at some point D along the path. Remove the glass and connect the points PO and OD with straight lines. The lines may be extended to any distance out from O. Choose some point along OD, say E, and determine the distance OE. Then make OE' on OP equal to OE. From E and E' erect perpendiculars to the normal NN' drawn through O. By definition of the index of refraction of light from glass to air we have (Fig. 217).

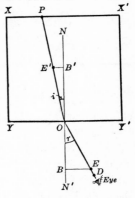

Fig. 217. Refraction through a rectangular plate of glass.

$$_g n_a = \frac{\sin i}{\sin r} = \frac{E'B'}{EB}$$

Measure the angles i and r, and the distances $E'B'$ and EB. Calculate $_g n_a$ by means of the two ratios $\dfrac{\sin i}{\sin r}$ and $\dfrac{E'B'}{EB}$. Repeat your experiment two or more times, using different values of the incident angle i.

ANGLES		DISTANCE		$\dfrac{\sin i}{\sin r}$	$\dfrac{E'B'}{EB}$	AVERAGE VALUE OF	
i	r	$E'B'$	EB			$\dfrac{\sin i}{\sin r}$	$\dfrac{E'B'}{EB}$

Average value of
$$\frac{1}{\dfrac{E'B'}{EB}} = {_a n_g} =$$

Average value of
$$\frac{1}{\dfrac{\sin i}{\sin r}} = {_a n_g} =$$

Part (c)   Place two pins A and B in your data sheet as in Figure 218. With your eye close to the sheet, look through the prism to-

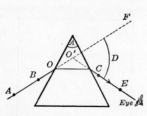

Fig. 218. Refraction through a glass prism.

wards the pins AB. When you get these pins in line, rotate the prism back and forth, around an axis at the apex of the angle A perpendicular to the paper, until the angle D becomes a minimum. You can tell when D is a minimum by noting the extreme excursion (towards the line OF) of the image of AB through the prism.* The rotation desired may be conveniently accomplished by causing a slight pressure at the apex of the angle A. When the minimum angle D is found, place pins at each of two points, such as C and E. Draw the line AB, extending it to F; also, the line CE, extending it to O'. The angle D, shown in the figure by $EO'F$, is also the angle of minimum deviation. Measure this angle with a protractor. The apex angle A of the prism will be given you by the instructor. If not, it can be measured accurately enough for this experiment by drawing carefully two thin pencil lines on paper along the edges of A and then using a protractor. The index of refraction from air to glass may be shown to be

$$_a n_g = \frac{\sin \dfrac{A + D}{2}}{\sin \dfrac{A}{2}}.$$

Repeat two or more times. Calculate the average index of refraction, also the per cent of error.

Questions

(a) In part (b) of your experiment, what was the least count of (1) your protractor, (2) your measuring rule?

(b) Which of the two ratios $\left(\text{i.e., } \dfrac{\sin i}{\sin r} \text{ and } \dfrac{E'B'}{EB} \right)$ did you find the more accurate for determining the value of $_g n_a$ in part (b)? State the reasons for your answer.

(c) Do the errors in part (a) and part (b) of your experiment appear to be influenced in any way by the magnitude of the angle i?

* If a narrow beam source of light is available then this position for minimum deviation can be quite easily located. See Chapter XXXIV, page 412.

EXPERIMENT 51

A SIMPLE REFRACTOMETER

To measure the refractive index of a small sample of a liquid.

APPARATUS: A simple refractometer consisting of a semicircular disk of glass mounted with a protractor and a guide for measuring angles (Fig. 213).

The platform supporting the semicircular glass disk (Fig. 213) contains a black reference line at its center. When the disk is in position on the platform, one notices that the black line will disappear at some point as the eye is started from its position vertically over the disk and is moved downward along the cylindrical edge. The angle, measured from the vertical, at which the line disappears is desired. Set the movable pointer on this position and look many times to see whether the setting is correct. Then measure this angle. Take at least five measurements of this angle. The average value of the critical angle will be θ_c. Design your own form of data sheet, recording all readings and the average. Calculate the index of refraction of the glass (i.e., $_an_g$) and the velocity of light in the glass. *Note:* These calculations are not all a necessary part for determining $_an_w$, which is the purpose of this experiment, but they help you understand the behavior of the light when entering a different medium. Use 3×10^{10} cm per sec as the velocity of light in air.

Now cover the reference line on the platform with a few drops of water and replace the semicircular disk. Take five readings of the critical angle under these conditions. The average value of the critical angle will be ϕ_c. Obtain the index of refraction from water to glass by means of equation (99). Calculate also the velocity of light in water. Obtain the index of refraction of water $_an_w$ by finding the ratio between v_a and v_w. Finally calculate the same index more directly by the use of equation (100).

Repeat the experiment for any other liquids to be measured.

Questions

(a) Show by calculation how much the measured index of refraction $_an_w$ will change if θ is too large and ϕ is too small, each by one degree.

(b) What do you estimate is the precision of your measured value with the given apparatus. Base your estimate on the readings which you obtained.

366   EXPERIMENTAL PHYSICS FOR COLLEGES

(c) Calculate $_g n_a$, $_w n_a$.

(d) Why can θ_2 not be larger than θ_c in this experiment?

(e) Will this experiment work if the refractive index of the liquid is greater than that of the glass? Illustrate by means of a diagram.

PROBLEMS

Experiment 50

1 Prove that the index of refraction ($_g n_a$) from glass to air is given by the relation

$$_g n_a = \frac{E'B'}{EB}.$$

(See Fig. 217.)

2 If a perpendicular PL (Fig. 219) is dropped from P and the line EO is extended to K, prove that

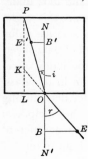

$$_g n_a = \frac{OK}{OP}.$$

Fig. 219.

3 Prove, if D is the angle of minimum deviation for a glass prism and A is the angle of the prism, that the index of refraction from air to glass is given by the equation,

$$_g n_a = \frac{\sin \dfrac{A + D}{2}}{\sin \dfrac{A}{2}}.$$

4 Show that if A is very small in the above problem, say 5°, we may write the deviation D as

$$D = A(_a n_g - 1)$$

Experiment 51

1 The refractive index $_a n_e$, for ethyl alcohol is 1.36. What is the velocity of light in this liquid. Assume that light travels 186,000 miles per sec in air.

2 What is the value of the critical angle for light traveling from air into the ethyl alcohol of the previous problem? Illustrate the path taken by such a ray.

3 A ray of light travels from water into glass as shown in Figure 215. If the index of refraction of water is 1.33 and the index of refraction of the glass is 1.5, what is the value of the critical angle ϕ_c?

4   Figure 220 shows a ray of light going from a denser medium (crown

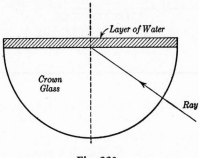

Fig. 220.

glass) into a lighter medium (water). Show how to find the refractive index from glass to water in such a case.

CHAPTER XXX

REFLECTION AND REFRACTION AT CURVED SURFACES

The laws of reflection and refraction of a narrow beam or ray of light as given in the last chapter for plane surfaces are applicable to curved surfaces if we apply these laws to each individual point of the curved surface where the light impinges. Consider a tangent plane to be drawn at every point where the light strikes. Then the laws of reflection and refraction apply to this tangent plane. Since every such plane will be inclined at an angle to all others, the reflected or refracted rays from an object will be spread out or brought together in some manner depending upon the curvature of the surface.

In dealing with light reflecting at or passing through curved surfaces, it is convenient often to speak of the *wave front* which is perpendicular to the direction of the ray of light. The wave front of any beam of light coming from a very distant source is, for all practical purposes, plane. Another way of stating this same fact is by saying that the radius of curvature of the wave front is infinite.

MIRRORS

Consider a plane wave front proceeding towards a curved mirror (Fig. 221). The latter can be thought of as being a small portion

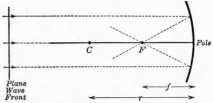

Fig. 221. Concave mirror with source at infinite distance.

of a sphere with its center at C and of radius r. The center of the mirror surface is called the pole (Fig. 221), and the line drawn from the pole perpendicular to the spherical surface at that point is called the principal axis. The beam will strike the mirror and be reflected so that, when the laws of reflection are applied to each point on the mirror, the new wave front is found to be spherical and converging towards one point F on the principal axis called the principal focus. The distance f from the pole to the principal focus is called the focal distance.

If the source P, the light of which is being reflected, is at a finite distance p from the mirror (Fig. 222) the reflected wave front (the

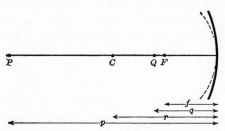

Fig. 222. Concave mirror with source at finite distance.

dotted line) will converge or focus at some point Q on the principal axis at a distance q from the pole. The relation between p, q, and r is known to be

$$\frac{1}{p} + \frac{1}{q} = \frac{2}{r}. \tag{101}$$

By definition, the focal length of a mirror is the distance from the pole to the point at which light will focus when coming from an infinite distance ($p = \infty$). Hence in the above equation, when $p = \infty$, $q = f$, or $\frac{2}{r} = \frac{1}{f}$. That is, we may write the above equation for mirrors as,

$$\frac{1}{p} + \frac{1}{q} = \frac{1}{f}, \tag{102}$$

if the focal length is given instead of the radius of curvature. The proof of this equation can be found in almost any textbook on college physics.

While equation (102) was written for concave mirrors (i.e., center of curvature towards source), it holds for all types of spherical mirrors. To make it applicable for all cases, note first that all distances (p, q, r) are positive for a real image formed by the concave mirror and that the object, image, and center of curvature are on the same side of the pole. When the image and object are on opposite sides of the pole, the distance of the image from the pole is negative. Likewise the radius of curvature (or focal length) is negative if the center of curvature and object are on opposite sides of the pole.

While the use of the wave-front method is convenient for developing mirror and lens formulas, it is not a convenient method for obtaining the more exact locations and relative sizes of images. Determination of the location and sizes of images is usually carried out by the ray method. Figure 223 represents the geometrical construction, using rays, for finding the image.

A convenient set of conventions for location of images follows: (1) Draw from any convenient point in the object a ray parallel to the principal axis; this ray, by definition, will reflect and pass on through the principal focus. (2) Draw a ray starting from the same point in the object, through the center of curvature; this ray will be reflected back along its same path. The image of the given point in the object will be found where these lines meet. Usually the two end points of the object are sufficient for the location of the whole image. In fact, if the image is considered perpendicular to the principal axis and half of the object is above the principal axis and the other half below, then the image is readily located by drawing the two lines mentioned above from one point only.

It will be noticed that the image in Figure 223 is inverted. This always happens when the two rays of light actually meet after

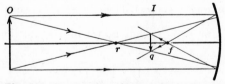

Fig. 223. Construction of images in a concave mirror—ray method.

reflection from the mirror. We call such an image, which is formed by the actual crossing of the rays, a real image. Images formed by rays which appear to cross, but actually do not, are called virtual images. They are always erect.

It may be shown that the ratio of the magnitude of the image to the object is given by the relation.

$$\frac{I}{O} = \frac{q}{p} = M,$$

where M is generally called the magnification.

The following general diagrams on the next page may be found helpful in the construction of images formed by mirrors in specific cases:

Concave Mirrors

Example 1. If $p > r$,

then $\qquad\qquad r > q > f$,

and $\qquad\qquad \dfrac{I}{O} < 1.$ $\qquad\qquad$ (Fig. 224)

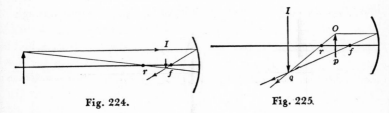

Fig. 224. $\qquad\qquad\qquad$ **Fig. 225.**

Example 2. If $r > p > f$,

then $\qquad\qquad q > r$,

$\qquad\qquad\qquad \dfrac{I}{O} > 1.$ $\qquad\qquad$ (Fig. 225)

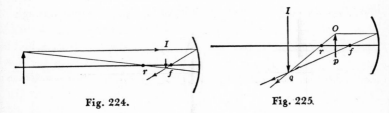

Fig. 226.

Example 3. If $\qquad\qquad p < f$,

then q is on the opposite side of the mirror and is negative numerically. $\qquad\qquad$ (Fig. 226)

Convex Mirrors

Example 4. If $\infty > p > 0,$

then $q < f.$

For these mirrors, the numerical magnitudes of r, f, and q are negative.   (Fig. 227)

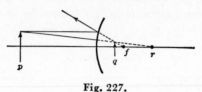

Fig. 227.

LENSES

Now, consider a plane wave advancing toward a double convex lens (Fig. 228) as shown in the diagram. Upon passing through

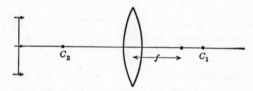

Fig. 228. Double convex lens with source at an infinite distance.

the lens, it will come to a focus at a point on the principal axis called the principal focus, which is at a distance f from the center of the lens. The direction of the ray of the advancing wave is parallel to the principal axis, which is defined as a line, joining the two centers of curvature (C_1 and C_2) of the spherical surfaces of the lenses.

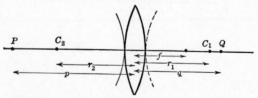

Fig. 229. Double convex lens with source at finite distance.

If we consider a wave front (see Fig. 229) starting from a source P at a distance p from the center of the lens, it will, upon passing through the lens, be refracted (dotted curve) so as to converge to a point Q which is a distance of q units from the center of the lens. The relation between p, q, and f is known to be

$$\frac{1}{p} + \frac{1}{q} = \frac{1}{f}, \tag{103}$$

where

$$\frac{1}{f} = (n-1)\left(\frac{1}{r_1} + \frac{1}{r_2}\right). \tag{104}$$

This formula holds not only for converging lenses, which are thick at the center and thin at the edges, but also for diverging lenses, which are thin at the center and thick at the edges. A common form of a diverging lens is the double concave lens shown in Figure 230. As in the case of mirrors, if any of the distances (i.e., q, f, r_1, r_2) are measured in a direction compared to the source, opposite to that shown in Figure 229 the sign becomes negative. Thus

Fig. 230. Double coneave lens.

the focal length of a convex lens is positive, while that of a double concave lens is negative.

While the formula for a lens is readily obtained from the curvature of the wave fronts, the geometrical construction of images is, again, more readily obtained by use of the ray, or geometrical method. We will redraw Figure 229 using the ray method. Our new figure (Fig. 231) shows the object, of size O, at a distance p

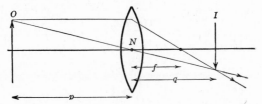

Fig. 231. Construction to find image position by convex lens.

from the center of the lens. The method of locating the image of size I is as follows: (1) Draw from some point in the object a ray parallel to the principal axis; it will pass through the focal point.

(2) Draw another straight line, starting from the same point O, through the optical center of the lens and continue this line until it crosses the other ray which was refracted. If the object is perpendicular to the principal axis and symmetrical with it, the location and size of the image can be found without further image construction.

The optical center N is the point through which the light passes from one side of the lens to the other without change of direction. There is a lateral displacement but this is negligible for thin lenses.

Just as in the case of mirrors, real images are inverted and the refracted rays actually intersect. Virtual images are erect and the refracted rays only appear to intersect.

It may be shown that the ratio of the magnitude of the image to the object is

$$M = \frac{I}{O} = \frac{q}{p}.$$

The following general examples are given for reference:

Converging Lenses

Example 1. If $\infty > p > 2f,$

then $f < q < 2f,$

and $\dfrac{I}{O} < 1.$ (Fig. 232)

Fig. 232.

Example 2. If $2f > p > f,$

then $2f < q < \infty,$

and $\dfrac{I}{O} > 1.$ (Fig. 233)

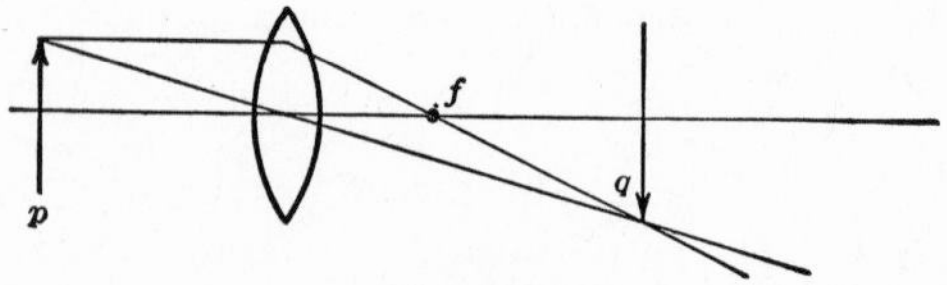

Fig. 233.

Example 3. If $\qquad f > p > 0,$

then $\qquad \infty > q > 0,$

and q is negative and the image virtual. (Fig. 234)

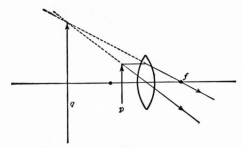

Fig. 234.

Diverging Lenses

Example 4. If $\qquad \infty > p > 0,$

then $\qquad f > q > 0,$ (Fig. 235)

where both f and q have negative values and the image is virtual.

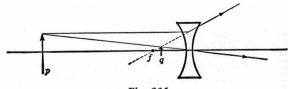

Fig. 235.

The power of a lens The quantity $(n - 1)\left(\dfrac{1}{r_1} + \dfrac{1}{r_2}\right)$, used in equation (104) for calculating the focal length of a lens, involves only measurable physical properties of the lens. If is often referred to as the optical *power D* of a lens. The power of a lens is, therefore, the reciprocal of the focal length.

Hence $\qquad D = \dfrac{1}{f} = (n - 1)\left(\dfrac{1}{r_1} + \dfrac{1}{r_2}\right)$

The unit of power is the *diopter*, which is the power of a lens with a focal length of one meter. For example, a lens having a focal length of 25 cm has a power of 4 diopters.

When thin lenses are placed in contact to form a lens combination, it can be shown that the combined focal length F can be found from the individual focal lengths by using the relationship

$$\frac{1}{F} = \frac{1}{f_1} + \frac{1}{f_2}$$

or in terms of diopters

$$D = D_1 + D_2$$

Using these latter units the power of unknown lenses can readily be found by combining them with lenses of known power and then measuring the power of the combination. The power is positive for converging lenses and negative for diverging lenses.

EXPERIMENT 52

SPHERICAL MIRRORS

Part (a)   *To determine the focal length of a concave mirror using a parallel beam.*

Part (b)   *To determine the radius of curvature of a concave spherical mirror by means of parallax.*

Part (c)   *To locate, in general, any image by the method of parallax for both concave and convex mirrors.*

APPARATUS: Mounted concave and convex mirrors, several mounted pins or arrows which can be illuminated, ruler, screen.

Part (a)   For this part of the experiment one uses an object which is at a relatively large distance from the concave mirror. For mirrors having focal lengths of 20 cm or less an illuminated object 30 feet away will, for all practical purposes, give a parallel beam with respect to the mirror. If it is more convenient, open a window and focus the sun or any other distant object on a screen. The distance from the screen to the mirror will represent the focal length. In order to obtain a sharp image, keep the rays as nearly parallel to the mirror axis as possible. Make several trials and calculate the focal length.

Part (b) From the equation for mirrors, it is seen that, for a concave mirror, when the object is at the center of curvature, the image will be formed at the same place. Hence, place a pin in a movable block and slide it towards the concave mirror until a position is reached such that there is no observable parallax between the pin and the inverted image of the pin as observed in the mirror.

The distance from the pin to the center of the mirror gives the radius of curvature of the mirror. Repeat the adjustment two or more times. Record all data. Note also the size of the image and whether it is erect or inverted. Calculate r and f.

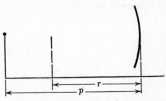

Fig. 236. Concave mirror.

Part (c) Place a pin in front of your concave mirror so that its distance p in front of the mirror is greater than the radius of curvature r (Fig. 236). Locate the image of this pin by means of parallax. That is, place another pin where you think the image of the object O should be (Fig. 223). Move your head back and forth. The image is located where this latter pin and image are not displaced relative to each other upon to-and-fro motion of the head. Measure the distance p of the object and the distance q of the image from the mirror, and calculate r from the equation

$$\frac{1}{p} + \frac{1}{q} = \frac{2}{r}.$$

Repeat for two or more positions of the object O, and find the average value of r. What is the value of f? Note the relative size of object and image. Make up your own data form.

Replace the concave mirror by the convex mirror and use the method of parallax as in part (c). When an object is placed in front of a convex mirror no real image is formed (see Fig. 227). A second pin, however, can be placed behind the mirror in the position of the virtual image until no parallax exists between them. This will give the position of the virtual image. Measure p and q and calculate the values of r and f. Watch the signs to be used in this case (p is $+$, q is $-$. See page 370). Repeat for several positions of the pin in front of the mirror.

Questions

(a) Draw to scale a ray diagram for one measured position of the object and image in each of parts (a) (b) and (c).

(b) In each part of the experiment state whether the image is erect or inverted and whether real or imaginary.

(c) Would you use a concave or convex mirror to see your face better for shaving purposes?

EXPERIMENT 53

THE FOCAL LENGTH OF LENSES

Part (a) *To measure the focal length and power of a converging lens using parallel light.*

Part (b) *To find the focal length of a converging lens by image formation in general.*

Part (c) *Using a converging lens of known focal length to find the focal length of a diverging lens of smaller power — lenses in contact.*

Part (d) *To find the focal length of a diverging lens by determining two conjugate distances.*

APPARATUS: Converging and diverging* lenses mounted in movable supports (any form of optical bench), illuminated wire mesh as object, ruler for measuring distances, a distant bright source of light.

Part (a) Using a distant source of light as an object, form an image, by means of the converging lens, on a screen. If the rays can be considered as being parallel to each other, then the distance of the image to the lens will give the focal length. Repeat this measurement several times, recording each measurement of this distance, and so find the focal length. Express your answer in centimeters and diopters.

Part (b) Use an illuminated wire mesh as an object. Place the lens a short distance from the wire mesh and find the image on a screen placed on the opposite side of the lens. Measure the distances of the object and the image from the lens, and from the lens formula calculate the focal length and also the power in diopters. Repeat

---

* The diverging lens should have a power about one-half that of the converging lens.

several times by changing distances. Make similar measurements on another lens.

Part (c) Having found the focal length of the converging lenses place one in contact with an unknown diverging lens and find experimentally the focal length of the lens combination.

Then
$$\frac{1}{F} = \frac{1}{f_1} + \frac{1}{f_2}$$

or
$$D = D_1 + D_2$$

From the above calculate the power and focal length of the diverging lens.

Part (d) To measure the focal length of a diverging lens an image I_1 of an object is first formed on a screen by means of a converging lens (see Fig. 237). The position of the screen should be recorded. Next the screen is moved farther away from the converging lens and the diverging lens of unknown focal length is placed between the converging lens and the screen. The position of the diverging lens is adjusted until a sharp image (I_2) is again formed on the

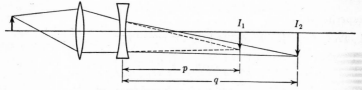

Fig. 237. Effect of a diverging lens.

screen. The first image I_1, can be considered then as the object for the diverging lens which forms an image of I_1 at I_2. The distances of I_1 and I_2 from the diverging lens are then said to be conjugate. Determine these distances and calculate the focal length of the diverging lens. Note that D in this case will be negative. Repeat by changing the screen and lens position and from all your data find the average value for the focal length. If this was the same lens used in part (c), compare the values of f found by the two methods.

Questions

(a) Why is it sometimes more convenient to deal with the power of a lens rather than its focal length? Illustrate your answer with figures taken from your data.

(b) How would your experiment be affected if in part (c) and (d) the focal length of the diverging lens were (1) the same and (2) shorter than the focal length of the converging lens?

(c) How will the measured focal length in part (a) be changed if the object used is not infinitely far away?

PROBLEMS

Experiment 52

1 Show by use of the formula for spherical mirrors that one would expect the image to appear at a distance behind a plane mirror equal to the distance of the object in front of the mirror.

2 When an object is placed 15 cm in front of a concave mirror, the image of that object appears, by the method of parallax, to be 60 cm behind the mirror. Is the image real or virtual, erect or inverted? What is the radius of curvature of the concave mirror? Find also the position of the image graphically.

3 An object 1 cm high is placed 3 cm in front of a convex mirror of focal length 10 cm. Where will the image be? Will it be real or imaginary and what will be the size?

Experiment 53

1 Prove for a double convex lens, the equation

$$\frac{1}{p} + \frac{1}{q} = (n - 1)\left(\frac{1}{r_1} + \frac{1}{r_2}\right)$$

2 In example 3 on page 375, let $p = 10$ cm and $f = 15$ cm. How far is the image from the lens? Draw a diagram showing the image, object, and lens position and construct the rays showing how the image is formed.

3 Suppose that the radii of curvature of the two spherical surfaces of a given double convex lens were 12 cm each. What would be the index of refraction of the lens if its focal length was 20 cm?

4 An object 2 cm high is placed 18 cm in front of a converging lens having a focal length of 10 cm. Find by calculation and graphical construction the position and size of the image.

5 Repeat the preceding problem for a diverging lens having the same focal length.

6 Design an experiment, including the theory, that uses the converging lens principle to find the index of refraction of water. The lens will be made by pouring water into a watch glass of constant radius of curvature.

CHAPTER XXXI

OPTICAL MAGNIFICATION

In order to see distant objects in more detail, we either bring the object nearer to the eye or go nearer to the object. That is, we increase the angle subtended at the eye by the object. Usually the eye, when normally adjusted and at ease, just brings objects at infinity to a focus on the retina or receiving surface of the eyeball. When we wish to see objects that are closer to the eye, the self-focusing lens in the eye has to be made more convex so as to bring the image again on the retina. This is done automatically by certain muscles attached to this lens. The *limit of accommodation* (i.e., distinct vision) is usually about 25 cm, and we shall use this figure in our calculations. Consequently, if we wish to see objects in still greater detail, a convex lens may be placed in front of the eye in order to make the effective focal length of the combination much less. This serves to decrease the distance of the object for distinct vision, so that it may be brought much nearer and thus subtend a much greater angle at the eye.

The magnifier The effect of a single convex lens is illustrated in Figure 238 (a) and (b). In Figure 238 (a), an object of length AB is seen at the limiting distance d of distinct vision (i.e., 25 cm). The angle subtended at the eye by AB is α. Now place a lens of focal length f between the object and eye as shown in Figure 238 (b). Adjust the object so that the image will appear at the limit of distinct vision d. *If the lens is close to the eye** so that the angle subtended at the eye is essentially the same as that at the lens, then the new angle subtended by AB is β. Hence we may define visual magnification M as the ratio of the angle subtended by the object at the eye when aided, to the angle subtended at the eye when unaided;* that is,

$$M = \frac{\beta}{\alpha}. \tag{105}$$

* The lens is used here as a magnifier. When used as a reading glass at larger distances from the eye the calculation for the magnification is not so simple. See Henry A. Perkins, *College Physics*. (Prentice Hall Inc., 1940), p. 425.

It is often convenient to work with linear magnification, especially when the instrument to be considered has a number of lenses, each producing a given magnification. Thus, if I is the length of the image produced by the object whose length is O, then the magnification M, as defined before, becomes in this case

$$M = \frac{I}{O} = \frac{q}{p},$$

where q and p represent the image distance and object distance, respectively, from the lens.

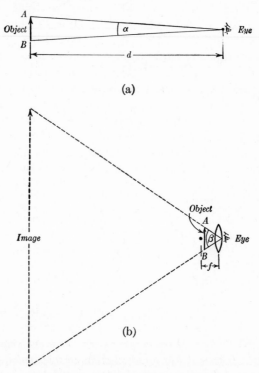

(a)

(b)

Fig. 238. Magnification by a convex lens.

Thus, in Figure 239 the magnification produced by a single double convex lens is

$$M = \frac{A'B'}{AB} = \frac{q}{p}, \tag{106}$$

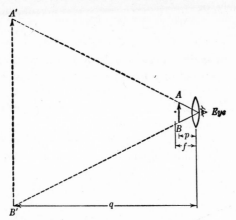

Fig. 239. Magnification by a convex lens.

and solving for p from the lens formula gives

$$M = \frac{d}{f} + 1, \tag{107}$$

where $q = d$, the limit of distinct vision.

The *astronomical telescope* (Fig. 240) consists essentially of an objective lens L_1 of focal length F and an eyepiece L_2 of focal length f.

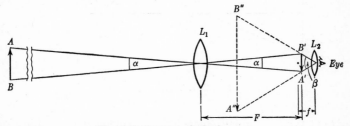

Fig. 240. Astronomical telescope.

Since the distance of the object AB is usually great compared to the length of the telescope, the angle is essentially the same as that subtended by AB with the unaided eye. Hence, the magnification of the image $A''B''$ over the object AB is given by

$$M = \frac{\dfrac{A'B'}{f}}{\dfrac{A'B'}{F}}$$

approximately, or

$$M = \frac{F}{f}. \tag{108}$$

That is, the magnification depends upon the relative magnitudes of the focal lengths of the objective lens and the eyepiece. The eyepiece consists very often of a combination of lenses. This does not change the magnification as given above, since f now represents the effective focal length of the combination.

The *microscope* (Fig. 241) consists essentially of an objective lens L_1 of very short focal length f_1 and an eyepiece L_2 also of short focal

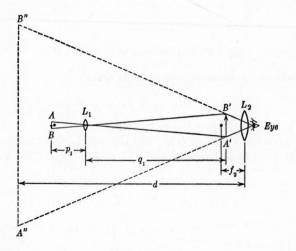

Fig. 241. Microscope.

length f_2. While in practice these lenses are made up of combinations to eliminate the various defects of a single lens, we shall treat them as simple lenses for purposes of obtaining an approximate magnifying power.

In order to calculate the approximate magnification of the microscope, we will first find the magnification of each lens by itself and then multiply the two separate magnifications to obtain the resulting magnification of the instrument as a whole. The object (Fig. 241) of length AB is placed just beyond the focal length f_1 of the objective. A real image of length $A'B'$ will be formed at a distance q_1 from the objective. Hence the linear magnification M_1, due to the objective, is given by the expression,

$$M_1 = \frac{A'B'}{AB} = \frac{q_1}{p_1}$$

The eyepiece is focused so that a virtual image $A''B''$ of the real image $A'B'$ is seen at the distance d of distinct vision. The eyepiece lens acts as a magnifier and as we have seen its magnification is

$$M_2 = \frac{A''B''}{A'B'} = \frac{d}{f_2} + 1$$

Hence the magnification of the microscope as a whole will be given by

$$M = M_1 M_2 = \frac{q_1}{p_1} \left(\frac{d}{f_2} + 1 \right) \tag{109}$$

EXPERIMENT 54

THE TELESCOPE AND THE MICROSCOPE

Part (a) *The magnification produced by a convex lens.*
Part (b) *The magnification produced by a compound microscope.*
Part (c) *The magnification produced by a telescope.*

APPARATUS:

Part (a) Lens of about 5 cm focal length in a vertical stand, two small xylonite rulers with millimeter divisions, one mounted on a vertical stand.

Part (b) Corrected lenses of focal lengths between 25 mm and 40 mm are satisfactory as objective and eyepiece lenses. They are mounted for vertical motion. Two small rulers as in part (a).

Part (c) Two lenses having a focal length of about $1\frac{1}{2}$ in. and 10 in., mounted on stands for horizontal motion and horizontal rays.

The measurement of the magnifying power of an instrument consists in observing uniform scale divisions through the instrument with one eye and simultaneously observing scale divisions of the same actual size with the other unaided eye. These images in the two eyes become superposed and with a little practice can be compared in size. The number of unmagnified divisions per magnified division is the magnifying power of the instrument.

First, measure the focal length of each lens supplied to you. This is done by forming a sharp image of a distant object (a light) on a screen, and measuring the distance from the lens to the screen.

Part (a)   Lay a millimeter scale on the table so that it points toward you. Place your eyes 25 cm above this scale and focus your attention on it. Hold the magnifier immediately below your right eye and bring a second millimeter scale into the focus of the magnifier. Now an enlarged scale seen with the right eye can be superposed on the first scale seen with the left eye (see Fig. 239). Compare the sizes of the millimeter divisions as seen with and without the magnifier. Measure the distance p from the magnifier to the upper scale. The conjugate distance q has been set at 25 cm. Calculate the value for q/p. What does it represent? Does this agree with the formula for magnifying power of a magnifier?

Part (b)   Measurement of the magnifying power of a compound microscope is accomplished just as for a magnifier: a common scale, 25 cm distant, is viewed with the unaided eye, and a second identical scale is viewed simultaneously through the instrument with the other eye. The eyepiece (and eyes) may be 25 cm from the table on which lies the comparison scale. The scale to be magnified is placed several centimeters above the table. Focusing is accomplished by adjustment of the objective lens between this latter scale and the eyepiece. When a clear magnified scale is seen superposed on the comparison scale note carefully the magnifying power as in part (a). Determine the distances p_1, d, and q_1 and the focal length f_2. The distance q_1 is found accurately enough by measuring the distance between the two lenses and subtracting f_2 (see Fig. 241). Calculate the total magnification. This is of course to be compared with the directly observed value. Repeat for a different value of p_1.

Part (c)   Again with both eyes open, view a distant vertical scale having uniform divisions. With the eyepiece of the telescope next to one eye bring the objective lens between the eyepiece and the scale and focus by adjusting the objective. A magnified image is obtained which can easily be superposed on the scale as seen with the unaided eye. A comparison of sizes is made, as before in parts (a) and (b). Measure the separation of the lenses (see page 383 and Fig. 240). Knowing the focal lengths of the lenses calculate the magnifying power, and compare with the measured value.

Questions

(a) Did you notice whether the image through the telescope was erect or inverted?

(b) How would you have proceeded to make a telescope the image of which is inverted compared to the one you observed?

(c) Draw diagrams to show the path of some rays through each of the optical magnifiers.

PROBLEMS

Experiment 54

1 What will be the approximate magnification of a simple microscope which has a focal length of 5 cm? (Assume 25 cm as the limit of distinct vision of these problems.)

2 Given that the objective and the eyepiece of a small telescope have focal lengths of 80 cm and 4 cm respectively. When viewing a distant object, what will be: (a) the magnification? (b) the distance between the objective and eyepiece?

3 Suppose that a building 200 ft high is viewed through the telescope of problem 2 at a distance of 5 miles. What is the size of the image due to the objective? What are the magnitudes of the angles α and β in radians?

4 Suppose that a real image due to the objective of a compound microscope is formed at a distance of 23 cm from the objective and is then magnified by the eyepiece of focal length 1.5 cm. What is the magnification? (Assume that the focal length of the objective is 1 cm.) How far is the object from the objective?

A physicist or a chemist in trying to discover new laws and facts in connection with the properties and behavior of matter finds very often that the eye is very limited in its scope. Of course this is no serious criticism when one considers what wonderful mechanisms and optical instruments our eyes really are. We marvel more and more when we try to extend the scope and vision of our eyes by building optical instruments based on the physical laws and facts familiar to us. By means of a telescope we can extend the limit of vision of the eye into larger distances, and by means of a microscope we can extend our limit of vision into smaller dimensions. In either case, however, the result achieved is insignificant compared with the fact that our eyes can see at all. Just imagine how interesting it would be if our eyes could see dimensions of the size of molecules of matter.

The *diffraction grating* is just another optical device, or part of an optical instrument, designed to aid our eyes in "seeing" smaller dimensions. The distances which interest us here are the wave lengths of light waves. By means of a diffraction grating wave lengths of the order of 0.00005 cm or even less can be measured with great accuracy. Very often a grating is used for the same purpose for which a prism would be used, namely, breaking up a complex light beam into its constituent colors or wave lengths in order to identify the nature of the source emitting the light beam.

A grating consists essentially of a number of very narrow and evenly spaced slits. The width of a slit or line is of the order 0.0001 inch. The difficulties of constructing or ruling such a grating are quite large and there are in existence only a very few machines capable of ruling such fine lines with accuracy. Depending upon whether the lines are ruled on a glass surface or a metal surface, the light either passes through, or is reflected from, the surface. The former is known as a transmission grating, the latter as a reflection grating.

For a detailed description the student should refer to a text. A few equations necessary to clear up the experimental procedure will be derived here. Let AB (Fig. 242) represent a cross section of a transmission grating with light falling normally on the surface from the left. The light, after emerging from the slits, produces little wavelets, according to Huyghens' principle, which in turn produce a wave front. It is easily seen that a wave front travels in direction Ⓢ. If necessary, this wave front can be converged by means of a lens to form a real image at the focus of the lens. There are, however, other directions in which wave fronts may be formed. In a direction designated by ① in the diagram it would be possible to have reinforcement of the light waves from the various successive slits, if the

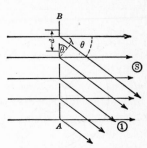

Fig. 242. Transmission grating.

difference in path is just equal to one wave length of light (λ). Along this direction ① then, it is possible to get another image. This is called the first order image. It is easily seen from Figure 242 that $\lambda = d \sin \theta$ where d is the distance between two slits or lines, and θ = angle between the direct image Ⓢ and the first order image ①. Similarly if the difference in path is $n\lambda$, we get the nth order image and hence in general we have,

$$n\lambda = d \sin \theta. \tag{110}$$

In practice it is found that the higher orders get so faint as to be invisible. The case treated above assumes that all light coming through the slits is of one wave length. This is never the case. Consequently, the image as seen really consists of several images close together. We usually say the light beam is spread out into a spectrum.

Let us suppose then that the problem is to find the wave length of a certain color. It becomes necessary only to measure θ in equation (110), since the distance d is usually known from the maker of the grating.

The instrument used for measuring the wave length of light is called a spectrometer. There are many forms of this instrument, and in most forms much skill and experience is required to make really precise measurements. In this course the student will not have sufficient time to master the detailed adjustments of such an instrument. In the laboratory, however, the instructor will have set up spectrometers, properly adjusted, in order to have the student see the instrument and then observe the various type of spectra. In general it can be said that the light from the source enters a very narrow slit in a tube called a collimator (see Fig. 243). Here the image of the slit is made into a parallel beam and then sent through either a diffraction grating or a prism.

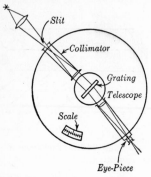

Fig. 243. Grating spectrometer.

The several wave lengths of light constituting the beam are deviated at various angles (hence separated) and then each wave length can be focused by means of a telescope back onto a screen or photographic plate. A typical spectrometer set up for a grating is shown in Figure 243. Provision is made in these instruments for measuring the angular deviation very exactly.

In Experiment 55 we will dispense with a standard form of spectrometer and set up the grating by eye as nearly normal to the incident beam as possible, then locate the positions of the central image and the first order image to the left on the rulings of the meter stick. In this way the angle θ can be determined for the first order image ($n = 1$). If the grating spacing d is known, an application of equation 110 enables one to calculate λ, the unknown wave length of the light being measured. If there are several wave-length components in the light then the angles θ will differ, and the wave length of each component can be found. The wave length of a light ray is very often stated in Ångstrom units (10^8 Å ≈ 1 cm).

LIGHT SOURCES

The grating, as we have seen, will spread out the light coming from a source into its characteristic spectrum. For a detailed description of the various types of spectra the student should refer to his lecture text. In the laboratory the three main types of spectra, i.e., continuous, absorption, and line spectra, should be produced and compared.

A continuous spectrum is obtained from an incandescent tungsten lamp, placed before a slit and its light focused on the slit, the latter acting as source.

A line spectrum can be produced by a bunsen burner having in the flame various salts of such elements as sodium, potassium, etc. A mercury arc placed in a corner of the room and having its light focused on the slit serves admirably. A neon- or hydrogen-filled glass tube with sealed-in electrodes, which has an electric discharge through it, will also furnish a line spectrum for purposes of comparison or calibration.

An absorption spectrum is perhaps best typified by the famous absorption lines (Fraunhofer lines) in the sun spectrum. Another example consists in a source of continuous spectrum (such as an incandescent lamp) of which the light has passed through various absorbing dye solutions or filters.

EXPERIMENT 55

THE DIFFRACTION GRATING

Part (a) *To measure the wave length of light using a diffraction grating mounted on a grating table.*

Part (b) *To examine several types of spectra.*

APPARATUS: Grating table, grating, slit, sodium burner, meter rule, spectrometer, several spectral sources such as neon, hydrogen, argon, incandescent lamp, etc.

The arrangement is as shown in Figure 244. A source of light giving out monochromatic rays (e.g., a sodium burner) is placed at S. A slit of width about 1 or 2 mm is placed in front of S. A grating is placed at G normal to the light coming from S. On placing the eye in front of the grating and looking along directions $G\,I_1$, and $G\,I_2$, several images I_1 and I_2, etc., of the slit will be seen. The eye serves the purpose here of focusing the beam emerging from the grating on the retina. Note that the image of the slit for sodium is yellow. It so happens that the spectrum of an excited atom consists very largely of two very intense yellow wave lengths so nearly alike in wave length that your instrument will not distinguish between them.

These images seen along directions ① I_1 and ② I_2 correspond to the first and second order images as described in this chapter. The angle θ is the angle of deviation of the beam of light coming from S.

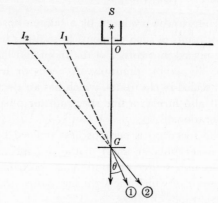

Fig. 244. Grating table.

In this experiment the data should be taken with the following points in mind:

1 To get a measurement on as many orders of images as is possible. Use the orders on the other side of the central image as well.

2 To measure the angle θ, or sin θ, and calculate the wave length in centimeters and Ångstrom units for each order. [*Note.* $\sin \theta = \dfrac{OI_1}{I_1G}$].

PROBLEMS

Experiment 55

1 Distinguish between a continuous spectrum, absorption spectrum, and line spectrum, both as regards appearance and also with respect to their physical interpretation. (See any textbook on types of spectra.)

2 Prove that for a diffraction grating, $n\lambda = d \sin \theta$, where θ is the angle of deviation for a beam incident normal to the grating.

3 What must be the wave length of a monochromatic beam of light if it falls normally on a grating and after having passed through the grating forms an image of the slit 10 cm from the direct or central image on a screen? The screen is 50 cm away and the grating has 10,000 lines per inch, the screen being parallel to the grating.

4 Write down the ranges of wave lengths in centimeters and in Angstrom units for the regions of the spectrum usually designated by ultraviolet, visible, infra-red. (Look up the wavelengths in a textbook.)

It is known that light is a wave motion whose velocity and wave length can be measured. Furthermore, Maxwell's brilliant mathematical analysis of electromagnetic phenomena and Hertz's experiments demonstrated very clearly that light is an electromagnetic phenomenon associated with varying electric and magnetic fields. As we shall see, *the fact that light can be polarized gives us the best proof that the waves must be transverse* in nature.

In talking about the vibration in the light beam, it is customary to refer to the vibrating electric field. Electromagnetic theory shows that this vibration is also accompanied by a vibrating magnetic field at right angles to the electric field. Both these fields, however, are always at right angles to the direction of travel of the light beam (or its velocity). In ordinary light the vibrations occur in *all* directions perpendicular to the ray. In plane-polarized light, however, the vibrations occur in only one of these directions. It is simpler to deal with the components of the vibrations rather than the vibrations themselves.

There are several ways in which a beam of ordinary light can be polarized, the degree depending upon conditions:

1 By reflection from a transparent medium

2 By double refraction through certain crystals (e.g., calcite)

3 By scattering of light from very small particles (Tyndall effect)

4 By refraction and selective absorption in certain crystals (e.g., tourmalin, quinine iodosulfate)

In Experiment 56 we will study only two of these in detail, namely, reflection and scattering. The last of the methods mentioned above has led to the discovery of a material called "polaroid." This material consists of small dichroic crystals embedded in a thin cellulose film and all lined up in such a way that a transmitted beam of ordinary white light will be almost completely plane polarized when passed through these crystals. The film is usually placed between two sheets of glass for protection. Such polaroid disks are very convenient for producing and analyzing polarized beams of light.

Polarization by reflection Consider a beam of ordinary light (*PO* in Fig. 245) striking the surface of a transparent medium such

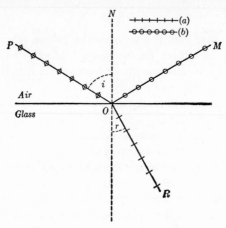

Fig. 245. Polarization by reflection.

as a glass of water. Although the vibrations are in all directions at right angles to the direction of the ray we can consider the light to have component vibrations in the plane of incidence [shown ++++++ = (a) in Fig. 245] and normal to the plane of incidence [shown ⊖⊖⊖⊖⊖⊖ = (b)]. The incident beam *PO* will be partly reflected *OM* and partly refracted *OR*. The amount of energy in each of these, and the degree of polarization in directions (a) and (b), will depend upon the angle of incidence i. In general it will be found that the refracted beam is partly polarized with the electric vector in the plane of incidence (a) and the reflected beam partly polarized at right angles to this (b). Furthermore, for most angles of incidence the two components behave differently in regard to the amount of energy reflected. In fact, for a particular angle of incidence *B*, called Brewster's angle, the vibrations (a) are not reflected at all. For this particular angle only about 10 per cent of the incident light is reflected, but all of this reflected light is plane polarized in a direction normal to the plane of incidence. A pile of parallel thin glass plates is sometimes used to increase the amount of polarized light reflected in direction OM. Experiment shows that for Brewster's angle ($i = B$), the angle $MOR = 90$ degrees.

Hence
$$_an_g = \frac{\sin i}{\sin r} = \frac{\sin B}{\sin (90\text{-}B)} = \frac{\sin B}{\cos B} = \tan B. \qquad (111)$$

Polarization of scattered light In order to understand this behavior of light consider what happens in the case of water waves. When water waves are passing a cork whose size is large compared with a wave length of the water waves, the cork is set into forced vibration with the same period as that of the waves. The cork then draws energy from the waves and sends it out in all directions over the water surface as a wave of the same period as the original wave. The cork is said to scatter the original wave.

The electromagnetic theory presents a similar view of the scattering of light by particles whose size is small compared to a wave

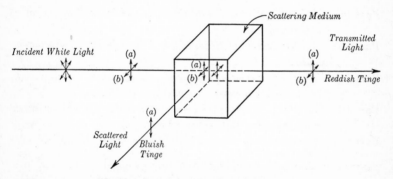

Fig. 246. Polarization of scattered light.

length. According to a celebrated formula devised by Lord Rayleigh the intensity of light scattered by such particles varies inversely as the fourth power of the wave length of the incident light. This means that violet light is scattered several times as strongly as red light. Hence white light is *scattered* as light with a bluish tinge. The blue color of the sky is attributed to the scattering of sunlight by air molecules. On the other hand, light *transmitted through* a scattering medium has a red tinge because blue light has been subtracted from it.

If there were no scattering particles in a beam of white light coming from the left in Figure 246, the beam would not be visible;

only the scattered light makes the beam visible. The degree of polarization of the scattered beam depends upon the direction from which one examines such scattered light. The figure should make it clear that if one views the beam at right angles then all *scattered light* in this direction should be plane polarized in a plane at right angles to the plane containing the incident ray and the scattered ray. As one views the scattered light at a smaller angle until one reaches the transmitted light direction, the degree of polarization becomes less and finally zero. Remember that no vibrations are supposed to exist along the ray since we have assumed that light waves are transverse.

EXPERIMENT 56

PLANE-POLARIZED LIGHT

Part (a)   *A determination of Brewster's angle and index of refraction of a glass plate.*

Part (b)   *A determination of Brewster's angle and index of refraction of water.*

Part (c)   *To study the color and plane of polarization of ordinary white light which has entered a scattering medium.*

Part (d)   *To study the effects produced by a scattering medium when plane-polarized light enters the medium.*

Part (e)   *Examination of strained plastics between two polaroids.*

APPARATUS: Two polaroid disks conveniently mounted for rotation in a stand, small flashlight bulb in a housing (see Chapter XXXIV, page 412), glass plate (or stack of glass plates) on a vertically adjustable stand, a screen with a ½-inch diameter hole to be placed in front of the polaroid disk, glass filter for mounting in front of lamp, meter rule, small low dish for water, a glass beaker with soap solution.

Part (a)   Set up the apparatus as shown in Figure 247. Place the lamp L just 40 cm above the table. Inquire from the instructor in regard to the exact position of the lamp in the housing. Next adjust the hole in the screen S to be also 40 cm above the table. Put the polaroid in its holder at P with the printed side toward the eye. Arrange the distance D to be exactly 80 cm. The thin glass plate G should be placed on the vertically sliding platform, equidistant from L and S. A glass filter is provided at F to cut off the red and violet rays which still pass through the polaroid.

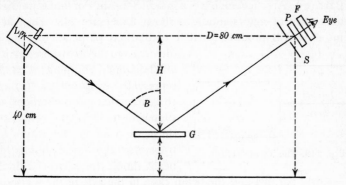

Fig. 247. Determination of Brewster's angle.

Rotate the polaroid in its holder until the intensity of the reflected light is least. Now move G up and down until the position of the least intensity is found. Next readjust P very carefully *for minimum intensity* and then readjust G. Read the position of the polaroid in its holder and note that in this position it does not transmit horizontal vibrations of the light, but it would transmit vertical vibrations if they were present. The angle of incidence is now Brewster's angle. To find it take ten measurements of h, being careful to readjust P as exactly as you can.

DATA FORM

h $\left(\begin{array}{l}\text{Three significant figures are}\\\text{required for each reading.}\end{array}\right)$	Deviations

Average_____   Average_____

$$h = \qquad \pm$$
$$D =$$
$$H = \qquad \pm$$
$$\tan B = \qquad \pm$$
$$B =$$

hence $_a n_g =$

Index of refraction of crown glass given in tables $\simeq$

Part (b) Repeat using a dish of water instead of the glass plate and find as before Brewster's angle and the refractive index.

Part (c) Arrange to have a parallel beam* of ordinary light enter a dish of soap solution as shown in Figure 248. Then at a point P it will produce particle oscillations perpendicular in all

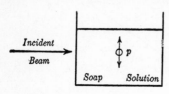

Incident Beam

Soap   Solution

Fig. 248. The Tyndall effect.

directions to the ray whose vertical and horizontal components can be represented by ⬍ and ○ or (a) and (b). Note that no oscillations are supposed to exist along the ray, since we assume the waves are transverse. For best results the beam should be narrow with the rays fairly parallel and the beam close to the side of the scattering medium being observed.

Examine the scattered light in a horizontal direction perpendicular to the beam by means of a polaroid placed in front of your eye. Record the orientations of the polaroid for the least and greatest intensity. How do these readings indicate that the vibrations are vertical?

Part (d) Instead of putting the polaroid in front of the eye, place it in the path of the light before it enters the soap solution. Observe the light scattered horizontally in a direction perpendicular to the original ray. Record the orientation of the polaroid for greatest and for least intensity of scattered light. Write a simple theory for these effects.

Part (e) Put a piece of crumpled cellophane between two polaroids and examine the transmitted light. The explanation is beyond the scope of this course.

Questions

(a) In not more than 25 words outline the argument presented by this experiment for the statement that light waves are transverse.

(b) In part (a), should the average deviation be equal to the difference between tan B and the accepted value of the index of refraction? *Explain.*

(c) In part (d) describe the direction of vibration of light scattered upward.

* The source of light which is described on page 412, Chapter XXXIV will do very well.

(d) Why is the scattering by droplets of water in a fog *not* classified as Rayleigh scattering?

(e) Compare quantitatively the Rayleigh scattering of green light (λ = 4000 Å) with that of red light (λ = 7200 Å) of the same intensity.

(f) Sunlight is ordinarily not polarized, whereas moonlight is partly polarized. Explain why.

PROBLEMS

Experiment 56

1 The index of refraction of water ($_an_w$) is 1.33. What is the value of Brewster's angle?

2 The index of refraction for crown glass is 1.52. What is the value of the polarizing angle? Draw to scale the reflected and refracted rays and indicate on your diagram the plane of polarization of each ray.

3 Heavy flint glass has a Brewster angle of 62°. What is the refractive index of this material.

4 Why are sunsets frequently red or orange?

5 Explain the blue colors of the sky.

PART 7   NOTES AND TABLES

DOUBLE AND TRIPLE BEAM TRIP SCALES

Trip scales (Fig. 249) are available with two weighing beams instead of one as illustrated in Figure 18, page 39. The second

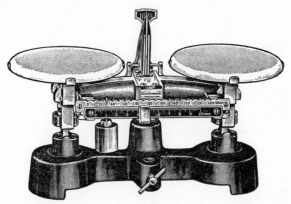

Fig. 249. Double beam trip scale. Courtesy Chicago Apparatus Company.

beam usually is not graduated but has notches at 10-gram intervals in which the knife-edge of the rider weight is placed. The second beam makes possible a wider range of weighings without use of loose weights. Trip scales are usually provided with an easy way to attach a string to the scale pan support under the iron frame, so that the loss of weight of a submerged body in experiments involving Archimedes' principle may be found easily.

Triple-beam trip scales, as shown in Figure 250 are very convenient since a still greater mass may be weighed without use of loose weights. They usually weigh up to about 600 grams before additional weights must be added. The balance will weigh additional loads by attaching an additional mass, or masses, in a slot or hole provided at or near the end of the combined beams. Notches are provided for correct positioning of the rider weight on two of the beams. Where notches are provided, serious weighing errors will be

Fig. 250. Triple beam trip scales. Courtesy Chicago Apparatus Company.

encountered unless the weights are in the notches. The *scale may be calibrated* for the initial, or zero position, *only* when the rider weights hung from the two notched beams are *set in the zero notches* and also when the graduated beam rider is *set for zero*. The maximum load that may be weighed depends upon the design but is usually about 2000 grams, or possibly 5000 grams.

Triple-beam balances made in the form shown in Figure 251 are very convenient for use in specific gravity measurements and

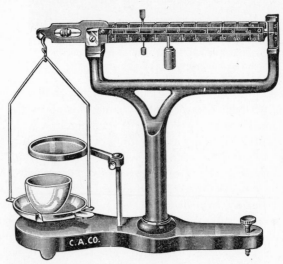

Fig. 251. Triple beam trip scale for determination of specific gravity. Courtesy Chicago Apparatus Company.

usually are about ten times as sensitive as those of Figures 249 and 250, weighing to about 0.01 gram. The total mass that may be weighed is about 111 grams without the use of extra weights. The maximum load is usually less than 300 grams.

LENGTHS

Spherometer   The principle of operation of this instrument (Fig. 252) is exactly the same as for a micrometer caliper, since the device consists of a movable micrometer screw attached to a head which is subdivided. The movable leg or micrometer screw is usually mounted vertically in a framework supported on three legs placed at equal distances from each other. The movable leg is placed so as to be equidistant from the three fixed legs. Attached to the framework is a vertical scale. In using the spherometer remember that it should be treated carefully and never forced, because the whole accuracy of such an instrument depends upon the screw remaining accurate. This will not be the case when subjected to excessive strains and excessive wear.

Fig. 252. Spherometer. Courtesy Central Scientific Company.

The *procedure* in using a spherometer is as follows:

1   First place the spherometer on a very flat and hard glass or metal surface and adjust the center leg until it touches the surface. When this has been done, the tips of all the four legs are in the same plane. This gives the zero reading.

2   Then the required thickness of a plate can be measured by placing the plate under the center leg only and measuring the amount which this leg has to be raised.

Difficulty will be experienced in determining exactly when the middle leg is just touching, unless the following or some similar method is used. Gently move one of the side legs back and forth while adjusting the center leg, and it will be found that as soon as the center leg becomes a little longer than the others, the instrument will rotate around this leg as a center. Perform the adjustment by having the center leg too short and then screwing it down until the spherometer just begins to turn on this middle leg and take the reading. Repeat the same adjustment but starting with the leg too long, and bring it back slowly until the instrument just does not rotate around this leg any more. Take a number of readings approaching the setting from both sides. With a little practice this method will give very accurate settings. Another way is to adjust the center leg so that the whole instrument will just fail to rock on this leg.

It will be found that this setting gives a reading somewhere in the neighborhood of the middle of the vertical scale. In many instruments the zero is consequently placed in the middle of the vertical scale. This leads to confusion in case we have to make a zero correction (which is almost always the case). It is a much

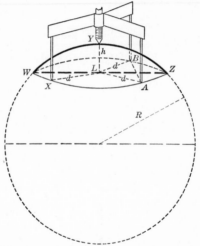

Fig. 253. Spherometer placed on a spherical surface.

better plan to call the lowest division mark on the vertical scale the zero of this scale, and then take the readings on the vertical scale with this point as zero.

Very often it becomes necessary to find the *radius of curvature* of *mirrors* and *lenses* since this is an important property in determining their optical behavior. The spherometer is admirably adapted for this purpose.

Let a portion of a lens, of which the radius of curvature R is desired, be represented by the spherical cap WYZ of Figure 253.

This spherical cap is pictured as representing a portion of a sphere with the desired radius R. We wish to express R in terms of XL and YL, which distances can be measured.

From symmetry, $\qquad XL = BL = AL = d.$

and if $\qquad\qquad YL = h$

then we can write,*

$$h(2R - h) = d^2$$

or, $\qquad\qquad 2Rh - h^2 = d^2$

i.e., $\qquad\qquad R = \dfrac{d^2 + h^2}{2h}.$

The spherometer is useful to measure small increments in length such as occur in linear expansion, Young's modulus (Fig. 255a), and bending beam experiments. The following five instruments are also very practical for the measurement of small distances.

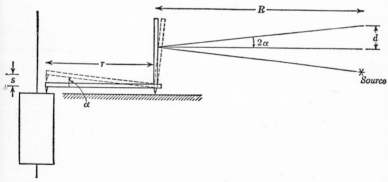

Fig. 254. Optical lever (see also Fig. 255-c).

Optical lever   The optical lever consists of a metal frame supported on three points, and carries an adjustable mirror in a frame placed at right angles to the previously mentioned frame. If the far left end of the lever of Figure 254 rises a distance s, the angle in radians through which the lever rotates will be $\alpha = s/r$ where r is the distance between supports. A source of light focused on the mirror and then reflected to a wall will be deflected through an

---

* This follows from the theorem in geometry which states that when two chords of a circle intersect within the circle, then the product of two parts of one chord is equal to the product of the two parts of the other.

angle $2\alpha = d/R$. Hence $2s/r = d/R$, or the increment in length s will be $s = dr/2R$. The distance d may be observed by setting up a telescope in front of the mirror with a vertical scale placed just to one side of the telescope. Any movement of the mirror will be ob-

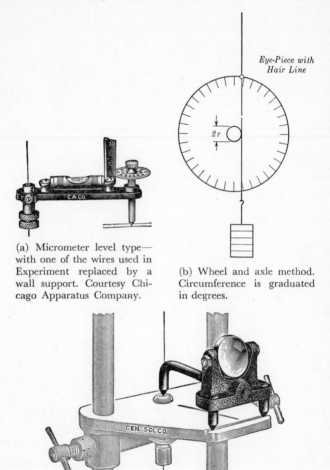

Eye-Piece with Hair Line

$2r$

(a) Micrometer level type—with one of the wires used in Experiment replaced by a wall support. Courtesy Chicago Apparatus Company.

(b) Wheel and axle method. Circumference is graduated in degrees.

(c) Optical lever type. Lever shown in use. Courtesy Central Scientific Company.

Fig. 255. Some devices used to measure changes in length as in Young's modulus experiments.

served by a corresponding displacement d on the scale when viewed through the telescope.

Wheel and axle bearing   In Figure 255 (b) a wire is wrapped around the axle of radius r for the purpose of determining the increase in length of the wire when an additional load is placed on the hanger. The disk is graduated in degrees, and the rotation in degrees is observed by an eyepiece. The ratio of the increase in length Δl to the circumference of the axle for any given increased load will be equal to the ratio of the rotation in degrees θ (caused by the increase in load) to 360 degrees. That is $\Delta l/2\pi r = \theta/360$, or $\Delta l = 2\pi r(\theta/360)$.

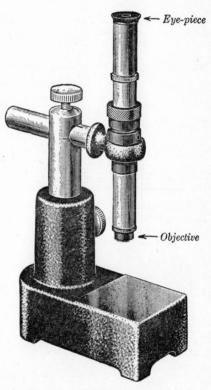

MICROSCOPES

Measuring microscope A typical measuring microscope is shown in Figure 256. The tube, which is about 16 cm long, has an eyepiece and an objective that give a total magnification of about 32 diameters. This magnification is sufficient for a very accurate setting. Thus one may measure the index of refraction of a rectangular piece of glass by measurement of the distance of the bottom (or any equivalent position) of the microscope tube to the base of the microscope with and without the

Fig. 256. Measuring microscope with scale in the eyepiece. Courtesy Central Scientific Company.

glass intercepting the region. The tube may be clamped by turning a knurled band. The objective is screwed to the body tube and may be removed. The eyepiece, or ocular, is located in a removable adaptor at the upper end and is held by friction.

A small eyepiece scale may be mounted right into the eyepiece for making measurements of very small distances. The image of the object being measured can be formed right on this scale and its size in terms of scale divisions found. Comparison of the eyepiece scale with a carefully made standard scale will make possible the calibration of the scale in the eyepiece.

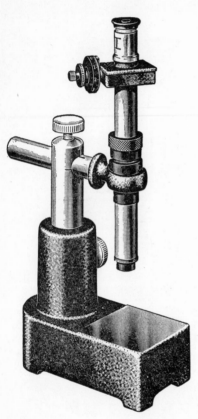

Fig. 257. Traveling filar micrometer microscope. Courtesy Central Scientific Company.

Traveling filar micrometer microscope   Figure 257 shows the complete micrometer microscope with a heavy support. A filar micrometer has been substituted for the adaptor with eyepiece described in the previous paragraph. Note that the micrometer has an attached adaptor of its own which houses the previously described eyepiece.

The micrometer screw which moves a cross wire in the eyepiece, usually has a pitch of 0.25 mm and is turned by a knurled head to which is attached a drum divided into 100 parts. Because of magnification in the eyepiece, the actual least count obtainable is greater than the indicated 0.0025 mm. Hence micrometer microscopes must be calibrated with a standard scale. The total distance measurable is about 3 mm.

The micrometer has at least one movable wire which advances at right angles to the screw axis, and may have a fixed parallel wire for reference.

A serrated scale placed at right angles to the moving wire measures the number of revolutions, each serration representing one revolution. Readings should be taken with the *screw advancing in the same direction* to avoid lost motion due to looseness in the nut.

This instrument is useful for measurement of diameters of capillaries, fibers, and other tiny distances.

Slide micrometer measuring microscope (comparator) Such an instrument is shown in Figure 258. The bedplate and measuring

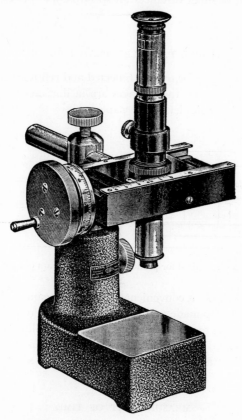

Fig. 258. Comparator or sliding measuring microscope. Courtesy Central Scientific Company.

microscope components have been described above. In the slide micrometer the complete microscope slides over a total possible distance of about 50 mm, whereas in the traveling filar micrometer microscope, only a tiny carriage within the micrometer slides. The pitch of the screw in such a comparator is usually 0.5 mm and the head is divided into 50 divisions. Details on use of the instrument must be given by the instructor, including instructions on correcting for zero error.

The comparator is useful in measurements of elongations caused by temperature, stresses, and the like, and for calibration of scales, measurement of small distances on spectroscopic plates, biological slides, etc.

SIMPLE PARALLEL BEAM SOURCE

The usual method for tracing reflected and refracted rays consists of placing pins so that their images are in line, and then drawing lines between pinholes left in the paper.

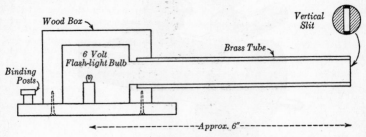

Fig. 259. Method for producing a narrow beam of light.

Figure 259 shows a convenient and simple beam of light for ray tracing. It is easily made and is cheap so that there is no difficulty with an even-front setup. The diagram is self explanatory. No lens is needed because the amount of spread in the beam over the distances used in tracing rays on an $8\frac{1}{2} \times 11$ inch sheet of paper is very small.

MEASUREMENT OF TIME

Measurement of time is the most difficult operation in determining the three fundamental quantities: length, mass, and time. There are several reasons for this inherent difficulty.

The scientific unit of time is the *mean solar second* which was chosen, not for its convenience, but for lack of a better unit. This unit of time has to be determined astronomically. Having once established this unit, the next operation was to try to construct a mechanically oscillating system which would give exactly isochronous (i.e., equal period) vibrations. No such system has yet been devised.

The greatest progress in this direction has been made within recent years at our large research laboratories by using vibrating crystals of quartz and recording their oscillations electrically. Fortunately for most of our scientific observations, such extreme accuracy is not demanded because other errors are much more important. Usually the procedure is to use a well-made clock and then find the correction factor for this clock by comparison with an astronomical clock.

Suppose for a moment that we did have a perfect clock, then how should we record or measure a certain interval of time exactly? It cannot be done! Personal errors, errors of lag, and inertia come in and offset the accuracy of our clock. These errors — i.e., errors which we make in starting and stopping a clock exactly at the beginning and end of an interval — are quite large and are difficult to determine.

Another error peculiar to a watch is that we cannot read a watch to parts of an oscillation of the flywheel. Every oscillation of the flywheel by means of a pawl actuates the seconds pointer and this pointer moves in jerks (e.g., $\frac{1}{5}$ sec jumps). This, then, limits the accuracy of reading such a watch to one-fifth of a second.

Assuming that the future will be able to produce oscillating systems with extremely constant oscillations, *the difficulties of recording intervals to accuracies even better than this become almost if not just as difficult a problem itself.* For most accurate work, therefore, measurement of time is extremely difficult and requires the highest degree of skill and technique.

Stop watches and clocks   Stop watches (and clocks) are made to operate mechanically or electrically. Hand-operated stop watches (or clocks) do not record time intervals shorter than $\frac{1}{10}$ second (usually $\frac{1}{5}$ second) since this is the approximate working limit for coordination between hand and mind. Electrically operated watches may be used for intervals not shorter than about $\frac{1}{100}$ second.

Very short time intervals   High-frequency oscillators, generating pulses or harmonic waves and coupled properly to cathode ray oscillographs, are now used to measure very short time intervals (i.e., shorter than $\frac{1}{100}$ second). This is the basic principle underlying radar, where time intervals of a few microseconds are accurately recorded.

Spark interval timers A successful method has been found to record accurately distances a body goes in short time intervals by use of equally timed sparks. The sparks punch holes in a paraffined paper and melt a tiny portion of the paraffin where the spark perforated the paper. The technique is used in many acceleration experiments (see Experiment 5). One type of spark interval timer operates much like a doorbell. The armature with striker is replaced by a constant-frequency bar. When the circuit containing the free end of the bar swings towards the electromagnet, the electric circuit opens. Then, another circuit between the battery and primary of an induction coil closes. When the bar returns, the circuit containing the induction coil in series with the battery breaks and a spark passes across the secondary terminals. The spark perforates the paraffined paper. The time interval of the above described instrument is usually $\frac{1}{120}$ second.

Typical earlier spark interval timers were operated by syncronous motors which operate a switch 30 times per second. The switch operates a spark inductor from the alternating current line giving time intervals of $\frac{1}{30}$ second.

MERCURIAL BAROMETER

The usual laboratory mercurial barometer will have a glass tube with wall thickness of about 3 mm and bore of about 4 mm. This diameter will be sufficient to prevent serious correction due to capillary effects. The barometers are adjusted for this error.

The steps taken to record accurately a barometer reading are given in the following numbered sentences: (1) Read the temperature. A thermometer will be found on the barometer. (2) Adjust the mercury level by turning the adjusting screw located either at the bottom (or top) of the well mounting. The mercury well level is moved up or down until the ivory point within the mercury well just makes contact. This is noted by reflection of the image of the point in the mercury or by lighting a neon lamp by contact of the point with the mercury surface when properly connected to a source of electric potential. (3) Adjust the vernier at the top of the mercury column until the edge of the vernier and its reflection are in line with the uppermost curved portion of the mercury surface. (4) Read the vernier. This will give the barometric reading before temperature correction is applied. (5) Subtract the temperature error which, for a brass scale and glass tube as described above, is approximately h_t 0.000161t,* where h_t is the reading of the barometric height in millimeters of mercury and t is the temperature in degrees centigrade. The factor 0.000161 comes from the subtraction of the coefficient of expansion of brass (0.0000188) from the coefficient of expansion of mercury (0.000180). To illustrate the temperature correction, suppose that the barometric reading (h_t) at temperature t°C is 760 mm. The correction to be subtracted at 20°C is 2.46 mm, and at 25°C is 3.07 mm. Corrections at 740 mm of mercury, sufficiently close for most sea level readings of the barometer are as follows:

Temperature °C.	Correction (mm) to be subtracted	Temperature °C.	Correction (mm) to be subtracted
18	2.1	24	2.9
20	2.4	26	3.1
22	2.6	28	3.3

CALORIMETERS

The ordinary calorimeter, consisting of an outer and an inner cup as described in the experiments on heat, has possibilities for considerable heat losses between the calorimeter (i.e., inner cup) and surroundings. The errors may be as high as 5 per cent under the usual conditions of elementary experimentation. These radiation losses may be considerably reduced by the use of vacuum-jacketed calorimeters or by use of some form of radiation loss correction curve.

Vacuum-jacketed calorimeters if used in such experiments as 28 and 29 will reduce the errors considerably. They are made by placing a Dewar flask with silvered surfaces within a polished metal case. The inner calorimeter cup has an outer and inner polished surface.

---

* The subtraction of h_t 0.000161t comes about because of the approximation made that $\dfrac{1}{1 + at} = 1 - at$, if a is a very small quantity.

RADIATION LOSS CORRECTIONS.   HEAT MEASUREMENTS

Rumford's method   This method assumes that the errors due to radiation losses or gains from the surroundings may be sufficiently accounted for by starting the experiment with inner-cup-calorimeter temperature correctly adjusted below (or above) room temperature so that at the end of the experiment the final temperature will be equally above (or below) room temperature. This method, used in the text, is simple but is none too accurate. Its inaccuracy is due chiefly to the fact that the time interval, following passage of the calorimeter temperature through room temperature, is greater than the interval previous to this passage. Figure 260 shows the type of

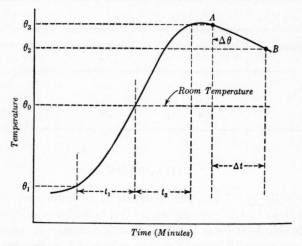

Fig. 260.   Temperature   vs.   time   curve—Rumford's method.

curve one might expect to get when temperature is plotted against time in Experiment 28 on specific heat. Note that at least one experiment must be completed before the approximately correct initial temperature can be estimated.

Correction by use of Newton's law of cooling   Newton's law of cooling assumes that the time rate at which heat is given off to surroundings is directly proportional to the difference between it and its surroundings. Thus, if the inner cup of the calorimeter is at temperature θ and room temperature is θ_0, then the time rate of change of temperature $(\Delta\theta/\Delta t)$ will be proportional to $(\theta - \theta_0)$. This law is sufficiently accurate if the temperature difference from room temperature does not exceed about 30 degrees.

The experiments may be performed as described in the experiments on heat measurement with the exception that the temperature is taken at intervals of every minute. Timing is begun for a short interval before the experiment begins and continues for several minutes after the experiment is completed (i.e., after the minimum or maximum temperature has been obtained). Assuming, for illustration purposes, that a maximum has been reached as in the specific heat experiment, continue the temperature readings until the solu-

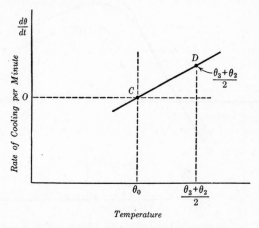

Fig. 261. Correction curve for rate of cooling.

tion continues to cool most rapidly as in the portion (Fig. 260) between points A and B. The temperature difference $(\theta_3 - \theta_0)$ should be at least as great as the maximum difference $(\theta_0 - \theta_1)$ below room temperature. With points A and B, Newton's cooling law curve may be plotted for *your* calorimeter. From your curve (Fig. 260) determine the value of $\Delta\theta/\Delta t$. This is the rate of cooling for the average temperature of $(\theta_3 + \theta_2)/2$. Plot the point D in Figure 261 by placing $\Delta\theta/\Delta t$ found above as ordinate and $(\theta_3 + \theta_2)/2$ as abscissa. Another point C is easily obtained since the rate of radiation is zero for room temperature θ_0.

The corrected curve of Figure 262 is obtained in the following way: The rate of cooling is obtained from the cooling curve (Fig. 261) for the average temperature in the first time interval (i.e., zero time to one minute). This correction is subtracted from the average temperature in this time interval to give the correct mean temperature in this time interval. The correction is subtracted, since $\Delta\theta/\Delta t$ is negative when the mean temperature is less than θ_0. Next, obtain the correction for the mean temperature for the time interval one to two seconds. The correct mean temperature in the interval one to two seconds is the mean temperature found on the graph of Figure 260 with both corrections subtracted, provided the second

Time (Minutes)

Fig. 262. Uncorrected and corrected temperature–time curves.

correction is negative also. The corrections are accumulative and the sum of the corrections gives the total correction. Thus the corrected mean temperature $(\bar{\theta}_c)$ for the nth time interval of one second will be the mean temperature $\bar{\theta}$ for that interval plus the sum of all the corrections with the signs properly taken into account, i.e., $\bar{\theta}_c = [\bar{\theta} + \Sigma(\Delta\theta/\Delta t)]$. If properly done, the corrected mean temperature in the time interval represented by the points A and B in Figure 260 will give a horizontal curve (Fig. 262) when plotted against time because presumably one has corrected for losses to the surroundings. The flat portion represents the final temperature which would have been reached if there were no losses.

In the table below is shown a list of the customary symbols used in circuit diagrams.

Electrical Symbols

Name	Symbol	Name	Symbol
Ammeter	—(A)—	Choke Coil	
Voltmeter	—(V)—	Transformer	
Resistor	—WWW— R	Cell	—‖+
Variable Resistor	—WWW—	Cells in Series	—‖‖+
Galvanometer	—(↘)— or —(G)—	d-c Motor	(DC)
Capacitor	—‖ C	a-c Motor	(AC)
Variable Capacitor	‖	Key	—∕—
Inductor	⟋⟋⟋⟋⟋ L	Diode	
Variable Inductor	⟋⟋⟋⟋⟋	Triode	or
		Ground	⏚ Gr.

NOTES ON ELECTRICAL MEASUREMENTS

Since electrical measurements are among the most accurate in the fields of physics, their applications have become very extensive and therefore important. Examination of any electric circuit reveals that the metals used are confined chiefly to copper, which is one of the best electric conductors, and to iron, which has very important magnetic properties. Since most sources of electric potential are reservoirs of potential energy, the chief danger to electric apparatus is overheating due to wrong connections. Study the digram carefully before making connections. If a diagram is not given, *draw a complete diagram before connecting the apparatus*. The diagram should be drawn so as to have as few wires crossing as is possible and the positions of the electric apparatus should be as nearly like the diagram as possible.

Connect all wires to binding posts or other appropriate terminals. *Never connect wires by twisting.* This introduces a variable resistance

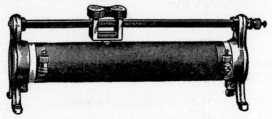

Fig. 263. Tubular rheostat. Courtesy Central Scientific Company.

that may mask results or blow out some ammeter. The electric *circuit should not be connected to the source of power* until examined by the instructor even though a switch may be a part of the circuit. After the wiring has been checked by the instructor, connect to the source of power by first touching each wire, by means of a side sweep to the appropriate power binding post. For simple circuits, without grounds, connection of the second wire to the appropriate binding post is the critical step. When a switch is included in the circuit, test cautiously by first closing it momentarily.

Resistors Two types of resistors are used in electric circuits: (1) heat-dissipating and (2) negligible-current or potential-dividing resistors. Figure 263 illustrates a typical heat-dissipating resistor.

The current-carrying capacity and resistance of each unit is marked on the slider. The current-carrying capacity should not be exceeded. The power dissipated may be increased further by blowing air or circulating water through the properly designed coil in accordance

Fig. 264. Plug type standard resistance box. Courtesy Central Scientific Company.

with manufacturer's directions. Only resistors of rugged construction will dissipate much power. These resistors have three terminals so that all or a variable portion only of the resistance can be placed in

Fig. 265. Dial type standard resistance box. Courtesy Central Scientific Company.

the circuit. A resistor with three terminals may be used as a potential divider also.

Resistance boxes (Figs. 264, 265) are used only where negligible current passes. All resistance boxes are made up to allow for a wide range in resistance values. The range for the box shown in Figure 264 is 111 ohms, in 0.1-ohm steps. The resistances in these standard boxes are connected *between* the brass blocks. Hence removal of a plug puts the designated resistance into the circuit. Removal of several plugs puts these resistances in series. The holes are tapered and the *plugs should be turned slightly and not forced when inserting or removing.* The plugs should not be placed on the table, and the metal portions should not be touched by the fingers. Lay the plugs on top of the box, or on a clean sheet of paper. The dial type resistance box is now becoming more common. It is convenient and the contacts are relatively free from dust hazards. One kind of dial resistance box is shown in Figure 265. Each dial operates one decade of resistance units. The one shown has a range of 9999 ohms in steps of 1 ohm.

Galvanometer The galvanometer is the fundamental electric current measuring instrument. It may be a suspension type as shown in Figure 266 or a jewel bearing type as shown in Figure 267. If used in d-c measurements, it will have a moving coil which is placed between two permanent magnetic poles, which are seen in Figure 266. The galvanometer of Figure 266, to be complete, must be furnished with a telescope arm, telescope, and scale. The ordinary suspension type galvanometer has a current sensitivity of 10^{-7} to 10^{-8} amperes per millimeter deflection (scale one meter away) while the jewel bearing galvanometer will have a sensitivity a little less than 10^{-6} amperes for perceptible deflection. The jewel bearing instrument shown has three buttons on the base. Pressing the first button to the left inserts a high resistance in series with the galvanometer, converting it to a voltmeter. This protects the galvanometer against a power overload. Press the two succeeding buttons in turn for increasing sensitivity if the magnitude of the deflection permits.

Fig. 266. Wall type D'Arsonval suspended coil galvanometer. Courtesy Central Scientific Company.

Ammeter An ammeter is a shunted galvanometer. Figure 268 shows the shunt arrangement that may be used to make the ammeter a two-range instrument. An ammeter must have negligible resistance compared to the resistance of other parts of the circuit. The *ammeter is an essential part of any circuit in which it is used* and is *always connected in series.*

Fig. 267. Portable type galvanometer. Courtesy Central Scientific Company.

Voltmeter   The voltmeter is not an essential part of a circuit and need not be connected permanently to the setup. The voltmeter

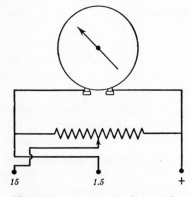

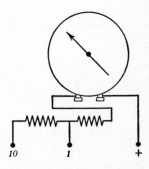

Fig. 268. Arrangement of shunts in an ammeter.

Fig. 269.   Series resistors used in a two-range voltmeter.

may be connected to prods with wire leads and connected momentarily where wanted. It *is connected always in parallel with that part of the circuit whose potential is desired.* Figure 269 illustrates a two-range voltmeter. Note that a voltmeter is a galvanometer with a high resistance in series.

Precautions in using voltmeters, ammeters, and galvanometers

(a)   If in doubt about the *amount* of potential difference or current which is likely to flow always begin by using the highest range on the instrument. Then go to the lower ranges if the indications are that this can safely be done.

(b)   Close the circuit momentarily if possible to see whether anything is wrong — this may save an instrument. If the deflections are not too great, close the switch definitely while performing the experiment. Open the circuit as soon as the necessary readings have been taken.

(c)   Always read the instruments as accurately as you can. Avoid parallax and *do not read* only to the nearest line — estimate the most exact reading by interpolating between the smallest divisions on the scale.

CLEANING SOLUTION

Should a *cleaning solution* be found necessary, the following alkali bath is very useful, especially when heated:

Sodium carbonate	60 grams per liter
Sodium hydroxide	15 grams per liter

or

Sodium carbonate crystals ($Na_2CO_3 \cdot 10\ H_2O$)	165 grams per liter
Sodium hydroxide	15 grams per liter

The object should be dipped into the alkali bath, then into water, and finally into very weak sulfuric acid. The last dipping in the sulfuric acid is desirable when the object is to be plated in an acid copper sulfate solution. For cleaning glass capillaries this last dipping is unnecessary.

TABLE 1

CONVERSION TABLES — MECHANICS

Symbol	Quantity	cgs unit	fps unit	mks unit	Ratio, size of mks unit to cgs unit	Ratio, size of mks unit to fps unit (approximate)
l, s, L	Length	centimeter	foot	meter	10^2	3.28
m, M	Mass	gram	pound	kilogram	10^3	2.2
t	Time	second	second	second	1	1
ρ	Density	g per cm^3	lb per ft^3	kg per meter^3	10^{-3}	0.0624
v	Velocity	cm per sec	ft per sec	meters per sec	10^2	3.28
a	Acceleration	cm per sec^2	ft per sec^2	m per sec^2	10^2	3.28
F, T	Force	dyne	poundal	newton	10^5	7.23
L	Torque	dyne·cm	foot-poundal	newton-meter	10^7	23.7
I	Moment of inertia	g·cm^2	lb·ft^2	kg·m^2	10^7	23.7
W	Work	dyne·cm (erg)	foot-poundal	newton-meter	10^7	23.7
P	Power	erg per sec	foot-poundal per sec	joule per sec (watt)	10^7	23.7

425

TABLE 2

CONVERSION TABLES — ELECTRICITY*

Symbol	Quantity	Electrostatic unit	Electromagnetic unit	mks unit (un-rationalized)	Ratio, size of mks unit to electrostatic unit	Ratio, size of mks unit to electromagnetic unit	Ratio, size of electrostatic unit to electromagnetic unit (c = velocity of light)
Q	Charge	statcoulomb	abcoulomb	coulomb	3×10^9	10^{-1}	c^{-1}
I	Current	statampere	abampere	ampere	3×10^9	10^{-1}	c^{-1}
V, E	Potential difference	statvolt	abvolt	volt	$(\tfrac{1}{3}) \times 10^{-2}$	10^8	c
R	Resistance	statohm	abohm	ohm	$(\tfrac{1}{9}) \times 10^{-11}$	10^9	c^2
C	Capacitance	statfarad	abfarad	farad	9×10^{11}	10^{-9}	c^{-2}
L, M	Inductance	stathenry	abhenry	henry	$(\tfrac{1}{9}) \times 10^{-11}$	10^9	c^2
W	Work	erg	erg	joule	10^7	10^7	
P	Power	erg per sec	erg per sec	Joule per sec (watt)	10^7	10^7	
H	Magnetic field intensity	statoersted	oersted (gilberts per cm)	1 mks oersted = $(\tfrac{1}{4}\pi)$ ampere-turn per m	3×10^7	10^{-3}	c^{-1}
B	Magnetic flux density	statweber per cm²	gauss (maxwells per cm²)	weber per m²	$(\tfrac{1}{3}) \times 10^{-6}$	10^4	c
B	Magnetic flux	statweber	maxwell	weber (volt-sec)	$(\tfrac{1}{3}) \times 10^{-2}$	10^8	c
m	Magnetic pole strength	statunit	abunit	1 mks unit	$(\tfrac{1}{3}) \times 10^{-2}$	10^8	c

* Taken in part from G. E. M. Jauncey and A. S. Langsdorf, *M. K. S. Units and Dimensions and a Proposed M. K. O. S. System.* Copyright, 1940, by The Macmillan Company and used with their permission.

TABLE 3

PHYSICAL PROPERTIES OF METALS AND ALLOYS (APPROXIMATE)

Substance	Specific gravity	Young's modulus (dynes per cm²)	Thermal coef of expansion per deg	Specific heats (cal per g per deg C)	Heat conductivity (cal per cm per sec per deg C)	Specific resistance at 0° C (ohm — cm)	Temp coef of resistance (per deg C at 20° C)	Velocity of sound (m per sec at 20° C)
Aluminum	2.70	6.96×10^{11}	23.8×10^{-6}	0.217	0.50	2.63×10^{-6}	0.0034	5,104
Brass (rolled)	8.56	9.2	19.2	0.092	0.20	7	0.002	3,500
Bronze	8.8	10.6	18	0.086	0.18	18	0.005	3,560
Copper	8.92	10	14.9	0.0912	0.918	1.60	0.0043	3,560
Iron (wrought)	7.86	20.0	11.4	0.113	0.16	10	0.0062	5,130
Lead	11.34	1.7	27.1	0.0305	0.083	20	0.0042	1,227
Mercury	13.55		30.0	0.033	0.20	94.1	0.00088	
Nickel	8.90	22	12	0.114	0.14	6.93	0.006	4,973
Steel (annealed)	7.82	22	10.9	0.11	0.11	6	0.003	5,000
Zinc	7.1	9.0	26.3	0.092	0.26	5.75	0.0040	3,700

427

TABLE 4

PHYSICAL PROPERTIES OF LIQUIDS (APPROXIMATE)

Substance	Temperature (deg C)	Specific gravity	Surface tension (dynes per cm)	Absolute coef of viscosity (poises)	Specific heat (cal per gram per deg C)	Boiling point (deg C at 76 cm mercury)
Alcohol, (ethyl)	0	0.806	23.5	0.0177	0.548	78.4
	20	0.789	21.7	0.0119		
Alcohol, (methyl)	20	0.793	23.0	0.00591	0.601	64.6
Benzene	0	0.894		0.00906		80.08
	20		29	0.00649		
Carbon tetrachloride	20	1.595		0.0096		76.0
Castor oil	20	0.97		9.86		
Ether	20	0.72	16.8	0.00234		35.0
Ethylene glycol	15	1.115				197
Glycerin	20	1.260	65.1	8.3	0.576	290
Mercury	0	13.596		0.0170	0.03346	
	20	13.546	520	0.0150	0.03326	356.9
	40	13.497		0.0145	0.03309	
Toluene	20	0.866	28.4	0.00586		111
Turpentine	20		27.1	0.0149	0.41	
Water	0	0.9998	75.6	0.0179	1.00874	
	10	0.9997	74.2	0.0131	1.00185	100.0
	20	0.9982	72.8	0.0100	0.99859	
	30	0.9956	71.4	0.0080	0.99745	

TABLE 5

PHYSICAL PROPERTIES OF GASES (APPROXIMATE)

Substance	Density (g per cm³ at 76 cm mercury at 0° C)	Coef. of expansion of gases at constant volume (referred to deg C)	Velocity of sound at 0° C (m per sec)
Air (dry)	0.001293	0.003666	331.5
Carbon dioxide	0.00188	0.003698	258.0
Hydrogen	0.00008988	0.003664	1269.5
Methane	0.000717		432
Nitrogen	0.001251	0.003672	
Oxygen	0.001429	0.003672	317.2
Illuminating gas			490.4

TABLE 6

MISCELLANEOUS CONSTANTS

CHANGE OF STATE

SOLIDS			LIQUIDS		
Substance	Heat of fusion (cal per g)	Melting point (deg C)	Substance	Heat of vaporization (cal per g)	Boiling point (deg C at 76 cm mercury)
Beeswax		60.5–62	Ammonia	327.1	−33.35
Naphthalene	35.6	79.9	Carbon tetrachloride	46.4	76.75
Paraffin	35.1	52.4	Ethyl ether	83.9	34.6
Salol		42.5	Ethylene glycol (anti-freeze)	191.0	197.
Sodium acetate		97.7	Sulfur dioxide	94.9	−10.1
Sodium thiosulphate	47.8	45–50	Water	539.5	100.
Water (ice)	79.2	0			

TABLE 6 *(Continued)*

INDEX OF REFRACTION FOR SODIUM LIGHT RELATIVE TO AIR

Crown glass (light to heavy)	1.51–1.61
Flint glass (light to heavy)	1.61–1.75
Flint glass (very dense)	1.9
Carbon bisulfide	1.62
Canada balsam	1.53
Ethyl alcohol	1.36
Ethylene glycol (anti-freeze)	1.43
Glycerin	1.47

ELECTRICAL CHARACTERISTICS OF WIRES

Substance	Specific resistance (ohm-cm at 20° C)	Ohms* per ft for No. 24	Temp coef at 25° C
Nichrome	100×10^{-6}	1.49	0.0004
Manganin†	44	0.655	0.00000
Copper	1.724	0.0257	0.00393
Constantan	44.1	0.657	0.000002
Iron	10	0.149	0.0052
Silver	1.63	0.0243	0.0038
Aluminum	2.83	0.042	0.0034

* For an increase or decrease of three numbers in the B & S gauge, the area is changed approximately by a factor of 2. For example, the area of No. 24 B & S wire is 0.2047 mm² and of No. 21 is 0.4105 mm².

† The temperature coefficients at 0° C and 100° C are +0.000006 and −0.00004, respectively.

WIRE SIZES

B & S gage	Diameter in mm	Area in sq mm	Diameter in in.	Area in circular mils	Area in sq in.
10	2.588	5.261	0.1019	10380	0.008155
12	2.053	3.309	0.08081	6530	0.005129
14	1.628	2.081	0.06408	4107	0.003225
18	1.024	0.8231	0.04030	1624	0.001276
22	0.6439	0.3255	0.02535	642.4	0.0005046
24	0.5105	0.2047	0.02010	404.0	0.0003173
28	0.3211	0.0810	0.01264	159.8	0.0001255
30	0.2548	0.05093	0.01003	100.5	0.00007894
32	0.2019	0.03203	0.007950	63.21	0.00004964
36	0.1270	0.01267	0.00500	25.00	0.00001963
38	0.1007	0.00797	0.003965	15.72	0.00001235

TABLE 7

ABSOLUTE HUMIDITY AND PRESSURE* OF SATURATED WATER VAPOR

Temperature (centigrade)	Grams per cubic meter	Pressure (cm of mercury)	Temperature (centigrade)	Grams per cubic meter	Pressure (cm of mercury)
—20	0.892	0.079	23	20.355	2.086
—12	1.81	0.165	24	21.546	2.215
— 8	2.54	0.235	25	22.796	2.352
— 4	3.52	0.330	26	24.109	2.496
— 2	4.13	0.390	27	25.487	2.647
0	4.83	0.457	28	26.933	2.806
2	5.54	0.527	29	28.450	2.974
4	6.33	0.607	30	30.039	3.151
6	7.22	0.697	40		5.486
8	8.21	0.799	50		9.198
10	9.33	0.914	60		14.888
11	9.93	0.977	70		23.331
12	10.57	1.043	80		35.487
13	11.25	1.114	90		52.547
14	11.96	1.119	95		63.366
15	12.71	1.267	96		65.740
16	13.50	1.351	97		68.188
17	14.34	1.444	98		70.713
18	15.22	1.533	99		73.316
19	16.14	1.632	100		76.000
20	17.12	1.736	101		78.759
21	18.14	1.847	102		81.601
22	19.22	1.963	103		84.528
			104		84.541
			105		90.641

Part of a table from the 23rd Edition of the Handbook of Chemistry and Physics, The Chemical Rubber Publishing Co., Cleveland, Ohio.

* Between an atmospheric pressure of 700 and 800 mm of mercury, the correct boiling temperature for water within 0.1 deg. C may be obtained by adding to or subtracting from 100° C the factor 0.037 deg. C for each millimeter of pressure by which the atmospheric pressure differs from 760 mm of mercury.

TABLE 8

CONDENSED RELATIVE HUMIDITY TABLE* FOR WET AND DRY BULB THERMOMETERS (CENTIGRADE SCALE)

$t - t_w$															
t	1	2	3	4	5	6	7	8	9	10	11	12	13	14	15
7	87	74	62	50	38	26	15								
10	88	77	66	55	44	34	24	15	6						
13	89	79	69	59	50	41	32	23	15	7					
16	90	81	71	63	54	46	38	30	23	15	8				
19	91	82	74	65	58	50	43	36	29	22	16	10			
22	92	83	76	68	61	54	47	40	34	28	22	17	11	6	
25	92	84	77	70	63	57	50	44	39	33	28	22	17	12	8
28	93	85	78	72	65	59	53	48	42	37	32	27	22	18	13
31	93	86	80	73	67	61	56	51	45	40	36	31	27	22	18
34	93	87	81	75	69	63	58	53	48	43	39	35	30	26	23

* Taken from the 23rd Edition of the Handbook of Chemistry and Physics, The Chemical Rubber Publishing Co., Cleveland, Ohio. Calculations are based on a pressure of 74.27 cm of mercury. Use of the condensed table will not be impaired if the actual pressure differs by about 5 cm of mercury from the pressure used in calculations.

TABLE 9

MENSURATION; CONVERSION OF UNITS

The circumference of a circle (radius r) $= 2\pi r$.
The area of a circle (radius r) $= \pi r^2$.
The area of the surface of a sphere (radius r) $= 4\pi r^2$.
The volume of a sphere (radius r) $= \frac{4}{3}\pi r^3$.

1 mile	= 5280 feet	1 kilometer	= 1000 meters
1 foot	= 12 inches	1 meter	= 100 centimeters
1 inch	= 2.54 centimeters	1 centimeter	= 10 millimeters
1 meter	= 39.37 inches	1 pound	= 453.6 grams
1 liter	= 61.0 cubic inches	1 kilogram	= 2.205 pounds

TABLE 10

THE TRIGONOMETRIC FUNCTIONS FOR 30°, 45°, AND 60°

In any right-angled triangle:

The sine of an angle $= \dfrac{\text{side opposite}}{\text{hypotenuse}}$.

The cosine of an angle $= \dfrac{\text{side adjacent}}{\text{hypotenuse}}$.

The tangent of an angle $= \dfrac{\text{side opposite}}{\text{side adjacent}}$.

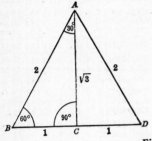 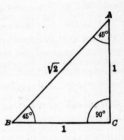

Fig. 270.

Function	0°	30°	45°	60°	90°
Sine	0	$\dfrac{1}{2}$	$\dfrac{1}{\sqrt{2}}$	$\dfrac{\sqrt{3}}{2}$	1
Cosine	1	$\dfrac{\sqrt{3}}{2}$	$\dfrac{1}{\sqrt{2}}$	$\dfrac{1}{2}$	0
Tangent	0	$\dfrac{1}{\sqrt{3}}$	1	$\sqrt{3}$	∞

TABLE 11

FOUR PLACE LOGARITHMS

N	0	1	2	3	4	5	6	7	8	9	1 2 3	4 5 6	7 8 9
10	0000	0043	0086	0128	0170	0212	0253	.0294	0334	0374	4 8 12	17 21 25	29 33 37
11	0414	0453	0492	0531	0569	0607	0645	0682	0719	0755	4 8 11	15 19 23	26 30 34
12	0792	0828	0864	0899	0934	0969	1004	1038	1072	1106	3 7 10	14 17 21	24 28 31
13	1139	1173	1206	1239	1271	1303	1335	1367	1399	1430	3 6 10	13 16 19	23 26 29
14	1461	1492	1523	1553	1584	1614	1644	1673	1703	1732	3 6 9	12 15 18	21 24 27
15	1761	1790	1818	1847	1875	1903	1931	1959	1987	2014	3 6 8	11 14 17	20 22 25
16	2041	2068	2095	2122	2148	2175	2201	2227	2253	2279	3 5 8	11 13 16	18 21 24
17	2304	2330	2355	2380	2405	2430	2455	2480	2504	2529	2 5 7	10 12 15	17 20 22
18	2553	2577	2601	2625	2648	2672	2695	2718	2742	2765	2 5 7	9 12 14	16 19 21
19	2788	2810	2833	2856	2878	2900	2923	2945	2967	2989	2 4 7	9 11 13	16 18 20
20	3010	3032	3054	3075	3096	3118	3139	3160	3181	3201	2 4 6	8 11 13	15 17 19
21	3222	3243	3263	3284	3304	3324	3345	3365	3385	3404	2 4 6	8 10 12	14 16 18
22	3424	3444	3464	3483	3502	3522	3541	3560	3579	3598	2 4 6	8 10 12	14 16 17
23	3617	3636	3655	3674	3692	3711	3729	3747	3766	3784	2 4 6	7 9 11	13 15 17
24	3802	3820	3838	3856	3874	3892	3909	3927	3945	3962	2 4 5	7 9 11	12 14 16
25	3979	3997	4014	4031	4048	4065	4082	4099	4116	4133	2 4 5	7 9 10	12 14 16
26	4150	4166	4183	4200	4216	4232	4249	4265	4281	4298	2 3 5	7 8 10	11 13 15
27	4314	4330	4346	4362	4378	4393	4409	4425	4440	4456	2 3 5	6 8 9	11 12 14
28	4472	4487	4502	4518	4533	4548	4564	4579	4594	4609	2 3 5	6 8 9	11 12 14
29	4624	4639	4654	4669	4683	4698	4713	4728	4742	4757	1 3 4	6 7 9	10 12 13
30	4771	4786	4800	4814	4829	4843	4857	4871	4886	4900	1 3 4	6 7 9	10 11 13
31	4914	4928	4942	4955	4969	4983	4997	5011	5024	5038	1 3 4	5 7 8	10 11 12
32	5051	5065	5079	5092	5105	5119	5132	5145	5159	5172	1 3 4	5 7 8	9 11 12
33	5185	5198	5211	5224	5237	5250	5263	5276	5289	5302	1 3 4	5 7 8	9 11 12
34	5315	5328	5340	5353	5366	5378	5391	5403	5416	5428	1 2 4	5 6 8	9 10 11
35	5441	5453	5465	5478	5490	5502	5514	5527	5539	5551	1 2 4	5 6 7	9 10 11
36	5563	5575	5587	5599	5611	5623	5635	5647	5658	5670	1 2 4	5 6 7	8 10 11
37	5682	5694	5705	5717	5729	5740	5752	5763	5775	5786	1 2 4	5 6 7	8 9 11
38	5798	5809	5821	5832	5843	5855	5866	5877	5888	5899	1 2 3	5 6 7	8 9 10
39	5911	5922	5933	5944	5955	5966	5977	5988	5999	6010	1 2 3	4 5 7	8 9 10
40	6021	6031	6042	6053	6064	6075	6085	6096	6107	6117	1 2 3	4 5 6	8 9 10
41	6128	6138	6149	6160	6170	6180	6191	6201	6212	6222	1 2 3	4 5 6	7 8 9
42	6232	6243	6253	6263	6274	6284	6294	6304	6314	6325	1 2 3	4 5 6	7 8 9
43	6335	6345	6355	6365	6375	6385	6395	6405	6415	6425	1 2 3	4 5 6	7 8 9
44	6435	6444	6454	6464	6474	6484	6493	6503	6513	6522	1 2 3	4 5 6	7 8 9
45	6532	6542	6551	6561	6571	6580	6590	6599	6609	6618	1 2 3	4 5 6	7 8 9
46	6628	6637	6646	6656	6665	6675	6684	6693	6702	6712	1 2 3	4 5 6	7 7 8
47	6721	6730	6739	6749	6758	6767	6776	6785	6794	6803	1 2 3	4 5 6	7 7 8
48	6812	6821	6830	6839	6848	6857	6866	6875	6884	6893	1 2 3	4 5 6	7 7 8
49	6902	6911	6920	6928	6937	6946	6955	6964	6972	6981	1 2 3	4 4 5	6 7 8
50	6990	6998	7007	7016	7024	7033	7042	7050	7059	7067	1 2 3	3 4 5	6 7 8
51	7076	7084	7093	7101	7110	7118	7126	7135	7143	7152	1 2 3	3 4 5	6 7 8
52	7160	7168	7177	7185	7193	7202	7210	7218	7226	7235	1 2 3	3 4 5	6 7 7
53	7243	7251	7259	7267	7275	7284	7292	7300	7308	7316	1 2 2	3 4 5	6 6 7
54	7324	7332	7340	7348	7356	7364	7372	7380	7388	7396	1 2 2	3 4 5	6 6 7
N	0	1	2	3	4	5	6	7	8	9	1 2 2	4 5 6	7 8 9

TABLE 11 (Continued)

FOUR PLACE LOGARITHMS

N	0	1	2	3	4	5	6	7	8	9	1	2	3	4	5	6	7	8	9
55	7404	7412	7419	7427	7435	7443	7451	7459	7466	7474	1	2	2	3	4	5	5	6	7
56	7482	7490	7497	7505	7513	7520	7528	7536	7543	7551	1	2	2	3	4	5	5	6	7
57	7559	7566	7574	7582	7589	7597	7604	7612	7619	7627	1	1	2	3	4	5	5	6	7
58	7634	7642	7649	7657	7664	7672	7679	7686	7694	7701	1	1	2	3	4	4	5	6	7
59	7709	7716	7723	7731	7738	7745	7752	7760	7767	7774	1	1	2	3	4	4	5	6	7
60	7782	7789	7796	7803	7810	7818	7825	7832	7839	7846	1	1	2	3	4	4	5	6	6
61	7853	7860	7868	7875	7882	7889	7896	7903	7910	7917	1	1	2	3	3	4	5	6	6
62	7924	7931	7938	7945	7952	7959	7966	7973	7980	7987	1	1	2	3	3	4	5	5	6
63	7993	8000	8007	8014	8021	8028	8035	8041	8048	8055	1	1	2	3	3	4	5	5	6
64	8062	8069	8075	8082	8089	8096	8102	8109	8116	8122	1	1	2	3	3	4	5	5	6
65	8129	8136	8142	8149	8156	8162	8169	8176	8182	8189	1	1	2	3	3	4	5	5	6
66	8195	8202	8209	8215	8222	8228	8235	8241	8248	8254	1	1	2	3	3	4	5	5	6
67	8261	8267	8274	8280	8287	8293	8299	8306	8312	8319	1	1	2	3	3	4	5	5	6
68	8325	8331	8338	8344	8351	8357	8363	8370	8376	8382	1	1	2	3	3	4	4	5	6
69	8388	8395	8401	8407	8414	8420	8426	8432	8439	8445	1	1	2	3	3	4	4	5	6
70	8451	8457	8463	8470	8476	8482	8488	8494	8500	8506	1	1	2	3	3	4	4	5	6
71	8513	8519	8525	8531	8537	8543	8549	8555	8561	8567	1	1	2	3	3	4	4	5	6
72	8573	8579	8585	8591	8597	8603	8609	8615	8621	8627	1	1	2	3	3	4	4	5	6
73	8633	8639	8645	8651	8657	8663	8669	8675	8681	8686	1	1	2	2	3	4	4	5	5
74	8692	8698	8704	8710	8716	8722	8727	8733	8739	8745	1	1	2	2	3	4	4	5	5
75	8751	8756	8762	8768	8774	8779	8785	8791	8797	8802	1	1	2	2	3	3	4	5	5
76	8808	8814	8820	8825	8831	8837	8842	8848	8854	8859	1	1	2	2	3	3	4	4	5
77	8865	8871	8876	8882	8887	8893	8899	8904	8910	8915	1	1	2	2	3	3	4	4	5
78	8921	8927	8932	8938	8943	8949	8954	8960	8965	8971	1	1	2	2	3	3	4	4	5
79	8976	8982	8987	8993	8998	9004	9009	9015	9020	9025	1	1	2	2	3	3	4	4	5
80	9031	9036	9042	9047	9053	9058	9063	9069	9074	9079	1	1	2	2	3	3	4	4	5
81	9085	9090	9096	9101	9106	9112	9117	9122	9128	9133	1	1	2	2	3	3	4	4	5
82	9138	9143	9149	9154	9159	9165	9170	9175	9180	9186	1	1	2	2	3	3	4	4	5
83	9191	9196	9201	9206	9212	9217	9222	9227	9232	9238	1	1	2	2	3	3	4	4	5
84	9243	9248	9253	9258	9263	9269	9274	9279	9284	9289	1	1	2	2	3	3	4	4	5
85	9294	9299	9304	9309	9315	9320	9325	9330	9335	9340	1	1	2	2	3	3	4	4	5
86	9345	9350	9355	9360	9365	9370	9375	9380	9385	9390	1	1	2	2	3	3	4	4	5
87	9395	9400	9405	9410	9415	9420	9425	9430	9435	9440	1	1	2	2	3	3	4	4	5
88	9445	9450	9455	9460	9465	9469	9474	9479	9484	9489	0	1	1	2	2	3	3	4	4
89	9494	9499	9504	9509	9513	9518	9523	9528	9533	9538	0	1	1	2	2	3	3	4	4
90	9542	9547	9552	9557	9562	9566	9571	9576	9581	9586	0	1	1	2	2	3	3	4	4
91	9590	9595	9600	9605	9609	9614	9619	9624	9628	9633	0	1	1	2	2	3	3	4	4
92	9638	9643	9647	9652	9657	9661	9666	9671	9675	9680	0	1	1	2	2	3	3	4	4
93	9685	9689	9694	9699	9703	9708	9713	9717	9722	9727	0	1	1	2	2	3	3	4	4
94	9731	9736	9741	9745	9750	9754	9759	9763	9768	9773	0	1	1	2	2	3	3	4	4
95	9777	9782	9786	9791	9795	9800	9805	9809	9814	9818	0	1	1	2	2	3	3	4	4
96	9823	9827	9832	9836	9841	9845	9850	9854	9859	9863	0	1	1	2	2	3	3	4	4
97	9868	9872	9877	9881	9886	9890	9894	9899	9903	9908	0	1	1	2	2	3	3	4	4
98	9912	9917	9921	9926	9930	9934	9939	9943	9948	9952	0	1	1	2	2	3	3	3	4
99	9956	9961	9965	9969	9974	9978	9983	9987	9991	9996	0	1	1	2	2	3	3	3	4
N	0	1	2	3	4	5	6	7	8	9	1	2	3	4	5	6	7	8	9

435

TABLE 12

NATURAL TRIGONOMETRIC FUNCTIONS

DE-GREES	Sine	Cosine	Tangent	DE-GREES	Sine	Cosine	Tangent
0	000	1.000	000	46	719	695	1.03
1	017	1.000	017	47	731	682	1.07
2	035	999	035	48	743	669	1.11
3	052	999	052	49	755	656	1.15
4	070	998	070	50	766	643	1.19
5	087	996	087	51	777	629	1.23
6	104	994	105	52	788	616	1.28
7	122	992	123	53	799	602	1.33
8	139	990	140	54	809	588	1.38
9	156	988	158	55	819	574	1.43
10	174	985	176	56	829	559	1.48
11	191	982	194	57	839	545	1.54
12	208	978	213	58	848	530	1.60
13	225	974	231	59	857	515	1.66
14	242	970	249	60	866	500	1.73
15	259	966	268	61	875	485	1.80
16	276	961	287	62	883	469	1.88
17	292	956	306	63	891	454	1.96
18	309	951	325	64	899	438	2.05
19	326	945	344	65	906	423	2.14
20	342	940	364	66	913	407	2.25
21	358	934	384	67	920	391	2.36
22	375	927	404	68	927	375	2.47
23	391	920	424	69	934	358	2.60
24	407	913	445	70	940	342	2.75
25	423	906	466	71	945	326	2.90
26	438	899	488	72	951	309	3.08
27	454	891	509	73	956	292	3.27
28	469	883	532	74	961	276	3.49
29	485	875	554	75	966	259	3.72
30	500	866	577	76	970	242	4.01
31	515	857	601	77	974	225	4.33
32	530	848	625	78	978	208	4.70
33	545	839	649	79	982	191	5.14
34	559	829	674	80	985	174	5.67
35	574	819	700	81	988	156	6.31
36	588	809	726	82	990	139	7.11
37	612	799	754	83	992	122	8.14
38	616	788	781	84	994	104	9.51
39	629	777	810	85	996	087	11.4
40	643	766	839	86	998	070	14.3
41	656	755	869	87	999	052	19.1
42	669	743	900	88	999	035	28.6
43	682	731	932	89	1.000	017	57.3
44	695	719	966	90	1.000	000	∞
45	707	707	1.000				

INDEX

QC
37
.53
1960